# THE BEST OF
# MR. PUNCH

DOUGLAS JERROLD

# THE BEST OF

# ᏩᎡ. ᏢᏌᏁᏟᎻ

## THE HUMOROUS WRITINGS OF
## DOUGLAS JERROLD

*Edited with an introduction by*

RICHARD M. KELLY

THE UNIVERSITY OF TENNESSEE PRESS : KNOXVILLE

*Library of Congress Card Number: 73–111045*
*Standard Book Number: 87049–115–6*

*Frontispiece: Douglas Jerrold
from an engraving by T. A. Prior*

*62.*

# FOREWORD

SOME OF the pieces in this collection, including the "Q" Papers, "The English in Little," and the "Jenkins" Papers, have not been reprinted previously and are taken directly from *Punch*. While the other works have been reprinted in miscellaneous nineteenth-century collections, they have long been out of print. The texts of "Punch's Letters to His Son," "Punch's Complete Letter Writer," "Mrs. Caudle's Curtain Lectures," "The Cockney," "The Undertaker," and "The Wine Cellar" are taken from *The Writings of Douglas Jerrold* (8 vols.; London, 1851–1858). Unless otherwise indicated, the various works offered in the present edition are complete.

I have attempted to gloss peculiar words and phrases, allusions, names of people and places, customs, and quotations which the reader might not readily identify. A few references and quotations, however, have not been traceable.

I wish to thank the Graduate School of the University of Tennessee for a summer grant which facilitated the completion of the manuscript. I am also indebted to the following people for their generous assistance in my annotating the volume: James Gill, Bob Leggett, Albert Lyles, Michael McDonald, Norman Sanders, John Wagner, and Thomas Wheeler.

R. M. K.

Caricature of the *Punch* staff.

# ONTENTS

MR. PUNCH'S FANCY BALL.
Orchestra comprised of *Punch* staff, with Jerrold on the drums; Queen Victoria, Tom Thumb, Lord Brougham, and other dignitaries are pictured below the orchestra.

# ︫LLUSTRATIONS

# THE BEST OF
# MR. PUNCH

# INTRODUCTION

## THE LIFE OF DOUGLAS JERROLD

ALTHOUGH born in London, Douglas William Jerrold spent most of his youth in Blue Town, Sheerness, where his father managed a small theater. The excitement of this thriving seaport town during a period of great naval activity made a lasting impression on young Jerrold. Shortly before Christmas in 1813, at the age of ten, he volunteered for service on board the guardship *Namur*, anchored at the Nore, and was accepted. The ship's captain, Charles Austen, a brother of the novelist Jane Austen, allowed Douglas to keep pet pigeons on board, as well as a small library which served to further the youth's education. With the help of a friend, he produced small theatricals to offset the monotonous routine aboard ship. The tedium quickly passed, however, when in 1815 the war with France reached its climax and Douglas was transferred to the gunbrig *Earnest*, which conveyed wounded soldiers from the battlefield at Waterloo to Ostend. Although he was never engaged in actual combat, the ghastly sights of bleeding and dying countrymen instilled in the midshipman a hatred for war and Frenchmen that was later to find expression in his essays for *Punch*. He also saw his own shipmates flogged until unconscious for acts of disobedience, the memory of which served him later in his ceaseless campaign against man's brutality towards his fellowman.

With the peace came the depopulation of Blue Town, forcing the Jerrold family to move to London, where Mrs. Jerrold and her two daughters obtained employment as actresses, while Mr. Jerrold, a disappointed and tired old man, stayed at home reading to his son. In an effort to do his share in helping with the family's expenses, Douglas became a printer's apprentice and quickly learned the mechanics of book printing, a first step towards his career in journalism and editorship. He spent his spare hours at the famous London playhouses, where he saw the great actors of the day—Edmund Kean, John Kemble, and Charles Matthews.

In 1818 he wrote his first play, a farce entitled *The Duellists*, and sent it to the English Opera House, where it remained unread for two years. The piece was finally accepted and performed in 1821 at Sadler's Wells Theatre. Rechristened *More Frightened Than Hurt*, it won a favorable reception that led to subsequent productions in Paris and at Madame Vestris' Olympic Theatre. Greatly pleased with his initial success, the young dramatist followed it quickly with a number of other melodramas.

Jerrold's future reputation as a radical liberal was anticipated in 1823 by a romantic scheme he devised with his friend Laman Blanchard. The two idealistic young men planned to join Byron in Greece to help the cause of liberty threatened by the Turkish tyrants. The idea was soon relinquished, however, in favor of practicality. On August 15, 1824, Jerrold married Mary Ann Swann, the daughter of a postal worker. Their marriage appears to have been happy and peaceful, although outside of the fact that she bore her husband seven children little is known about Mary Ann.

As salaried playwright for the Coburg Theatre, Jerrold wrote more than seven plays for which the manager, George Bowell Davidge, paid outrageously small fees. After a quarrel with Davidge, Jerrold began writing for the Surrey Theatre, managed by Robert William Elliston, the actor-manager immortalized in Lamb's famous essay. Jerrold's first great theatrical success came in 1829 when *Black-Eyed Susan; or, All in the Downs* appeared at the Surrey. The play enjoyed a near record run of four hundred nights at six theaters during the first year. Nevertheless, Jerrold's profit amounted to a mere sixty pounds, ten of which he obtained by selling the copyright. The success of the play, however, earned him the reputation of an exciting new dramatist, and the two patent houses, Drury Lane and Covent Garden, eagerly solicited his works.

It was sometime in 1835 that Jerrold, recovering from a serious attack of rheumatism, first met Charles Dickens, then a reporter for the *Morning Chronicle*. Dickens recorded his impressions of the meeting: "I remember very well that when I first saw him in about the year 1835—when I went into his sick room in Thistle Grove, Brompton, and found him propped up in a great chair, bright-eyed and quick and eager in spirit, but very lame in body, he gave me the impression of tenderness.

It never became dissociated from him."[1] From that day on the two men were fast, lifelong friends.

Jerrold's output for the theater increased at an incredible rate; it was not unusual to find three or four of his plays being performed in London during the same month. Besides his work for the stage, he was busily writing essays and stories for *Blackwood's Magazine*, the *Freemason's Quarterly Review*, and other journals.

In 1841 he began his long and fruitful career with *Punch*. A small group of writers and artists in constant argument and conviviality gathered weekly around the dinner table of the *Punch* office to discuss the material to be included in the next number. Here Jerrold was in his glory, showing off his sparkling wit and drawing roars of laughter. Thackeray, however, disliked his co-worker's habit of monopolizing the conversation; sides were chosen and the gentlemanly and Bohemian factions began to clash—John Leech and Thackeray against Mark Lemon and Jerrold. Thackeray was repulsed by Jerrold's vulgar habit of eating peas with a knife, and Leech used to imitate his eating with the gusto of a starving animal. Gradually Jerrold and Thackeray came to compete for supremacy in the pages of the magazine. During *Punch*'s first five years Jerrold was the unrivalled genius of comic journalism. He was *Punch*'s highest paid and most illustrious contributor. In the words of *Punch*'s historian he was "the man to whom, more than anyone else, the paper owed the enormous political influence it once enjoyed, and to whom it is indebted for much of the literary reputation it still retains."[2] By 1845, the year "Mrs. Caudle's Curtain Lectures" appeared, Jerrold was the undisputed claimant for the title "Mr. Punch." Not even Thackeray's "Snob Papers" could surpass the success of Mrs. Caudle.

Besides his association with *Punch*, Jerrold founded and edited the *Illuminated Magazine*, dedicated to the "masses of the people." Wilkie Collins made his literary debut in the pages of this magazine with his story entitled "The Last Stage Coachman." In 1844 Jerrold dropped the *Illuminated Magazine* to edit and write for *Douglas Jerrold's Shilling Magazine*, a venture supported by the publishers of *Punch*. By breaking away from the standard half crown then charged for such monthly miscellanies, the periodical marked an innovation in publishing. The theme of the magazine, "that it shall appeal to the hearts of the Masses of England," was in accord with its low price. Jerrold's serialized novel

---

[1] Quoted in Walter Jerrold, *Douglas Jerrold, Dramatist and Wit* (2 vols.; London, 1914), I, 265.

[2] M. H. Spielmann, *The History of Punch* (London, 1895), p. 284.

of social protest, *St. Giles and St. James*, decidedly did appeal to the social and economic underdog who turned to the *Shilling Magazine* in
hopes of better days to come. As editor of *Douglas Jerrold's Weekly
Newspaper*, Jerrold continued to support the cause of the lower class.
His opening editorial praised Lord John Russell and the Whigs for
their promise to help the poor and oppressed of England.

Between 1851 and 1854 Jerrold's publisher issued his collected writings gathered from numerous periodicals, books, and playscripts, although only a select few of the more than sixty plays were included.
Meantime, his new comedy, *St. Cupid* (1853), was given a command performance at Windsor Castle. Jerrold, however, was not invited to attend. The snub was obviously meant to inform him that the Queen
and her husband were not amused by his satirical portraits of them in
*Punch.*

Editing *Lloyd's Weekly Newspaper*, writing an occasional essay for
*Punch*, working on new plays, and crusading for freedom on the Continent, Jerrold remained active until his death. The best portrait of the
aging satirist is that given by Nathaniel Hawthorne, who met Jerrold
the year before his death:

> He was a very short man, but with breadth enough and a back excessively
> bent—bowed almost to deformity; very gray hair, and a face and expression
> of remarkable briskness and intelligence. His profile came out pretty bold-
> ly, and his eyes had the prominence that indicates, I believe, volubility in
> speech, nor did he fail to talk from the instant of his appearance, and in
> the tone of his voice, and in his glance, and in the whole man, there was
> something racy—a flavour of the humourist. His step was that of an aged
> man, and he put his stick down very decidedly at every footfall; though,
> as he afterwards told me, he was only fifty-two, he need not yet have been
> infirm.[3]

Many celebrities were among the two thousand mourners at Jerrold's
funeral. His pallbearers included such distinguished men as Thackeray,
Dickens, Richard Monckton Milnes, John Forster, Sir Joseph Paxton,
Mark Lemon, and Horace Mayhew. Jerrold died intestate, leaving his
wife and daughter with what little money accrued from royalties on his
plays and books. Later, both Dickens and Thackeray gave public read-
ings of their works and donated the proceeds to a fund that had been
established to help the Jerrold family.

3 *Notes of Travel* (4 vols.; New York, 1900), II, 92.

ON OCCASION, humorous verse and prose were combined with the serious news in most of the daily or weekly papers from the beginning of the nineteenth century and earlier, as when Lamb included poems and jokes in his fashionable intelligence for the *Morning Post*, and when Thomas Moore contributed his squibs in rhyme to the *Morning Chronicle*, competing with Theodore Hook and R. H. Barham in *John Bull*. Independent comic journalism, however, was a novelty in 1831 when Gilbert à Beckett and Henry Mayhew founded *Figaro in London*, the earliest predecessor of *Punch*. *Figaro*, like its many imitators that followed within months of its inception, poked fun at the passing events of popular interest, contained witty "brevities" and funny paragraphs, and had a column or two of theatrical criticism as its most solid contribution. The humor, however, was feeble and coarse. Only with the founding of *Punch* in 1841 did comic journalism mature into an art, with Jerrold as its most illustrious exponent. His humanitarian spirit and satiric artistry assured a depth of meaning and lasting relevance to his humor. Jerrold, unlike his predecessors, was keenly alive to the grave and serious, an awareness that paradoxically made him a superior humorist. He once criticized his fellow workers at *Punch* for lacking a serious point of view in their comic visions:

> After all, life has something serious in it. It cannot all be a comic history of humanity. Some men would, I believe, write the Comic Sermon on the Mount. Think of a comic History of England; the drollery of Alfred; the fun of Sir Thomas More in the Tower; the farce of his daughter begging his dear head, and clasping it in her coffin on her bosom! Surely the world will be sick of such blasphemy![4]

Writing over the signature "Q," Jerrold contributed hundreds of essays on political and social topics that firmly established the radical tone of *Punch*. Writing as Mr. Punch, he set forth the magazine's non-partisan position: "As for my politics, men of London, they are of all sides, and all parties: hence, Tory, Whig, Conservative, and Radical, may with perfect consistency give me their vote: for as the pine-apple . . . combines in itself a smack, a relish of every other fruit, so do I possess a shade and hue of every party under the sun." In practice, however, *Punch* was decidedly liberal, always crusading on behalf of the poor and oppressed in

---

[4] Quoted in *Douglas Jerrold, Dramatist and Wit*, II, 445.

England and on the Continent. Jerrold's political beliefs were those of
a radical democrat: he argued for sweeping changes in legislation and
governmental practices but refused to sanction physical violence, such
as that exhibited by the Chartist mobs. As a political and social satirist,
he always exaggerated and caricatured the two nations of the rich and
the poor. The aristocracy were always the villains and the London poor
were the brutalized innocents.

Jerrold's first "Q" papers appeared in 1841, when Sir Robert Peel was
struggling with the Bedchamber Crisis, and they portray his apparent
inadequacy at controlling the young Queen and her retinue of women:
"What minister shall answer for the sound repose of Royalty, if he be
not permitted to make Royalty's bed?"

Despite Peel's abolition of many dutiable articles, he believed that sugar and corn imports must continue to be taxed. The Corn Law League,
which had been organized to repeal the Corn Laws, sent Peel some velveteen for trousers, in which were secretly woven ears of wheat and the
word *free*. When he discovered the joke he returned the material and
wrote a solemn letter of refusal to the *Times*. Jerrold capitalized on the
absurdity of the incident: "Great, indeed, would have been the triumph
of the League, if the Minister had donned the insidious trousers, and,
taking his seat in them in the House of Commons, had, without knowing it, based his ministry upon—'free corn!' "

Jerrold's range of subjects was as broad as that of the *Times*: Queen
Victoria, Prince Albert, the Duke of Wellington, various London magistrates and other public officials, Disraeli, Czar Nicholas I, and President Polk were just a few of the hundreds of people he converted into
literary caricatures that blended well with the cartoon caricatures drawn
by *Punch*'s master artists, John Tenniel, John Leech, Richard Doyle,
and others.

Directed by Jerrold, *Punch*'s attack upon the prejudicial nature of
certain civil laws found its victim in the notorious London alderman,
Sir Peter Laurie. In 1841 the *Times* recorded in a few small paragraphs
the case of William Simmons, an unemployed tailor, who was charged
by a policeman with having attempted to cut his own throat with a razor. Alderman Laurie asked Simmons why he had tried to commit suicide, and he replied that he was in a perishing condition and could get
nothing to do. Then Laurie said:

> Suicides and attempts, or apparent attempts, to commit suicide very
> much increase, I regret to say. I know that a morbid humanity exists, and
> does much mischief, as regards the practice. I shall not encourage attempts

of the kind, but shall punish them; and I sentence you to the treadmill for a month, as a rogue and vagabond. I shall look very narrowly at the cases of persons brought before me on such charges.

Jerrold expanded this small notice in the *Times* into a full-page editorial in *Punch* in order to expose the foolishness and callousness of the magistrate. "Sir Peter Laurie on Human Life" was only the first of many essays ridiculing the alderman that Jerrold contributed to *Punch*. Joined by his fellow writers and cartoonists, he continued his attack for the next four years. Laurie's notoriety, largely inspired by Jerrold's savage caricatures, was finally crowned by Dickens in *The Chimes,* where Laurie appears as Alderman Cute, whose ruling passion is to "Put Down!" Among the things he would put down are distressed wives, shoeless children, wandering mothers, sick babies, and, of course, suicide.

Occasionally, as in some of his essays on Laurie, Jerrold's weapons were blunt sarcasm, invective, and sermonizing. On the other hand, his irony in " 'Gentlemen Jews' " was so accomplished that it backfired upon him. Poking fun at the *Morning Post*'s use of the term "gentlemen Jews," he observed that Jews had risen from being called "accursed dogs" to "individuals of the Jewish persuasion" to "persons of the Hebrew faith" and now to "gentlemen Jews." Jerrold called for a reversion to the good old days when "good, strong, stringent prejudices" were "intended to hold society together." Many readers mistook the irony for anti-Semitism and wrote complaining letters to the *Times*, the *Morning Chronicle,* and *Punch*. In " 'Gentlemen Jews' and Punch" Jerrold, red-faced and amazed, explained to his more obtuse readers the irony of his earlier article.

*Punch* was so outspoken on foreign affairs that in 1843 it was banned in France. A cartoon captioned "Punch turned out of France," showing a seasick puppet received on the Boulogne quay at the point of a bayonet, heralded the magazine's encounter with Louis Philippe. The cartoon referred the reader to an essay by Jerrold, one of the authors chiefly responsible for the embargo, who explained "The Wrongs of Punch." Two months later France allowed the magazine to return to the newsstands, but soon an incendiary article by Thackeray once again secured its expulsion.

Like so many satirists, Jerrold directed his thrusts at hypocrisy, both personal and national. He saw slavery as America's Achilles' heel: "The eagle steals its prey—America steals her blacks. The eagle will feed upon human flesh—so does America; that is, if the flesh have within it negro blood. The eagle—that is—the free American eagle—lays putrid eggs; nought wholesome, nought vital is produced from them."[5] Delighting in matching a country's symbol with its practices, and having already driven the British Lion back to the jungle, Jerrold turned to America as ready-made prey.

Although he stated that the purpose of his political essays was "to give brief suggestions for the better government of the world, and for the bringing about the millennium," Jerrold's primary effect was not to cure the ills of his world so much as to make people laugh at other people. He achieved this end—as the essays sufficiently illustrate—through irony, ridicule, downright invective, name-calling, and exaggeration or caricature. Whether or not his "Q" papers provided any kind of social therapy is now irrelevant: today they are literary documents. It does not matter that Prince Albert failed to heed Jerrold's attacks upon his person and to mend his ways, for he remains a vital literary presence in the satiric imagination of his delineator, Mr. Punch, and we can no more be interested in his reform than in the reform of Thomas Shadwell, Arabella Fermor, or any other character ridiculed in literature.

Jerrold eventually dropped the signature "Q," for, when he had educated his readers to his unique style of comic journalism, his identity was quickly recognized through his characteristic style. By the middle of the 1840's he was truly *Punch's* Prime Minister.


## PUNCH'S LETTERS

### LETTERS TO HIS SON

IN THE PREFACE to *Joseph Andrews* Fielding explains that hypocrisy and vanity are the two causes of affectation which provide the source of the "true Ridiculous": "for as vanity puts us on affecting false characters, in order to purchase applause; so hypocrisy sets us on an endeavour to avoid censure, by concealing our vices under an appearance of their opposite virtues."

As one of the chief vices of the Victorian age, hypocrisy was frequently exposed and attacked by critics from Carlyle to Morley. Because the Victorians made a cult of sincerity they were keenly aware of hypocrisy and outspoken concerning its demoralizing effects upon society. Froude

---

[5] "American Liberty—American Eggs," *Punch*, XIII (1847), 154.

said that the discrepancy between practice and principles "has made the entire life of modern England a frightful lie." Kingsley accused Victorians of worshipping God and Mammon at the same time and deplored the fact that "the very classes among us who are most utterly given up to money-making, are the very classes which, in all denominations, make the loudest religious professions."[6]

The Victorian novelists also contributed greatly to the onslaught upon hypocrisy. Dickens, for example, created such arch-hypocrites as Uriah Heep, Mr. Pecksniff, and Sir John Chester, savage caricatures who all reap the terrible justice of exposure and comic deflation.

Among journalists Jerrold was the most outspoken on the subject of hypocrisy. Besides making isolated attacks upon people and institutions over the signature "Q," he wrote a number of serials. His first extended satire in *Punch*, "Punch's Letters to His Son," both pokes fun at the political, social, and moral hypocrisy of the day and parodies Lord Chesterfield's *Letters to His Son*. He creates as a persona an experienced scoundrel who imparts his pernicious wisdom to a younger generation, and unifies the epistolary series through the theme of education set forth by Mr. Punch: "I have sought to paint men as they are—to sketch the scenes of the world as they have presented themselves to my observation—to show the spring of human motives—to exhibit to the opening mind of youth the vulgar wires that, because unseen, make a mystery of commonplace." In short, each letter is aimed at teaching his son how to get ahead in life through devious means or, in Mr. Punch's phrase, "how to secure the best cut of the shoulder."

Chesterfield's central theme in the letters is the necessity of acquiring perfect manners and of learning how to please as prerequisites for success in diplomacy. Jerrold parodies this theme by having Mr. Punch teach his son how to deceive others as a prerequisite to becoming "Nothing," that is, being in a position "ready to accommodate yourself to any profitable circumstance that may present itself." Chesterfield counsels cleanliness, proper grammar, flattery, truthfulness (and white lies), and sobriety; Mr. Punch advises his son to marry a dirty woman ("there is a fine natural religion in dirt"), to employ rhetoric to deceive his peers, to lie judiciously, and to gamble and drink his way to success.

In one letter, describing how his son may acquire learning with the most economical use of time, Mr. Punch suggests he read Blackstone's

---

6 James Anthony Froude, *The Nemesis of Faith* (London, 1904), p. lii; Charles Kingsley, "God and Mammon," *Westminster Sermons* (London, 1874), p. 319.

*Commentaries* while shaving. Jerrold acknowledges his debt to Chesterfield for this idea by cleaning up for his parody an anecdote that readers of *Punch* would consider vulgar and indecent. Mr. Punch's advice to
learn while shaving is meant to conjure up Chesterfield's example of a
man "who was so good a manager of his time, that he would not even
lose that portion of it which the calls of nature obliged him to pass in
the necessary-house; but gradually went through all the Latin Poets in
those moments." After he studied them, he tore the pages out and "sent
them down as a sacrifice to Cloacina." Remaining innocent of any in-
decency himself, Jerrold manages to suggest this piece of comic vulgarity
to his well-informed readers. Those who did not recognize the allusion
and had to check its source had only their curiosity to blame for any
shock their sensibilities might have suffered.

"Punch's Letters to His Son" converts Chesterfield's "course of polite
education" into an art of hypocrisy offered not only as a parody but as a
criticism of moral principles in Victorian society. Both Mr. Punch and
Sir John Chester (Dickens's caricature of Lord Chesterfield in *Barnaby
Rudge*) only vaguely recall the historical Earl of Chesterfield. The Victorian public laughed at these literary figures because they recognized in
the exaggerated and distorted characters their own (and perhaps more
vividly their neighbors' and superiors') shortcomings.

Most comic journalism ceases to be funny as soon as the people and
events with which it deals are forgotten. In "Punch's Letters to His Son,"
however, Jerrold discovered the proper form for his satire. By focusing
upon a character type, the arch-hypocrite and conniving success hunter,
who subverts solid moral principles, Jerrold assured himself a subject
that would endure. Furthermore, he provides his readers with a lasting
point of reference by basing his satire upon Chesterfield's *Letters*. Finally, he unifies the serial through the parodic theme of education and by
creating a persona, Mr. Punch, to write all the letters.

### COMPLETE LETTER WRITER

Jerrold broadened the range of his epistolary satire in "Punch's Complete Letter Writer" by including all manner of authors, from a hypocritical bishop to a complaining servant girl. Although both sides of the
correspondence are given, Jerrold does not allow the reader to mistake
his point of view. He sympathizes with servants, governesses, debtors,
drunkards, peasants, penniless relatives, downtrodden husbands, and
impoverished children. The epistolary villains are the aristocrats, heart-

less creditors, hypocritical clergymen, self-righteous moralizers, henpecking wives, and threatening landlords.

If there was any one group of women on whose behalf Jerrold fought most vigorously it was the governesses of England, or, as he called them, the "Sisters of Misery." He began his defense in "Punch's Complete Letter Writer" and renewed it with greater force in 1848, the same year that *Jane Eyre* depicted a governess as a woman of intelligence, sensibility, and deep feeling. Unmarried girls in middle-class families who were forced to work, or girls of upper-class families that were suddenly impoverished, turned to the only respectable way open to them and became governesses. The majority of applicants lacked the qualifications of Jane Eyre but were desperate to salvage their self-respect. Aware of this situation, as well as of the degradation that fell upon any woman who endeavored to support herself, those who hired governesses paid unjustly low wages and increased the duties and working hours with impunity. Governesses were often treated with scornful patronage or veiled contempt because they had committed the unforgivable sin of falling from social grace. It is against this background that the letters of Honoria Asphalt, Dorothea Flint, and Mary Wilton are to be read.

The letters to and from members of the clergy represent another aspect of the immorality of the age. As a young writer Jerrold was notorious for his anti-clericalism. In fact, Thackeray was so violently opposed to his satiric treatment of the English clergy that he came to the point of resigning from *Punch*. In his essay "On Clerical Snobs" he reproved those journalists who constantly poked fun at the clergy and argued that most Victorian parsons lived good lives. Jerrold took this to be a direct reproof of himself and moderated his anti-clericalism. "From a Bishop to a Young Friend about to Take Orders" provides a worthy example of the sarcasm, directed at the complacency and self-righteousness of bishops, that upset Thackeray, not to mention innumerable clergymen.

Jerrold's focus throughout "Punch's Complete Letter Writer" is upon hypocrisy and self-aggrandizement. His satire sweeps across the breadth of English society during the hungry forties and presents a stinging indictment of its moral decay. Although this work lacks the unity of "Punch's Letters to His Son," it allows Jerrold to present a "general prologue" to the Victorian age as each character, drawn from a different class or profession, unwittingly reveals the depth of his comic self.

# MRS. CAUDLE'S CURTAIN LECTURES

STRUCTURE

IN THE *Punch* Almanac for 1845 there appeared on the January page the adaptation of a popular advertisement: "Worthy of attention. / Advice to persons about to marry,—Don't." This notice aptly preceded the first installment of "Mrs. Caudle's Curtain Lectures" and prophetically suggested its moral. As the title of the serial indicates, all the lectures are given in bed; the story progresses through Mrs. Caudle's complaints and through shifting the location of the bedroom. Job is lectured each night because Margaret knew that he "was too much distracted by his business as toy-man and doll-merchant to digest her lessons in the broad day."

Although consisting basically of loosely connected psychological episodes, the serial has unity. Mrs. Caudle's suspicion of Job's fidelity, aroused by Miss Prettyman, who continually looms in the background as a marital threat, adds an element of suspense. And Margaret's self-pity, announced early in the serial by such typical statements as "I know that I'm sinking every day" and "when I'm gone, we shall see how your second wife will look after your buttons," prepares the reader for the only psychologically satisfying conclusion—her actual death. The action is confined almost exclusively within the minds of the characters, and the effect of movement, obtained by the few changes of scene (from London, through Herne Bay, Margate, France, back to London, and finally to the "Turtle-Dovery"), is restricted by the exclusive focus upon the bedroom as the center of the Caudles' world.

Jerrold reports that Job recorded only the best thirty-six lectures out of his thirty years of marriage, which presumably means that 10,914 lectures were judiciously rejected. When Job died he left his manuscript for publication; and Jerrold, acting as the anonymous editor, expresses the hope that he has "done justice to both documents," that is, the lectures and Job's comments upon them. Job's authorial comments are usually of a mechanical nature, relating how either Margaret or he finally fell asleep. Sometimes, however, the tailpiece is psychologically related to the lecture and presents an amusing consequence of it. After a long scolding for having lent an acquaintance the family umbrella, Job tells that at length he fell asleep and dreamed that "the sky was turned into green calico, with whalebone ribs; that, in fact, the whole world turned round under a tremendous umbrella."

Most of the lectures were written according to a basic formula. The theme of each lecture is stated at the outset. Mrs. Caudle then begins her harangue, which invariably includes the accusation that some innocent act of Job has caused her and the children to suffer. Job's two or three mild remonstrances agitate her still further until finally she or Job falls asleep.

A number of variations on the pattern keep it from becoming tedious. When Margaret wants her mother to come to live with them she reverses her usual approach: instead of nagging Job to sleep, she takes a positive view, explaining how her mother will prepare his favorite dishes and save them money by brewing beer at home. Margaret's domestic optimism, needless to say, is as oppressive to Job as her invective. Sometimes the variation is achieved by a surprise ending to a lecture. Usually Mrs. Caudle's theme, no matter how much it exaggerates Job's innocent actions, is based on fact: he does stay out late, he does lend the family umbrella, and so forth. One night, however, he is severely lectured for putting up bail for his friend Harry Prettyman. Job finally manages to get a word in to explain that it was not Harry but her own brother for whom he put up bail, and Mrs. Caudle goes to sleep amidst repentant tears.

All the characters—Job, his wife, and his friends—are drawn from the middle or working class of the 1840's. They are all without exceptional endowments and have lived through the ordinary experiences of love, marriage, and parenthood. Life is rather unhappy and dull for them, and their world is largely limited to domestic affairs. In Thackeray's words, "almost all the events and perplexities of Cockney domestic economy pass before her [Mrs. Caudle] . . . a foreigner, or a student in the twentieth century, may get out of her lectures as accurate pictures of London life as we can get out of the pictures of Hogarth."[7]

Jerrold's ambiguous attitude towards the Caudles contributes to their credibility. Although he sympathizes with the psychologically oppressed Job, whom he presents as an object of both pity and contempt, he does not completely identify with him and at times seems to relish exercising his own powers of invective through Mrs. Caudle. Similarly, Jerrold enlarges the shrewish character of Mrs. Caudle with pathos. When she tries to persuade Job to spend the vacation at Margate she declares, "the ocean always seems to me to open the mind. I see nothing to laugh at; but you always laugh when I say anything. Sometimes at the seaside— specially when the tide's down—I feel so happy: quite as if I could cry." Her final lecture, delivered from her deathbed, eschews sentimentality in favor of genuine pathos: "And after all, we've been very happy. It hasn't been my fault, if we've ever had a word or two, for you couldn't help

[7] The *Morning Chronicle* (Dec. 26, 1845), p. 5.

now and then being aggravating; nobody can help their tempers always,
—specially men. Still we've been very happy, haven't we, Caudle?"

### BASIS OF SATIRE

A significant part of the fun in "Mrs. Caudle's Curtain Lectures" is its
satire on the idealized picture of married life drawn in Victorian conduct
manuals and literature. Mrs. Sarah Ellis, for example, wrote a series of
standard manuals during the late 1830's and early 1840's (*Daughters of
England, Wives of England,* and *Women of England*) in which she con-
tends that since the life of business debases the mind by making its goals
materialistic, a wife should be solicitous to advance her husband's intellectual, spiritual, and moral nature. She should be "a companion who
will raise the tone of his mind from . . . low anxieties and vulgar cares"
and "lead his thoughts to expatiate or repose on those subjects which
convey a feeling of identity with a higher state of existence beyond this
present life." At every turn Mrs. Caudle is the comic opposite of Mrs.
Ellis' good wife: she reinforces materialistic interests in Job's mind by
arguing over domestic finances and by urging him to find a wealthy godfather for the new baby. Rather than advancing his moral stature, she
uses him to smuggle French lace past customs. "Low anxieties and vulgar
cares" are her forte, and she would not dream of raising the tone of his
mind above them.

Domestic felicity was also portrayed in literature, where the home
gradually became sentimentalized and the wife was given wings with
which to fly above the debased world of pots and pans. The very title of
Coventry Patmore's long poem *The Angel in the House* suggests that
married love was more than mortal. Dickens, too, presents an idealized
and sentimentalized picture of marriage in David Copperfield and Agnes
Wickfield. A number of other Victorian authors showed that the love
between a man and a woman frequently transcended mortality, that
when one partner died romantic love continued in heaven. When Mrs.
Caudle dies Job calls her "that angel now in heaven," but that angel, instead of fostering eternal romantic love, continues to harass Job with her
lectures from the grave. Jerrold's "Curtain Lectures" helped bring fiction
to terms with real life. They not only satirized the ideal Victorian family
but too clearly portrayed families who fell short of the ideal.

The basic ingredient of "Mrs. Caudle's Curtain Lectures" that guar-
antees its survival as literature is the presence of characters who convince us of their reality and of the reality of the world they inhabit.
Commenting upon the serial, Thackeray observed that "to create these

realities is the greatest triumph of a fictitious writer." One may recognize in "Mrs. Caudle's Curtain Lectures" the presence of a genuine artist who, unlike Thackeray, remained a dedicated contributor to *Punch* and assured a place of respectability for the profession of comic journalism.

## THE ENGLISH IN LITTLE

THE MOST FAMOUS American in London in the year 1844 was a midget named Charles Stratton, better known as General Tom Thumb. His manager, the celebrated P. T. Barnum, determined that the best way to establish Tom Thumb financially was to make him the darling of fashion, trusting the common people to follow in the tracks of their betters; consequently, he directed all of his efforts toward seeking the approval of Queen Victoria. Barnum's cunning led to Thumb's appearance at Buckingham Palace, where he so charmed the Royal Family that they received him three times. Victoria presented Thumb with several expensive souvenirs, including a gold pencil case with the initials "T. T." and his coat of arms engraved on it. His subsequent appearances at the Egyptian Hall brought thousands of people to watch the little man strut about in his famous imitation of Napoleon and to see his representation of Grecian statues. Even the Duke of Wellington frequently called at the Hall and was particularly amused by Thumb's Napoleonic pose.

The historian's or biographer's account of Barnum's invasion of England little resembles that of Douglas Jerrold. His series of satirical papers, "The English in Little," appeared in *Punch* simultaneously with Thackeray's "The Snobs of England." The first installment explains that because "the English have idolised a dwarf . . . the pigmy, duly returning the compliment, paints 'The English in Little.'" Drawing upon current topics, Jerrold satirizes the societies of both England and America. The dual satire is effectively achieved by having the papers written in dialect under the persona of Tom Thumb. By dangling Thumb like a rash puppet in the midst of Buckingham Palace and making him raise the regal roof, Jerrold mocks royalty for lavishly favoring the foreign performer over many of England's gifted writers and artists. The aristocracy, upon whom Jerrold heaps the blame for most of England's ills, are also attacked for neglecting their country's poor while applauding and enriching the frivolous American visitor. Because of his hatred for war and Toryism, Jerrold singled out the Duke of Wellington for special ridicule.

Interwoven and contrasting with the local satire is a critical and satiric portrayal of American society—its vulgarity and egotistical patriotism, its pragmatic ethical standards, and its hypocrisy in proclaiming itself a free republic while practicing slavery. On the other hand, one may detect beneath the satire Jerrold's respect for the forthrightness and stamina inherent in the American's brash independence. Jerrold's pseudo-American dialect not only adds local color to the series but emphasizes the moral insensitivity of the American. Through Barnum's speech on the value of money, Jerrold portrays the English as modest and reserved and the American as amoral, pragmatic, avaricious, and vulgar—and he does this not only through what Barnum says but also through how he says it:

> . . . there is nothing—no moral pinte on the airth that money will not illustrate, if only you know how to set about it. Well, modesty is jist as stupid a thing as this; it is for all the world as if a full weight goolden sov'reign was to insist upon going for only nineteen shillins, and not a farden more. That is modesty; by which you will understand that modesty is always a thing that a man loses by . . . . Why it's as if a whole hog should beleetle himself down to a suckin pig.

Here is a savage caricature of the vulgar American who glibly illustrates even moral problems in terms of money. Applied to Thumb, Barnum's pragmatic philosophy implies that the midget is "a full weight goolden sov'reign" simply receiving his just evaluation from the English.

The entire serial is well conceived and balanced. Progressing from Barnum's and Thumb's arrival in London, through their rise to popular acceptance, to their departure to America, the series is further unified by being told from the point of view of Tom Thumb. By maintaining double points of view, satirically mocking both the American and the Englishman, Jerrold achieves a complexity and fullness of comic vision worthy of the finest satirists in a rich English tradition.


# CHARACTER SKETCHES

### MISCELLANEOUS PORTRAITS

YEARS BEFORE DICKENS began his *Sketches by Boz*, Jerrold was busily rendering his portraits of London characters in various magazines. His "Full Lengths," which comprised a group of characters drawn from everyday life and everyday people, appeared in the *Monthly Magazine* during

1826, and included such figures as the Greenwich Pensioner, the Drill Sergeant, the Tax-Gatherer, the Jew Slop-Seller, and the Ship's Clergyman. Under the influence of Theodore Hook, Jerrold published "Sketches of Character" in *Blackwood's Magazine* (1835–1836). "Job Pippins: the Man Who 'Couldn't Help it,' " "Adam Buff: the Man 'Without a Shirt,' " and "Christopher Snub: Who Was 'Born to Be Hanged' " are among the various portraits of men whose characters are rigidly determined by the sayings appended to their names. In 1839 Jerrold contributed fifteen "Portraits of the English" to a collection entitled *Heads of the People*, which contained works by Leigh Hunt, Thackeray, and other prominent authors. Once again, Jerrold focused upon the common man, including "The Pew Opener," "The Undertaker," "The Postman," "The Hangman," "The Cockney." In 1844 he wrote eleven sketches for *Punch* entitled "Exhibition of the English in China," which featured a number of portraits of individuals as well as types, including Shakespeare and Lord Brougham.

Unlike the classical and seventeenth-century character writers, Jerrold roams freely over his subject, and the structure of each sketch varies. He builds "The Cockney," for instance, upon a series of contrasts; the early and contemporary Cockney, the young and middle-aged Cockney, and the Cockney in England and abroad. He unifies the subject through the Cockney's timeless characteristics of cleverness, judiciousness, sprightliness, wit, and pride. These traits focus the contrasts into one comprehensive image of the eternal Cockney embodying "infinite fun and humor."

In the "Exhibition of the English in China," Jerrold varies his technique by writing from the point of view of a naïve Chinaman. Although each portrait is only a paragraph long, it is more satirical and sarcastic than the earlier sketches. Jerrold shifts his emphasis away from external appearances, background scenes, and verisimilitude in order to underscore such traits as hypocrisy, selfishness, and callousness. The focus has now moved from the outer to the inner man. In the earlier portraits men's faces and dress reveal their souls, but in the Chinaman's sketch of the Bishop, Jerrold goes beyond the facade of righteousness to the heart of the clerical hypocrite.

### JENKINS PAPERS

The "Jenkins Papers," which appeared in *Punch* intermittently between 1843 and 1848, began as a lampoon of the *Morning Post*, which specialized in news of fashionable society. Gradually, however, the character of Jenkins, intended as the personification of the newspaper, emerged as a portrait of a snob who was amusing in his own right. It is very possible that Thackeray used the character as the prototype for his "Snob" papers, especially since he contributed a few Jenkins numbers himself a year after Jerrold first conceived the idea.

The original of Jenkins was a *Morning Post* reporter named Rumsey Forster, whose duty it was to record the names of guests at fashionable receptions. By making him an opera critic, Jerrold could employ the opera house as a microcosm of England's aristocracy and the opera pit as a vantage point from which Jenkins views all society: "He very properly looks upon the condition of opera boxes as the barometer of 'society.' If Duchesses turn out in their best diamonds and sweetest smiles,— why, the weavers must be doing better at Bolton and Paisley."

Jerrold's technique is to take actual passages from the *Morning Post*, credit them to Jenkins, and develop his character out of these quotations by means of satiric embellishments. Jenkins is pictured as being more concerned with the genteel audience than with the performance itself. The splendor with which he surrounds himself is made a recurrent contrast to the smallness of his own character: "Behold him in his glory in the opera pit—and then view him, as we a hundred times have seen him, creeping furtively from his three-pair back to buy his herring, or the green luxury of water-cresses."

In "The Perennial Jenkins!" Jerrold not only deflates Jenkins' pomposity with a sartorial-anatomical analysis of his character, but in the following passage conjures up a coarse, comical image of Jenkins as a baboon, an animal with a distinctive rump of bare red calluses: "There is the monkey soul of Jenkins! And see you not his nether monkey, glowing in red plush? That is Jenkins' soul in full livery." Jerrold also weaves his earlier satire into the present one by repeating such bombastic words of Jenkins as "virtuosi," and by alluding to his earlier inane suggestion that the lower class eat nettles.

Thackeray's contributions to the "Jenkins" papers are more restrained than Jerrold's, being directed mostly at Jenkins' pretentious and uneducated use of French to raise the dignity of his prose. Although Thackeray wrote "Punch's Parting Tribute to Jenkins," the farewell proved premature. In the next volume of *Punch*, Thackeray revived him in "Gems from Jenkins." Soon after this essay Jenkins disappeared from the pages of *Punch*, but the editorial office received so many letters inquiring about his fate that Jerrold replied to his readers in "Jenkins!" that the *Punch* staff did not murder the flunky, but that he was to be found "mesmerized past hope of recovery at a neighbouring pot-house." This article was the real farewell to Jenkins. By leaving him in a trance "with slumbers light," Jerrold allows his readers to hope for Jenkins' reappearance in future issues of *Punch*. Two years later, in 1846, and again in 1848, Jerrold fulfills the letter of his promise to notify his readers should Jenkins awake, by having him appear at a royal wedding and later at Drury Lane to comment upon "Monte Cristo," but for all intents and purposes he was, in Thackeray's phrase, a "chose qui montre la corde" in 1844.

## TALES

JERROLD published over a hundred pieces of short fiction in most of the popular magazines of his day, from the lowly *New Monthly Magazine* to the highbrow *Blackwood's Magazine*. The majority of these tales are either farcical or didactic; the latter, which he labelled "moralities," inculcate a specific moral, usually domestic, virtue.

Devils and diabolical creatures figure largely in Jerrold's stories. "The Tutor Fiend and his Three Pupils," for example, bristles with the grotesque and the melodramatic. A variation on Chaucer's "Pardoner's Tale," it tells the story of a father who wants his sons tutored in the art of "getting on." The tutor, whose name is Rapax (Latin for "greed"), instills in his pupils a fascination for gold. They all travel to a primitive island, bringing guns, disease, and superstition with them. "In fine," writes Jerrold, "the island was civilized." Rapax becomes king; after he dies the oppressed natives rush into his home to capture his gold. Meanwhile, two of the three brothers have fled with their mentor's wealth, leaving the other behind to be hanged by the islanders because he cannot pay them for his passage. Then one of the two remaining brothers kills the other for his treasure, but unknowingly buries the keys to the gold hoard with the body. He goes mad and beats himself to death upon the locked chest.

Rapax is a fiend who personifies the commercial spirit of England in the early 1830's. Both the settlement in Australia and commercialism in India are suggested by Jerrold's satirical account of the tutor and his pupils' civilization of the island. Fifteen years later Harriet Martineau's *Dawn Island* balances Jerrold's account by singing the praises of the material well-being which the English merchants bring to an ignorant, savage group of natives.

Another devil appears in "The Wine Cellar," a story which curiously anticipates "The Cask of Amontillado." While not as subtle as Poe's tale, the fantastic irony of its conclusion, reminiscent of "The Tutor Fiend and His Three Pupils," is impressive. Although "The Wine Cellar" assumes a typical Victorian theme—that alcohol is destructive of mind and body—Jerrold ends the story with a piece of comic moralizing that burlesques the theme of sobriety. The contrast between the humor of the conclusion and the tone of horror that sustains the rest of the tale makes the whole work comically grotesque. Such burlesque of moral endings is in keeping with the cult of the comic-horrible, best exemplified in R. H. Barham's *The Ingoldsby Legends,* and reveals an aspect of Victorian humor seldom discussed.

Besides short fiction, Jerrold wrote three novels, *The Story of a Feather* (1843), *St. Giles and St. James* (1845–1847), and *A Man Made of Money* (1848). Read and admired by thousands of people, including Dickens, these works are too heavily laden with social propaganda and moralizing to be palatable today. Nevertheless, they provide a fascinating glimpse into the horrors of lower-class life during England's hungry forties. Because he was more concerned with social issues and the condition of the poor than he was with the creation of great art, Jerrold's novels, more than those of his famous contemporaries, contain reportage of the first order.

## THE ART OF JERROLD

In an essay on the cartoonist John Leech, Thackeray concisely summarizes the central theme of Jerrold's contributions to *Punch*:

> Mr. Leech surveys society from the gentleman's point of view. In old days, when Mr. Jerrold lived and wrote for that famous periodical, he took the other side; he looked up at the rich and great with a fierce, a sarcastic aspect, and a threatening posture, and his outcry, or challenge was: "Ye rich and great, look out! We, the people, are as good as you. Have a care, ye priests, wallowing on a tithe pig and rolling in carriages and four; ye landlords grinding the poor; ye vulgar fine ladies, bullying innocent governesses, and what not—we will expose your vulgarity; we will put down your oppression; we will vindicate the nobility of our common nature", and so forth. A great deal was to be said on the Jerrold side, a great deal was said—perhaps, even a great deal too much.[8]

8 "Mr. Leech's Sketches in Oil," The *Times* (June 2, 1862), p. 5.

Jerrold carried out in deadly earnestness his radical, democratic crusade on behalf of the poor and oppressed. A moralist concerned with equal justice for all people, he worked diligently at perfecting the art of comic journalism in order to capture the imagination of a lethargic public as a first step towards winning their sympathy for the common man and their outrage at his oppressors. Writing about himself as Mr. Punch, Jerrold outlined his satiric approach to current events:

> Whenever he has condescended to chronicle the events of the times, he has generally contrived to enrich his narrative with incidents which have altogether escaped the attention of his soberer contemporaries; nay, he has often reported circumstances wholly unknown to the actors thereof. Nevertheless, by so doing, he has endeavoured to deliver himself in the true spirit—if truly developed—of the event. If in his reports he narrates not precisely what really happened, but what—tested by the thing professed—*ought to have taken place*, he may certainly violate historic fidelity, but he submits that the fiction may have its moral utility.

Behind all his satire and distinguishing it from the superficial humor of the earlier comic journalists is Jerrold's utopian vision for England's future:

> Surely there will come a time when the Rich and the Poor will fairly meet, and have a great human talk upon the matter; will hold a parliament of the heart, and pass acts that no after selfishness and wrong—on either side—shall repeal! The Rich will come—not with cricket-balls or quoits in their hands—to make brotherhood with the Poor; but touched with the deep conviction that in this world the lowest created man has a solemn part to play, directed to solemn ends; that he is to be considered and cared for, in his condition, with tenderness, with fraternal benevolence; that there is something more than alms due from the high to the low; that human sympathy can speak otherwise than by the voice of money; and that, too, in at once a loftier and sweeter tone of hope and comforting.

# $\mathcal{S}$elections from "Q" PAPERS

## SIR PETER LAURIE ON HUMAN LIFE.*

SIR PETER LAURIE has set his awful face against suicide! He will in no way "encourage" *felo-de-se*. Fatal as this aldermanic determination may be to the interests of the shareholders of Waterloo, Vauxhall, and Southwark Bridges, Sir Peter has resolved that no man—not even in the suicidal season of November—shall drown, hang, or otherwise destroy himself, under any pretence soever! Sir Peter, with a very proper admiration of the pleasures of life, philosophises with a full stomach on the ignorance and wickedness of empty-bellied humanity; and Mr. Hobler—albeit in the present case the word is not reported—doubtless cried "Amen!" to the wisdom of the alderman. Sir Peter henceforth stands sentinel at the gate of death, and any hungry pauper who shall recklessly attempt to touch the knocker, will be sentenced to "the treadmill for a month as a rogue and vagabond!"

One *William Simmons*, a starving tailor, in a perishing condition, attempts to cut his throat. He inflicts upon himself a wound which, "under the immediate assistance of the surgeon of the Compter,"[1] is soon healed; and the offender being convalescent, is doomed to undergo the cutting wisdom of Sir Peter Laurie. Hear the alderman. "Don't you know *that that sort* of murder (suicide) *is as bad as any other?*" If such be the case— and we would as soon doubt the testimony of Balaam's quadruped[2] as Sir Peter—we can only say, that the law has most shamefully neglected to

*Punch*, I, 210.

[1] surgeon of the Compter, the physician at the debtors' prison.

[2] Balaam, in the Old Testament, a prophet summoned by Balak, king of Moab, to pronounce a curse upon the Israelites; three times during his journey his ass balked, and each time Balaam struck it in anger; the animal then spoke, reproaching him for his cruelty.

provide a sufficing punishment for the enormity. Sir Peter speaks with the humility of true wisdom, or he would never have valued his own throat for instance—that throat enriched by rivulets of turtle soup, by streams of city wine and city gravies—at no more than the throat of a hungry tailor. There never in our opinion was a greater discrepancy of windpipe. Sir Peter's throat is the organ of wisdom—whilst the tailor's throat, by the very fact of his utter want of food, is to him an annoying superfluity. And yet, says Sir Peter by inference, "It is *as bad,* William Simmons, to cut your own throat as to cut mine!" If true Modesty have left other public bodies, certainly she is to be found in the court of aldermen.

Sir Peter proceeds to discourse of the mysteries of life and death in a manner that shows that the executions of his shrievalty were not lost upon his comprehensive spirit. Suicides, however, have engaged his special consideration; for he says—

> Suicides and attempts, or apparent attempts, to commit suicide, very much increase, I regret to say. *I know that a morbid humanity exists,* and does much mischief as regards the practice. *I shall not encourage attempts of the kind,* but shall punish them; and I sentence you to the treadmill for a month, as a rogue and vagabond. I shall look *very narrowly at the cases* of persons brought before me on such charges.

Sir Peter has, very justly, no compassion for the famishing wretch stung and goaded "to jump the life to come." Why should he? Sir Peter is of that happy class of men who have found this life too good a thing to leave. "They call this world a bad world," says Rothschild[3] on a certain occasion; "for my part, I do not know of a better." And Rothschild was even a greater authority than Sir Peter Laurie on the paradise of £ *s. d.*

The vice of the day—"a morbid humanity" towards the would-be suicide—is, happily, doomed. Sir Peter Laurie refuses to patronise any effort at self-slaughter; and, moreover, threatens to "look very narrowly at the cases" of those despairing fools who may be caught in the attempt. It would here be well for Sir Peter to inform the suicidal part of the public what amount of desperation is likely to satisfy him as to the genuineness of the misery suffered. *William Simmons* cuts a gash in his throat; the Alderman is not satisfied with this, but having looked very narrowly

3 Rothschild, prominent family of international bankers. Nathan Meyer Rothschild (1777–1836), founder of the London branch of the family, died in 1836, after which the house of Rothschild was dominated by Baron Lionel Nathan de Rothschild (1808–1879).

into the wound, declares it to be a proper case for the treadmill. We can well believe that an impostor trading on the morbid humanity of the times—and there is a greater stroke of business done in the article than even the sagacity of a Laurie can imagine—may, in this cold weather, venture an immersion in the Thames or Serpentine, making the plunge with a declaratory scream, the better to extract practical compassion from the pockets of a morbidly humane society; we can believe this, Sir Peter, and feel no more for the trickster than if our heart were made of the best contract saddle-leather; but we confess a cut-throat staggers us; we fear, with all our caution, we should be converted to a belief in misery by a gash near the windpipe. Sir Peter, however, with his enlarged mind, professes himself determined to probe the wound—to look narrowly into its depth, breadth, and length, and to prescribe the treadmill, according to the condition of the patient! Had the cautious Sir Peter been in the kilt of his countryman *Macbeth*, he would never have exhibited an "admired disorder" on the appearance of *Banquo*, with his larynx severed in two; not he—he would have called the wound a slight scratch, having narrowly looked into it, and immediately ordered the ghost to the guard-house.

The Duke of Wellington, who has probably seen as many wounds as Sir Peter Laurie, judging the case, would, by his own admission, have inflicted the same sentence upon the tailor *Simmons* as that fulminated by the Alderman: Arthur and Peter would, doubtless, have been of one accord, *Simmons* avowed himself to be starving. Now, in this happy land— in this better Arcadia—every man who wants food is proved by such want an idler or a drunkard. The victor of Waterloo—the tutelary wisdom of England's counsels—has, in the solemnity of his Parliamentary authority, declared as much. Therefore it is most right that the lazy, profligate tailor, with a scar in his throat, should mount the revolving wheel for one month, to meditate upon the wisdom of Dukes and the judgments of Aldermen!

We no more thought of dedicating a whole page to one Sir Peter Laurie, than the zoological Mr. Cross[4] would think of devoting an acre of his gardens to one ass, simply because it happened to be the largest known specimen of the species. But, without knowing it, Sir Peter has given a fine illustration of the besetting selfishness of the times. Had Laurie been born to hide his ears in a coronet, he could not have more strongly displayed the social insensibility of the day. The prosperous saddler, and

4 Edward Cross, animal dealer who owned the Zoological Collection at Exeter 'Change in the Strand. In 1829 the collection moved to King's Mews, where the National Gallery now stands. In 1831 the Surrey Zoological Gardens acquired his collection.

the wretched, woe-begone tailor, are admirable types of the giant arrogance that dominates—of the misery that suffers.

There is nothing more talked of with less consideration of its meaning and relative value than—Life. Has it not a thousand different definitions? Is it the same thing to two different men?

Ask the man of independent wealth and sound body to paint Life, and what a very pretty picture he will lay before you. He lives in another world—has, as *Sir Anthony Absolute*[5] says, a sun and moon of his own—a realm of fairies, with attending sprites to perform his every compassable wish. To him life is a most musical monosyllable; making his heart dance, and thrilling every nerve with its so-potent harmony. Life—but especially *his* life—is, indeed, a sacred thing to him; and loud and deep are his praises of its miracles. Like the departed Rothschild, "he does not know a better;" certain we are, he is in no indecent haste to seek it.

Demand of the prosperous man of trade—of the man of funds, and houses, and land, acquired by successful projects—what is Life? He will try to call up a philosophic look, and passing his chin through his hand —(there is a brilliant on his little finger worth at least fifty guineas)—he will answer, "Life, sir—Life has its ups and downs; but taken altogether, for my part, I think a man a great sinner, a very great sinner, who doesn't look upon life as a very pretty thing. But don't let's talk of such dry stuff —take off your glass—hang it!—no heel-taps."

Ask another, whose whole soul, like a Ready Reckoner, is composed of figures,—what is Life? He, perhaps, will answer, "Why, sir, Life—if you insure at our office—is worth more than at any other establishment. We divide profits, and the rate of insurance decreases in proportion," &c. &c.; and thus you will have Life valued, by the man who sees nothing in it but a privilege to get money, as the merest article of commercial stock.

Inquire of many an Alderman what is Life? He will tell you that it is a fine, dignified, full-bellied, purple-faced creature, in a furred and violet-coloured gown. "Life," he will say, "always has its pleasures; but its day of great delight is the Ninth of November.[6] Life, however, is especially agreeable in swan-hopping season, when white-bait abounds at Blackwall[7] and Greenwich,[8] and when the Lord Mayor gives his Easter-ball;

5 Sir Anthony Absolute, in Sheridan's *The Rivals*, the strict but well-meaning father of Captain Absolute.

6 Ninth of November, Lord Mayor's Day, when the Lord Mayor goes in procession with the Aldermen to and from Westminster, where he receives from the Lord Chancellor the assent of the crown to his election.

7 Blackwall, a popular shipyard and location of Lovegrove's Tavern, famous for its whitebait dinners.

8 Greenwich, a borough of London, located on the south bank of the Thames.

and 'keeps up the hospitalities of his high office.' " Not, however, that life is without its graver duties—its religious observations. Oh, no! it is the duty of well-to-do Life to punish starving men for forgetting its surpassing loveliness—it is a high obligation of Life to go to church in a carriage, and confess itself a miserable sinner—it is the duty of Life to read its bible; and then the Alderman, to show that he is well versed in the volume, quotes a passage—"when the voice of the turtle is heard in the land."

Now ask the Paisley[9] weaver what is Life? Bid the famine-stricken multitudes of Bolton[10] to describe with their white lips the surpassing beauty of human existence. Can it be possible that the glorious presence—the beneficent genius that casts its blessings in the paths of other men—is such an ogre, a fiend, to the poor? Alas! is he not a daily tyrant, scourging with meanest wants—a creature that, with all its bounty to others, is to the poor and destitute more terrible than Death? Let Comfort paint a portrait of Life, and now Penury take the pencil. "Pooh! pooh!" cry the sage Lauries of the world, looking at the two pictures—"that scoundrel Penury has drawn an infamous libel. *That* Life! with that withered face, sunken eye, and shrivelled lip; and what is worse, with a suicidal scar in its throat! *That* Life! The painter Penury is committed for a month as a rogue and vagabond. We shall look very narrowly into these cases."

We agree with the profound Sir Peter Laurie that it is a most wicked, a most foolish act of the poor man to end his misery by suicide. But we think there is a better remedy for such desperation than the tread-mill. The surest way for the rich and powerful of the world to make the poor man more careful of his life is to render it of greater value to him.

Q.

## THE PRINCE OF WALES.—HIS FUTURE TIMES.*

A PRIVATE letter from Hanover states that, precisely at twelve minutes to eleven in the morning on the ninth of the present November, his Maj-

---

[9] Paisley, a town in Renfrewshire, Scotland, with a thriving textile industry, famous in the nineteenth century for patterned Paisley shawls.

[10] Bolton, a borough in Lancashire, England, known for its textile industry.

*Punch, I, 222.

esty King Ernest[11] was suddenly attacked by a violent fit of blue devils. All the court doctors were immediately summoned, and as immediately dismissed, by his Majesty, who sent for the Wizard of the North (recently appointed royal astrologer), to divine the mysterious cause of this so sudden melancholy. In a trice the mystery was solved—Queen Victoria "was happily delivered of a Prince!" His Majesty was immediately assisted to his chamber—put to bed—the curtains drawn—all the royal household ordered to wear list slippers—the one knocker to the palace was carefully tied up—and (on the departure of our courier) half a load of straw was already deposited beneath the window of the royal chamber. The sentinels on duty were prohibited from even sneezing, under pain of death, and all things in and about the palace, to use a bran new simile, were silent as the grave!

"Whilst there was only the Princess Royal there were many hopes. There was hope from severe teething—hope from measles—hope from hooping-cough—but with the addition of a Prince of Wales, the hopes of Hanover are below par." But we pause. We will no further invade the sanctity of the sorrows of a king; merely observing, that what makes his Majesty very savage, makes hundreds of thousands of Englishmen mighty glad. There are now two cradles between the Crown of England and the White Horse of Hanover.

We have a Prince of Wales! Whilst, however, England is throwing up its million caps in rapture at the advent, let it not be forgotten to whom we owe the royal baby. In the clamourousness of our joy the fact would have escaped us, had we not received a letter from Colonel Sibthorp,[12] who assures us that we owe a Prince of Wales entirely to the present cabinet; had the Whigs remained in office, the infant would inevitably have been a girl.

For our own part—but we confess we are sometimes apt to look too soberly at things—we think her Majesty (may all good angels make her caudle!) is, inadvertently no doubt, treated in a questionable spirit of compliment by these uproarious rejoicings at the sex of the illustrious little boy, who has cast, if possible, a new dignity upon Lord Mayor's day, and made the very giants of Guildhall[13] shoot up an inch taller at the

11 Ernest Augustus (1771–1851), fifth son of George III of England and king of Hanover; associated with the reactionary Tories in England and known for his ultra-conservative reign.

12 Charles de Laet Waldo Sibthorp (1783–1855), colonel of the militia and politician, belonged to the ultra-Tory and ultra-Protestant party in Parliament.

13 Gog and Magog, two huge wooden statues in Guildhall.

compliment he has paid them of visiting the world on the ninth of November. In our playful enthusiasm, we have—that is, the public *We*—
declared we must have a Prince of Wales—we should be dreadfully in the
dumps if the child were not a Prince—the Queen must have a Prince—
a bouncing Prince—and nothing but a Prince. Now might not an ill-
natured Philosopher (but all philosophers are ill-natured) interpret
these yearnings for masculine royalty as something like pensive regrets
that the throne should ever be filled by the feminine sex? For own part
we are perfectly satisfied that the Queen (may she live to see the Prince
of Wales wrinkled and white-headed!) is a Queen, and think Victoria the
First sounds quite as musically—has in it as full a note of promise—as if
the regal name had run—George the Fifth! We think there is a positive
want of gallantry at this unequivocally shouted preference of a Prince
of Wales. Nevertheless, we are happy to say, the pretty, good-tempered
Princess Royal (she is *not* blind, as the Tories once averred; but then the
Whigs were *in*) still laughs and chirrups as if nothing had happened.
Nay, as a proof of the happy nature of the infant (we beg to say that the
fact is copyright, as we purchased it of the reporter of *The Observer*),
whilst, on the ninth instant, the chimes of St. Martin's were sounding
merrily for the birth of the Prince, the Princess magnanimously shook
her coral-bells in welcome of her dispossessing brother!

Independently of the sensation made in the City by the new glory that
has fallen upon the ninth of November (it is said that Sir Peter Laurie
has been so rapt by the auspicious coincidence, that he has done nothing
since but talk and think of "the Prince of Wales"—that on Wednesday
last he rebuked an infant beggar with, "I've nothing for you, *Prince of
Wales*")—independently of the lustre flung upon the new Lord Mayor
and the Lord Mayor just out—who will, it is said, both be caudle-cup
baronets, the occasion has given birth to much deep philosophy on the
part of our contemporaries—so deep, that there is no getting to the end
of it, and has also revived much black-letter learning connected with the
birth of every Prince of Wales, from the first to the last—and, therefore,
certainly not least—newcomer.

An hour or so after George the Fourth was born, we are told that the
waggons containing the treasure of the *Hermione*, a Spanish galleon,
captured off St. Vincent by three English frigates, entered St. James's-
street, escorted by cavalry and infantry, with trumpets sounding, the
enemy's flags waving over the waggons, and the whole surrounded by an
immense multitude of spectators. Now here, to the vulgar mind, was a
happy augury of the future golden reign of the Royal baby. He comes
upon the earth amid a shower of gold! The melodious chink of dou-

bloons and pieces of eight echo his first infant wailings! What a theme for the gipsies of the press—the fortune-tellers of the time! At the present hour that baby sleeps the last sleep in St. George's chapel; and we have his public and his social history before us. What does experience—the experience bought and paid for by hard, hard cash—*now* read in the "waggons of treasure," groaning musically to the rocking-cradle of the callow infant? Simply, that the babe of Queen Charlotte[14] would be a very expensive babe indeed; and that the wealth of a Spanish galleon was all insufficient for the youngling's future wants.

We have been favoured, among a series of pictures, with the following of George the Fourth, exhibited in his babyhood. We are told that "all persons *of fashion* were admitted to see the Prince, under the following restrictions, viz.—that in passing through the apartment *they stepped with the greatest caution,* and did not offer to touch his Royal Highness. For the greater security in this respect, a part of the apartment was latticed off *in the Chinese manner,* to prevent curious persons from approaching too nearly."

That lattice "in the Chinese manner" was a small yet fatal foreshadowing of the Chinese Pavilion at Brighton—of that temple, worthy of Pekin, wherein the Royal infant of threescore was wont to enshrine himself, not from the desecrating touch of the world, but even from the eyes of a curious people, who, having paid some millions towards manufacturing the most finished gentleman in Europe, had now and then a wish—an unregarded wish—to look at their expensive handiwork.

What different prognostics have we in the natal day of our present Prince of Wales! What rational hopes from many circumstances that beset him. The Royal infant, we are told, is suckled by a person "named Brough, formerly a *housemaid* at Esher."[15] From this very fact, will not the Royal child grow up with the consciousness that he owes his nourishment even to the very humblest of the people? Will he not suck in the humanising truth with his very milk?

And then for the Spanish treasure—"hard food for Midas"—that threw its jaundiced glory about the cradle of George the Fourth; what is that to the promise of plenty, augured by the natal day of our present Prince? Comes he not on the ninth of November? Is not his advent glorified by the aromatic clouds of the Lord Mayor's kitchen?—Let every man, woman, and child possess themselves of a *Times* newspaper of the 10th ult.;

14 Queen Charlotte (1744–1818), consort of George III of England.
15 Esher, a fashionable residential suburb of London. Wolsey's Tower and the remains of Esher Place, founded by William Waynflete and occupied by Cardinal Wolsey, are here.

for there, in genial companionship with the chronicle of the birth of the Prince, is the luscious history of the Lord Mayor's dinner. We quit Buckingham Palace, our mind full of our dear little Queen, the Royal baby, Prince Albert—(who, as *The Standard* informs us subsequently, bows "bare-headed" to the populace,)—the Archbishop of Canterbury, Doctor Locock,[16] the Duke of Wellington, and the monthly nurse, and immediately fall upon the civic "general bill of fare,"—the real turtle at the City board.

Oh, men of Paisley—good folks of Bolton—what promise for ye is here! Turkeys, capons, sirloins, asparagus, pheasants, pine-apples, Savoy cakes, Chantilly baskets, mince pies, preserved ginger, brandy cherries, a thousand luscious cates that "the sense aches at!"[17] What are all these gifts of plenty, but a glad promise that in the time of the "sweetest young Prince," that on the birth-day of that Prince just vouchsafed to us, all England will be a large Lord Mayor's table! Will it be possible for Englishmen to disassociate in their minds the Prince of Wales and the Prince of good Fellows? And whereas the reigns of other potentates are signalised by bloodshed and war, the time of the Prince will be glorified by cooking and good cheer. His drum-sticks will be the drum-sticks of turkeys—his cannon, the popping of corks. In his day, even weavers shall know the taste of geese, and factory-children smack their lips at the gravy of the great sirloin. Join your glasses! brandish your carving-knives! cry welcome to the Prince of Wales! for he comes garnished with all the world's good things. He shall live in the hearts, and (what is more) in the stomachs of his people!     Q.

## OLD BAILEY HOLIDAYS.*

*You will not leave one behind you who will not think a good deed done when your life is put an end to.*

THUS SPOKE Lord Denman[18] from the judgment-seat of the Old Bailey

16 Sir Charles Locock (1799–1875), obstetric physician; in 1840 appointed first physician accoucheur to Queen Victoria, he attended at the birth of all her children.

17 "O thou weed / Who art so lovely fair and smell'st so sweet / That the sense aches at thee, would hadst ne'er been born!" (*Othello*, IV, ii, 68–70.)

18 Thomas, Lord Denman (1779–1854), lord chief justice, had gained a minor reputation for law reforms, such as the abolition of capital punishment for forgery and other lesser offenses. Jerrold, on the other hand, was opposed to capital punishment on principle.

*Punch, II, 240.

to a convicted murderer; and the mob assembled outside of Newgate sent forth many and joyous hurrahs, as they became assured of another Old Bailey holiday! A man was to be hanged—a good thing was to be done,—and the wise, and humane, and contemplative of this huge metropolis, would be gathered together to bear solemn witness to the merits and the great social utility of the deed. However, before the crowning sacrifice ordained by law to vindicate humanity was performed, it was necessary, most necessary to the ends of justice, that there should be acted a prefatory ceremony: the wretch should be made a *warning show* to the public—or, at least, to that happy and delighted section thereof with Newgate interest, or, better still, with private influence with the wife of London's Mayor. The "condemned sermon," with the real murderer, racked and torn, and convulsed with agony, was a great moral lesson not to be neglected by any who could command the enjoyment of so rare an excitement; and, therefore, many were the applicants, great was the knocking at the doors of Newgate, on the long-expected Sabbath!

However, *"at ten o'clock all were accommodated in the most satisfactory manner in the different parts of the chapel allotted to visitors. At about that hour the Lady Mayoress and some of her ladyship's friends entered the governor's pew!"*

They have all, in a few heartfelt sentences, addressed themselves to God, imploring that what they are about to hear *and see* that day may work to their soul's health. This duty done, the benevolence of the law, that on such occasions shows a murderer

——as men show an ape,[19]

is made manifest, for the real assassin—(and, oh! what a fluttering of hearts among the Mayoress's friends!)—is brought in by real turnkeys, and placed in a chair!

"His appearance indicated extreme mental suffering. He clasped his hands together sometimes, and sometimes he raised them up and pressed them against *his breast in great agony, the tears streaming from his eyes,* whilst he endeavoured to catch a glimpse of some old acquaintance or friend amongst the surrounding multitude. So strong *was the expression of horror* in his face and demeanour, that *a respectable female,* who was prompted by the curiosity which will induce even persons of the weakest nerves to witness the 'condemned sermon' once in their lives, *shrieked and fainted.* The culprit looked with evident anxiety towards the spot

[19] "Superior beings, when of late they saw / A mortal man unfold all Nature's law, / Admir'd such wisdom in an earthly shape, / And show'd a Newton as we show an ape." (Alexander Pope, *An Essay on Man*, Epistle II, ll. 31–34.)

from which the alarm proceeded; but, finding that a stranger was the cause of it, he seemed to retire *within the awful circle of his own meditations*, and to struggle with feelings beyond the power of any human being to describe."

Now, was not this a spectacle worthy of the curiosity of refined, gentle, sight-seeking woman! Who would seek the vulgar playhouse, and pay their money to witness only ideal woe, when—with Newgate interest—ladies may be on the free list for all condemned sermons?—when they may witness real agony—may see the scalding tears of hopeless remorse—may behold a real murderer, dyed from crown to sole in human blood, writhing in all the hell of horror and despair! Is not this a sight worthy of meek, soft-hearted woman? Is it not something to stare and gaze upon a wretch, and to strive to pry "within the awful circle of his own meditations," as if the ulcerous heart of human guilt were a puppet-show to sate the "curiosity" of "respectable" females? When Justice dooms the murderer to the gallows, is it not most fit, most decent, that she should make a stare-cap of him, so that "ladies," the "Mayoress's friends" and others, may witness out of "curiosity" the experiment of a sermon played upon the half-dead wretch? If we might suggest an enlargement of Newgate hospitalities, we would propose that all ladies admitted to the condemned sermon should be invited to behold the galvanic battery applied to the corpse of the murderer as early as possible after execution. Certain we are that the exhibition would be equally interesting, equally pleasurable to the nervous system; and more, if ladies are liable to the accidental excitement of "shriekings and faintings," they would not then call the ghastly object played upon "from the awful circle of his own meditations;" for *then* he would be—who among the best, the most spotless of us, shall say—*where*?

We think, however, that the great social good arising from the exhibition made at condemned sermons would certainly be increased by further carrying out the sentiment that induces ladies to attend them. Hence, they certainly should be present at the galvanic experiment; and more, what a wholesome, moral fillip it would give them, if, at midnight, they were to attend the burial of the assassin, and, to show their horror of his deeds, were to cast within his unblest, unsanctified grave, a handful or so of lime, duly provided on these occasions to consume the murderer's bones! We are convinced that those delicate ladies who attend the funeral discourses on yet living men, would feel an additional sentiment —an enlargement of piety—from this last act. They would—bless their delicacy!—scatter their lime, as the *Queen* in *Hamlet* scatters the flowers upon *Ophelia*'s tomb,—with the same tenderness, the same pathos!

But the "condemned sermon" is over; the Lady Mayoress's friends and other visitors having wept and shrieked, and gazed upon the livid, tortured brow of homicide, feel their Christianity and their morals mightily refreshed by the discipline, and not being of those

Who think they're pious when they're only bilious,[20]

they retire to their homes, more than ever odorous from the sanctity of the "governor's pew." They have seen a murderer—have stared at him— have seen his whole frame convulsed and tortured—have gazed upon his flesh-quakes as they would have watched an exquisite piece of mechanism,—and the sight has done them all "a world of good!"

The murderer is to die at eight o'clock. Hours before, "groups of persons assembled in the Old Bailey." Besides, so great was the determination of the denizens of the Old Bailey to afford to their fellow-citizens every convenience for the enjoyment of a great moral spectacle, that all the houses opposite the prison had been let to sight-seeking lovers at an enormous price, and, in several instances, the whole of the casements were taken out and raised seats erected for their accommodation. In one case a noble lord was pointed out to the reporter as having been a spectator at the last four or five executions; his price for his seat was said to be 15£. Ah, happy noble lord, whose purse can thus readily minister to his moral improvement! However, where Fortune denied her means of a comfortable seat at a window, men were yet so intent upon the instruction to be gathered from the gallows—that tree of public knowledge—that they passed the whole night in front of Newgate, watching the "unfolding star;"[21] discussing on the mystery of life and death, on the temptations of the devil, on the only means of fortifying weak and erring man against the assaults of sin, and resolving in themselves to check and castigate the lusts of the flesh, urged to the discipline by the awful event that drew them there together. Others spoke not, but, rapt in themselves, pondered on the pomps and vanities, the fleeting gilded follies of this world, and the enduring glories of the next; and thus divinely absorbed, saw, with their spiritual eye, "angels ascending and descending"[22] from the spire of St. Sepulchre's church!

---

[20] "No solemn sanctimonious face I pull, / Nor think I'm pious when I'm only bilious; / Nor study in my sanctum supercilious, / To frame a Sabbath Bill or forge a Bull." (Thomas Hood, "Ode to Rae Wilson, Esq.," ll. 43–46.)

[21] "Look, the unfolding star calls up the shepherd." (*Measure for Measure*, IV, ii, 219.)

[22] "And he dreamed, and behold a ladder set up on the earth, and the top of it reached to heaven: and behold the angels of God ascending and descending on it." Genesis, xxviii, 12.

The knell of the murderer sounds, and the dying wretch mounts the scaffold. How hushed the mob! Each man may hear his fellow's heart beat in that terrible moment of silence and suspense. The bolt is drawn, and as the culprit falls, thousands gasp as one man, and lock their palsied hands in breathless horror. A few minutes pass, and the enormous multitude, awe-stricken by what they have beheld, and casting terrified looks at the corpse yet turning in the air, silently disperse, and for that day at least are never seen to smile. Their daily labour done, they seek their early homes, and having read their bibles, pray *not* to be led "into temptation."

Moreover, throughout the Old Bailey, no man loses snuffbox, purse, or pocket-handkerchief!

And "this is the moral influence!" and it is with delight we quote these words from *The Times*—"this is the moral influence of capital punishments!"      Q.

## PEEL'S "VELVETEENS."*

THE INGENUOUS Sir Robert has been the victim of a shameful trick. For ourselves, we have not the slightest doubt that the Corn-Law Leaguers are at the bottom of the transaction, which we only hope it is within the reach of Parliament to punish. The conspiracy displays such subtlety— has in it such a wicked *animus*—that did we merely consult our own feelings, we should devote the whole of our present number to discuss the iniquity, in its every shade of turpitude; in its depth, length, and width. The careless world, however, has not the same interest as Punch in the feelings of a Prime Minister—has, of course, not the same intimate sympathies with the private emotions of a politician. We shall therefore narrate, with all our characteristic brevity, the circumstances of as dark a political conspiracy as ever blackened the human heart—will show how the peace—nay, more the consistency of a Prime Minister, has been aimed at in his hour of social confidence, threatened in his whole anatomy.

A week or two since, Mr. W. Barlow of Ancoats-vale having—we are convinced of this truth—by the instigation of the Corn-Law League, perfected "some printed velveteens" of a most novel and beautiful fabric, sent a few yards of his handiwork as a present to Sir Robert Peel. Gracious, unsuspecting Minister! No artless milkmaid on Drayton Manor could have received with less suspicion a bunch of ribands from Hodge,

*Punch*, IV, 36.

the carter; albeit given for the basest after-purposes by the designing clown. Sir Robert gazed upon the velveteen "made to look like silk," although of cotton,—gazed, and was lost. (Mr. Barlow has the honesty to allow that one of the excellences of the fabric is, that it appears much better than it really is; that it has a glossy, silky outside look, to captivate unthinking eyes; although, indeed, the stuff itself be of an inferior yarn— a thing of very cotton. Why, believing this, Mr. Barlow should have thought fit to select such a politician as Sir Robert to patronize his velveteen, we leave to the man's conscience to answer; and proceed with our story.) Sir Robert—courteous victim!—lost no time in acknowledging the present of velveteen, and—(how the Corn-Law League must have chuckled!)—further assured Mr. Barlow, that Lady Peel was so delighted with the stuff, that she purposed *"having a cloak"* made of part of it, whilst he, Sir Robert, would devote the remnant to his own bodily comfort, in some other fashion!

Reader, pause for a moment, and imagine the smothered laugh shaking the ribs of the League! How the master manufacturer grinned with all his heart and all his soul! Nay, it is said, that feeble smiles did "shoot and circulate" in the tax-ground faces of the tenants of Manchester cellars—that the very ghastliness of want was irradiated with the dim sense of a joke played upon the Prime Minister! Indeed, everywhere throughout Manchester, laughter abounded. It is said, the very knockers on the manufacturers' doors were dimpled with smiles—that the church vanes no longer creaked, but laughed audibly! Wherefore? Why this exultation at the courtesy of the most courteous of Prime Ministers? Why this rudeness of merriment at an act of gentlemanly condescension? With mingled feelings of contempt and pity for our species, we tell the why.

The velveteen was made into a cloak—(this we know from Lady Peel's milliner,)—the remainder stuff was worked into trousers for the Prime Minister—(this we know from Sir Robert's tailor, the same man who has made our own motley for many years),—when the fraud, the iniquity, lurking in the fatal gift was discovered.

It appears that some *ears of wheat* were gracefully worked into the pattern adorning the velveteen, and further, that the dreaded monosyllable "FREE,"—those four damning letters, like tares and poppies, grew among the corn, thus insidiously presented to the Minister. Lady Peel, with the quick feminine eye, discovered the device at once.[23] Why, then,

[23] Incredible as it may seem, such a gift was actually offered, and Peel's letter of refusal was printed in the *Times* (Jan. 12, 1843, p. 5), followed by Barlow's disclamation of any intention on his part of connecting Peel's acceptance of the velveteen with any subject of public controversy.

it may be asked, did so many days elapse ere Sir Robert returned the stuff—for return it, he did—to Mr. Barlow? Ere we answer, we subjoin the missive that accompanied the rejected velveteen:—

> Drayton Manor, Jan. 7, 1843.—Sir: I was not aware, until to-day, that the specimen of manufacture which you requested me to accept bore any allusion to matters that are the subject of public controversy. No mention whatever was made of this in the letter you addressed to me; and I thought it would be ungracious to reject what appeared to be a pure act of civility on your part. I must beg leave to return to you that which I accepted under an erroneous impression. I am, Sir, your obedient servant, ROBERT PEEL.— W. Barlow, Esq.

Lady Peel, like an excellent, devoted wife as she is, with a full knowledge of the wheat, and of those "idle weeds," the letters F. R. E. E. that "grew among the sustaining corn,"[24]—ordered her cloak to be made; and wherefore? Simply, because she knew that Sir Robert had, at the last election, used a cloak with some sort of corn-law device upon it, and that therefore, like a good wife, she could do no better than follow the example of a virtuous and beloved husband. How different the case with Sir Robert, the Prime Minister!

We have no doubt whatever, that as far as a cloak might have been got out of the stuff for himself, Sir Robert would have had no objection to retain the velveteen as a provision for future accidents; keeping it on, or putting it off as the wind might blow, or the sun might shine; but when once the velveteen was made into trousers, when once the minister had donned so succinct a garment, it must become to him a sort of tight-fitting principle, not under any circumstances to be cast aside, with the least respect for the usages of honourable society. It was then Sir Robert saw the trap that had been laid for him; it was then that, looking with an instructed eye upon the velveteen, he felt the full force of the political plot got up in a pair of trousers:

> The seed was cursèd that did grow the web,
> And it was dyed in mummy, which the Corn Laws
> Conserved of broken hearts![25]

Such, then, appeared the velveteen presented by Mr. W. Barlow, and the Prime Minister immediately resolved to put no foot in it.

We hope there is no admirer of Sir Robert who will not feel grateful for the escape of the Minister. Spells and incantations have been woven

[24] ". . . and all the idle weeds that grow / In our sustaining corn." (*King Lear*, IV, iv, 5–6.)

[25] "The worms were hallowed that did breed the silk; / And it was dyed in mummy which the skillful / Conserved of maidens' hearts." (*Othello*, III, iv, 77–79.)

in a web ere now; and these, we are convinced of it, lurked in every ear of law-taxed corn.

> See the griesly texture grow,
> (*'Tis of human entrails made*,)
> And the weights that play below,
> Each a starving Briton's head![26]

Might not the velveteen, the produce of Corn-law looms, have been manufactured from such horrid materials—by such ghastly machinery? Indeed, we fear it.

And then that fatal word "FREE." In the *Gesta Romanorum*[27] there is a story of a beautiful girl who, having been nurtured upon serpents, was sent as a slave to a certain king; the monarch kissed the rosy venom, and straightway died. We have not the slightest doubt that the word "free" in Peel's velveteen was composed of serpents—and that no sooner should the Prime Minister have taken the trousers to himself, than that the petty reptiles would have grown into boa-constrictors, and poor Sir Robert, the unwilling Laocoön[28] of "free" corn, would, as Minister, have been strangled by opposing principles!

However, thanks to the late sagacity of Sir Robert, our minister is saved. We have, let us be grateful for it, another plot to add to the unsuccessful machinations of democrats and knaves. We have had the Gunpowder Plot—the Rye-house Plot—the Thistlewood Plot—and now, as a crowning escape—the Velveteen Plot! Great, indeed, would have been the triumph of the League, if the Minister had donned the insidious trousers, and, taking his seat in them in the House of Commons, had, without knowing it, based his Ministry upon—"free" corn!          Q.

## THE WRONGS OF PUNCH:
### HIS EXPULSION FROM FRANCE—LETTER THEREON
### TO KING LOUIS-PHILIPPE.*

PACKET BOAT INN, DOVER, *Feb.* 11.

CITIZEN KING,—For once, indignation has been too much for sea-sickness.

[26] Suggested by the Witches' chant in *Macbeth*, IV, i, 4–5: "Round about the cauldron go: / In the poison'd entrails throw."

[27] *Gesta Romanorum*, a Latin collection of anecdotes and tales, probably compiled early in the fourteenth century.

[28] Laocoön, in Greek mythology, the priest of Apollo who warned the Trojans not to touch the wooden horse made by the Greeks in the Trojan War. Because he incurred the anger of one of the gods, he and his two sons were killed by sea serpents.

*Punch*, IV, 75.

PUNCH TURNED OUT OF FRANCE!

"I have this moment, in a half-tempest, arrived from Boulogne—thrust from the port by the point of the sword. Yes; it is true—*Punch* is no longer to be admitted into France."—*Vide* page 95.

I have this moment, in a half-tempest, arrived from Boulogne—thrust from the port by the point of the sword. Yes; it is true—*Punch* is no longer to be admitted into France. *Punch,* who—but I have swallowed another *goutte* of brandy, and will subdue my feelings.

And is it thus, Louis,—is it thus you use an old friend! You, whom I have counted upon as almost my idolater; you, whose wariness—whose ingenuity—whose fine sense of self-preservation made you seem to the eyes of all men the first disciple of the school of *Punch*—do you now use your old master as whilom Plato maltreated Socrates?

It is barely two days since, and with what a jocund heart did I leave my wife (I am proud to say with a complimentary mist in her eyes) at the wharf of London bridge! How did that heart sink as the boat boiled past the Reculvers[29]—how very ill, indeed, was I off the North Foreland[30]—how more than puppy-sick ere I reached the port of Boulogne? "Never mind," thought I, as I quitted the *Magnet*; "here, at least, is Balm of Gilead[31] at two francs a bottle!" and with the thought the violet hue of my nose subsided, my blood quickened, and I stept out airily towards the Custom-house.

"What is your name?" says the clerk, with a suspicious look—a look significantly answered by a corps of *douaniers*—"What is your name?"

You know the graceful bend of my back—the smile that ordinarily puckers up my mouth. With that bend and that smile then, I answered—"*Punch!*"

"*C'est bien*—it is henceforth not permitted that your blood shall circulate in France. *Otez ce coquin*—take the vagabond away!" Thus spoke the man in authority; and in a trice, I was escorted to the *Water Witch,* then starting for Dover, and was in two hours and a half seated in an English inn, where—

[I beg your pardon, but I am interrupted. A man (a Dover waterman) has followed me to my hotel to beg—that is, enforce—"sixpence" for the accommodation of a plank from the wharf to the boat, the steam company, the mayor and magistrates of Dover smiling blandly on the extortion.]

I sank back in my chair, and endeavoured to review my past doings. How—how, thought I, can I have stirred the philosophic bile of my good

29 Reculvers, a small English village on the north coast of Kent, nine miles west of Margate.

30 North Foreland and South Foreland are headlands of Kent, England, forming part of the boundary of the roadstead called the Downs.

31 balm of Gilead, a liquid made from Mecca balsam, a small evergreen tree, and believed to have healing powers.

friend, Louis Philippe? For what can he have thus turned me out of Boulogne—wherefore stop my travels in France!

Whilst in this exceedingly brown study, a Frenchman entered the
room. He threw a piercing look at me, lifted his hat with a mixture of
scorn and forced politeness, and said—"*Mille pardons—mais—n'est-ce pas
—Ponch?*"

"Then you know me, monsieur?" said I.

"*Oui, monsieur*—I have read your things in Boulogne—in Paris"—and
still the Frenchman scowled, then laughed, as I thought, vindictively.

"Sir, I am happy at this meeting. You may, perhaps, resolve a doubt
that just now eats up my brain. In the first place, I have—yes—*Punch*
has been turned out of France."

"*C'est bien—c'est fort bien,*" said the Frenchman, with open delight.

"Bless me!" I exclaimed—"Why, what have I done?"

"What have you not done?" roared the Frenchman.

With subdued voice, I begged of him to enumerate my written of-
fences. It seemed to him a labour of love, for he drew his chair close to
the table, squared his elbows upon it, and his eyes flashing, and his moustache twisting and working like a young eel, thus began.

"In the first place,—Did you not call Louis-Philippe hard names about
the Spanish business? When Orca, Leon, and others were tricked to be
shot by Christina, did you not accuse Louis-Philippe of having his finger
in the bloodshed?"[32]

"I did."

"Secondly,—Did you not place the Great Napoleon on a monument of
froth, spouting from a bottle of imperial pop?"

"It can't be denied."

"Thirdly,—Did you not sneer at our colonies? Did you not more than
doubt the justice of our cutting Arab throats, and extracting true glory
from bloodshed? Did you not laugh at the Trappists, and fling hard
names upon General Bugeaud?"[33]

[32] Maria Christina (1806–1878), fourth wife of King Ferdinand VII, regent of
Spain, and mother of Queen Isabella II. Warfare between the conservatives (the
Carlists) and the liberals (the Christinists) divided Spain. Britain, France, and Portugal supported the Christinists; France's aid reflected the hope of Louis Philippe
(1773–1850) to revive the Bourbon family alliance between Spain and France by
having his son marry Isabella's younger sister. Jerrold sympathized with the Carlist
insurrectionists Orca and Leon, "the trusting and the brave," as he called them,
who he felt were being used as mere puppets by Christina and Louis Philippe.

[33] General Thomas Robert Bugeaud (1784–1849), French colonial official and
marshal of France, served in Africa from 1836 to 1847, was governor of Algeria in
1840, and won the battle of Isly, in Morocco, in 1844. The Trappists in Algeria
supported Bugeaud's view that the Cross must follow the Flag.

"All quite true."

"Fourthly,—Did you not desecrate—yes, desecrate—the eloquence of Mons. Dumas, when he turned a funeral oration on poor Orleans[34] into a drama for the Porte St.-Martin?"

"I confess it."

"And do you not, almost every week, preach up what you insolently call the mischief of glory, and question the born right of every French-man to carry fire and bloodshed into every country he can get into—and more, do you not laugh at and denounce, what is as dear to every French-man as the recollection of his mother's milk, a hatred, an undying ha-tred, to England and all that's English?"

"I own to every word of it."

"And more—do you not . . . ?"

"I beg your pardon, monsieur," said a stage-coachman, at this point entering the room, "if you are the gentleman as is going to Canterbury, time's up."

The Frenchman did not finish his sentence, but rising, and again lift-ing his hat, he with a grim smile and flashing eyes, stalked away.

And now, my quondam friend Louis-Philippe, I have put the above colloquy to paper, that I may herewith ask you, if your subject and fel-low-citizen is right as to the causes which (under your orders) have shut me out of France? If they be not, you will drop me a line. If they be, I will take your silence (and smuggle accordingly) for affirmation.

Yours,

"As thou usest me,"

PUNCH.

## WANTED—SOME BISHOPS!*

THERE MUST be a statue of virgin gold—a colossal statue, too, wigged and gowned—to Henry, Bishop of Exeter.[35] He has, with a cat's-leap,

---

[34] Ferdinand-Philippe, duc d'Orleans (1810–1842), heir to throne, patron of let-ters and friend of Victor Hugo and Alexandre Dumas.

[35] Dr. Henry Phillpotts (1778–1869) won *Punch's* satiric title "Henry of Exeter" for the wealth and power which he represented. Jerrold frequently attacked him for his avoidance of the plight of the London poor.

*Punch,* IV, 226.

jumped at the identical cause of all our social evils. All our sufferings arise from a dearth of Bishops. This delicious, soul-reviving truth, was published a few days since in the House of Lords; though we regret to say—the regret, by the bye, is leavened with a touch of pride—that *Punch* has been the first to acknowledge it. The Bishop of Exeter observed—

> Holding, *as he did,* that episcopacy was necessary for the church, the first consideration ought to be, how was it to be made most effectual for the whole church? When such a question was put, the answer suggested itself instantly—it could only be done by having a sufficient number of bishops. *The church required far more than were now in existence. They ought not to be content with adding to her strength only a single bishop.*

This avowal is especially curious—as valuable, too, as curious. That a bishop himself should hold "episcopacy necessary" is, in itself, an extraordinary instance of mingled intelligence and disinterestedness. A certain bishop was once asked, "what he thought of original sin?" "Sir," replied the bishop, "I think we should have done very well without it." It is plain that if Henry of Exeter were asked what he thought of episcopacy, his answer would not be in the same spirit with the above response. He is quite right, too, in the comprehensiveness of his design. What is one bishop? Troubles, it is said, never come singly: why, then, should blessings? There is a pitiful, sneaking spirit in adding, "only a single bishop;" when the whole country abounds with the raw material of which bishops, *ad infinitum,* might be manufactured. A man with an acre of well-stocked cellars might as well limit his guests to one bottle, as ministers treat the country to only a single bishop. *Falstaff,* in the triumph of his passion, cried, "Now, let it rain potatoes!"[36] *Punch,* with like hilarity, exclaims—"Let it drizzle bishops!"

It is impossible for the most superficial biped of this most superficial age—for as those who follow us will abuse *their* times, why should not we have a fling at our own?—not to observe, and observing, rejoice at— the miracles of goodness worked in society by the example of even our present limited stock of bishops. "If"—as the fellow cried who vended peppermint-drops in a hard frost—"if one will warm you, what will a pound do?" Now, if we are so very good—if there be so much virtue abounding in the land with the few bishops at present vouchsafed to us,—how excellent shall we be—what a superfluity of goodness shall we have for exportation, if the voice of Henry of Exeter prevail, and clouds of lawn "turn forth their silver lining" on the darkness of this stumbling generation?

36 "Let the sky rain potatoes . . . ." (*The Merry Wives of Windsor,* V, v, 20–21.)

Consider, reader, what it is to create a bishop. You take a man by force from a humbler service in the Christian sheep-fold; and whilst he declares *nolo episcopari,*—with both his hands and all his voice exclaims against the benevolent violence that heaps wealth and worldly honours upon him,—whilst, despite all his spiritual strugglings to get away, you tie upon him the episcopal apron, force into his unwilling hand a banker's book, and make him a lord spiritual, you at once elevate forlorn humanity, only that its humility may beam forth with sweeter radiance. You give wealth and honours to a man, only that he may share the gold with the miserable, and prove by his meekness how poor is all mundane greatness compared to the aggrandizement to come. In a word, when you make another bishop, you add to the uncanonized saints.

Is not this proved—blessedly proved—by the experience of every day? Go where we will, do we not see the golden fruits of episcopal teaching? The Bench of Bishops—with an exquisite obedience to the divine precept —never will let the good they do be known. Nevertheless, much of their active benevolence must declare itself. Is famine howling and gnashing its idle teeth in the land? Away goes the bishop to the homes of the suffering; and with pious words, and more, with part of his own substance, he straightway solaces the wretched. Is sickness in the poor man's house? The bishop sits by the bed of the sufferer—prays with him—for him, and by all those nameless acts of brotherly love which draw forth the better sympathies of men,—proves to his smitten fellow that the episcopacy of the nineteenth century is vital with all that loving-kindness which consecrated *anno domini* i. Do we not meet bishops in pestilent courts where typhus breeds—in the cellars of manufacturing towns, where Christian men and women are huddled like beasts? Do we not there find these radiant elder sons of orthodoxy—these "bright ones" of the bench—despoiling themselves of their own comforts for the solace of the wretched? In a word, what is a bishop—say the Bishop of Exeter for instance—what is he but the almoner to the poor? The richer his diocese, the happier for the humble souls abounding in it. If you could give a bishop, aye £1,000,000 a year, you would make the very best use of the money, for nobody would know how much the poor would have of it. Therefore, let Bishops be increased and multiplied. What should we be without them? We shudder to think of it—no better than Quakers; and they, it is well known, for the want of the oil and honey bestowed by bishops, are a most pugnacious, quarrelsome set of people, who would, indeed, be a great social mischief, if so many of them, urged by their propensities for blood and slaughter, did not enlist into the army, and help to man our fighting frigates.

Henry of Exeter further observed, that though he would make a great-er number of bishops, he would not give them seats in Parliament.—No.

He was quite content that the number should remain as it was, and it would not be without a precedent to see a bishop without a seat in that house.

We here strongly protest against this. It is necessary—highly neces-sary—that every bishop should have a seat in the Lords, for how useful—how beneficent is their influence, throwing as they do, the oil of Canaan on the troubled waters of political strife—mingling as they do, the honey of Christian charity with the bitterness of party zeal. Is a war about to be waged? Do not the Bishops rise one by one—and with voices clear and awful as the silver trumpets of cherubim—denounce the unchristian act? Do they not paint war in all its haggard wretchedness—its ghastly wrong —its agony—its defilement? Do they not conjure up to the startled imagi-nations of their hearers the terrors of the sacked city—the murdered ma-trons—outraged virgins, and infants writhing on the pikes of a blasphem-ing soldiery? Did they not one and all do this at the commencement of the Chinese war, prophecying the horrors to come, with such fearful elo-quence, that even "the iron Duke" wept drops of burning metal, (which Lord Brougham[37] in his admiration of the warrior has since had mount-ed for shirt-studs?)

Is there any tyranny, vast or petty, done or contemplated at home? At the very whisper of the wrong, up rises a Bishop in the House of Lords, and with Heaven-gifted eloquence champions the wretched. Is there one Bishop of the whole Bench, who is not a very Nathan pleading with re-sistless speech for the one "ewe lamb" of the English pauper, outraged and despoiled by the tyranny of wealth?[38] Are not the speeches of the Bishops on Poor Law iniquities written in leaves of brass? Even Lord Brougham owns as much; and Heaven knows! he is an indisputable judge of the material.

An Act of Parliament would be a poor, profane thing, unless blessed by a bishop. In the Lords, the Bishops say prayers over the statutes (as my Lord's chaplain always says grace over meat.) It is for this reason that our English laws are all so exquisitely perfect: that they are all informed,

37 Lord Henry Brougham (1778–1868), Whig statesman who championed and ini-tiated many liberal reforms of England's legal and educational systems. *Punch* fre-quently held him up to contempt, however, for his subservience to the Duke of Well-ington.

38 Nathan, prophet in the time of David and Solomon. With his parable of the ewe lamb he denounced David for his abduction of Bathsheba.

and sublimated with such charity towards the poor—such tenderness for their infirmities—such compassion for the inevitable inequalities of human nature!

The readers of *Punch* may remember a report of a late meeting of the Bishops, drawn together by the miseries in the manufacturing districts. This report was strangely overlooked by our active—and *Punch* is not ashamed to own it—formidable rival *The Times*. Well, the Bishops immediately went into the distressed districts; and the public is yet to be astonished by the report of their doings! How they went from coal-mine to coal-mine—from cottage to cottage—soothing, assuaging, comforting, relieving the poor!

The Catholic Church has her hundred legends of the liberality of her saints, who have stripped themselves to clothe the naked pauper. But with all her triumphs—amidst all her relics, can she show the pawn-broker's duplicate of a Bishop's watch, left with the Lombardy merchant in default of ready money, for hard cash wherewith to relieve the poor?

(We would not raise an honest blush upon the cheek of a benevolent man. But this much we must say. Since the Bishop of Exeter left town for that Christian expedition, he has never been seen with his gold repeater.)

Shall we then deny to Henry of Exeter even a multitude of Bishops? Certainly not; and therefore, let there be circulated throughout every village where a curate vegetates, handbills with these words—

WANTED—SOME BISHOPS!

Q.

## PUNCH, MEMBER FOR THE CITY OF LONDON.*

TO THE ELECTORS.

GENTLEMEN,—A vacancy having occurred in the representation of your magnificent city, I lose no time in replying to the two thousand and one invitations to offer myself as your new member for Parliament. Although I feel it to be altogether unnecessary to enumerate the many qualifications of *Punch* for that distinction—although they are as plain as Gog and Magog in the eyes of an admiring generation, I nevertheless con-

*Punch, V, 148.

form to custom, and shall inflict upon you the usual number of elegant romantic asseverations customary on such occasions.

Having, in the course of my long and useful life, three times occupied a most commodious cell in Newgate, I cannot be considered a stranger to the City. Having twice stood in the pillory in the Old Bailey, it will be conceded that I know something of at least one of the most valuable of your civic institutions. Hence, my claims must be allowed above all other competitors not enriched by such experience, although no doubt equally deserving with myself of that distinction. That, as your representative, I shall make the public money go farther than any other man, will be evident from the fact that I have been four times before as many Aldermen, charged with putting off gilt sixpences for sovereigns, a measure of economy that it will be my first object to force upon the Government.

My dear friend, Lord Brougham, has informed me that the money got rid of by the City of London amounts to nearly one million per annum: I am very happy to hear it; inasmuch as, from such an immense sum, there will be no difficulty in providing very handsomely for your representative.

Gentlemen, it will be my unceasing study to add to the moral majesty and physical dignity of the City of London; and with this object, I shall compel the Government to double the number of all the civic dignities, beginning with the Giants of Guildhall, and ending with the ticket-porters. Hence, you shall have two Lord Mayors, and a double number of Aldermen. And whereas, to properly provide for these functionaries, it will be necessary to add to the revenues of the City, all imposts and fees should be increased to three times their present amount, so that, with additional dignity of person, there will also remain additional surplusage of purse.

And next, as to city improvements. I shall obtain a government grant to whitewash Saint Paul's, face Temple Bar[39] with Bath brick, and insert cut-glass eyes in the heads of Gog and Magog. And feeling how intimately connected with the greatness of a city is a city's literature, I shall bring in a bill to make eternal copyright of the wit of Sir Peter Laurie to himself and his heirs for ever. I shall also vindicate my reverence for high art by securing to Mr. Sheriff Moon[40] the exclusive publication of

39 Temple Bar, a gateway of Portland stone which, until 1878, separated the Strand from Fleet Street.

40 Sir Francis Moon (1796–1871), printseller and publisher; sheriff of London and Middlesex County in 1843.

the portraits of Whittington's Cat,[41] to be annually raffled for at the Mansion House; making it compulsory upon all "foreigners" (as the savages west of Temple Bar are properly denominated,) to take a guinea ticket.

With respect to the fees for the freedom of the City,[42] I shall considerably add to their amount, by compelling the customers of freemen to become free themselves. Hence, if any "foreigner" be eating oysters in the City, it shall be compulsory upon him to take up the freedom of the Fishmongers[43]—if swallowing ginger-pop, to join the Vintners.

And as the duties falling upon corn and periwinkle-meters, aleconners, sworn-brokers, and other offices of your gorgeous city, are onerous and harassing, I shall double their number—so that one half of these valuable public servants may year and year about visit Naples, Rome, (or, if they prefer it, Macquarrie Harbour,[44]) for the benefit of their health and the relaxation of their intellects.

And, remembering that the hospitality of the City of London has made her the "envy of surrounding nations," I shall advocate the passing of an act that shall secure to the Court of Aldermen two dinners a day, with permission to invite their paupers from their country lodgings at Peckham and other places, to dine with them. My poor friend, Chatterton, has said of London—

Her shield's a turtle-shell, her spear a spit:—

This shield I will have flung before the houseless poor—this spit shall kill, and roast them, food.

It shall also (by my efforts) be made lawful for every Alderman out of the City funds to provide for his children, his grandchildren, and indeed, for all relatives within kinship of German cousin. I will also relieve Aldermen from the necessity of attending the Old Bailey Court during Sessions, believing that justice will get on just as well without them.

41 Richard Whittington (d. 1423), thrice lord mayor of London. According to popular legend, he started in life as a poor orphan employed as a scullion by a rich merchant. When he ventured to send his only possession, a cat, on one of his master's ships, the cat was sold for a great fortune to a Moorish ruler whose dominions were overrun with rats. Dick's master was so pleased with the transaction that he granted him his daughter in marriage, and Dick succeeded to the business.

42 freedom of the City, the right to enjoy the privileges of membership or citizenship; one of the highest honors a city can grant.

43 freedom of the Fishmonger, the enjoyment of full privileges and rights of the company of Fishmongers. The Fishmongers and Vintners, are among the numerous city companies of London.

44 Macquarie Island, in the Pacific Ocean, lies about 850 miles SE of Tasmania, Australia, to which it belongs.

As for my politics, men of London, they are of all sides, and all parties: hence, Tory, Whig, Conservative, and Radical, may with perfect consistency give me their vote: for as the pine-apple—as my friend Moon says—combines in itself a smack, a relish of every other fruit, so do I possess a shade and hue of every party under the sun. Therefore, Electors of London, rush to the poll; and place as the representative of your most enlightened and most economical City,

PUNCH.

P. S.—No objection to the votes of dead electors.

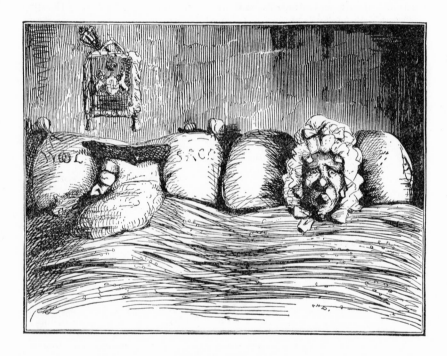

THE MRS. CAUDLE OF THE HOUSE OF LORDS.

"What do you say? *Thank heaven! You're going to enjoy the recess—and you'll be rid of me for some months?* Never mind. Depend upon it, when you come back, you shall have it again. No: I don't raise the House, and set everybody in it by the ears; but I'm not going to give up every little privilege; though it's seldom I open my lips, goodness knows!"—*Caudle Lectures (improved).*

# "GENTLEMEN JEWS."*

It is a cry, common as the cry of mackerel,[45] that we are fast approaching social destruction. All things, great and small, show it. The globe that we inhabit suffered a slight crack on Catholic Emancipation—another crack on the passing of the Reform Bill; and if it do not go clean in half on the abolition of the Corn Laws, why Colonel Sibthorp is no conjuror. What, however, are we to expect, when we find all our pet prejudices taken from us? The truth is, we then cease to be a people worth saving. Good, strong, stringent prejudices are intended to hold society together, even as iron hoops bind the staves of a cask. The world was much wiser and better when King John drew bills[46] upon the teeth of a Jew, and throughout the land the Israelite was a thing of abomination. We have long since ceased to look for gold in the jaws of the Hebrew; and, in the weakness of our benevolence, have given the creature liberties and privileges innumerable. Nevertheless, we put it to *The Morning Post*, whether, with all our liberality, it is not a gross affront to every respectable person of the Christian persuasion to call a Jew—"a gentleman?" Yet do we find it reported of Mr. Thomas, barrister, that a few days since he averred, that "gentlemen Jews were now sworn in Westminster Hall like other persons," that is, with their hats off!

At one time there was a very wholesome belief that the Jewish anatomy betrayed itself by an unpleasant odour inherent in it. This belief is still strong in the *Morning Post*; for, in one of its late leaders, dictated at the Russian Embassy, it spoke in its own peculiar vein of satire, of "those odoriferous people, the Jews." Sir Thomas Browne, among his other vagaries, touches upon the prejudice. "For," he says, "unto converted Jews, who are of the same seed, no man imputeth this unsavoury odour; as though, *aromatised by their conversion*, they lost their scent with their religion, and smelt no longer than they savoured of the Jew!"[47]

We have long been silent—indignantly silent—hearing the verbal changes rung upon, whilom, the abominable name of Jew. From "accursed dogs," they have risen to "individuals of the Jewish persuasion," "persons of the Hebrew faith," and so on. But to call a Jew a "gentleman," oh, Mr. Ralph Thomas! we hand you over to the virtuously or-

*Punch, VI, 79.

45 the cry of mackerel, one of the famous London street cries by which vendors advertised their wares.

46 drew bills, that is, borrowed money.

47 *Pseudodoxia Epidemica*, Bk. IV, chap. 10.

thodox indignation of the *Morning Post*. May you for ever be cheated by the Hebrew in oranges, and buy for ever of the tribe "black-lead pencils," innocent of lead!


## "GENTLEMEN JEWS" AND PUNCH. *

A MAN certainly looks awkward, even when called upon by dulness itself, to explain his joke. *Punch* is at this moment in such predicament. In the Number before last, *Punch* wrote what indeed he thought a small, yet very pretty piece of satire, on those times when our ancestors conceived that they best aired their Christianity by persecuting the Jews. We therein observed that the world still held together, albeit compelled to forego those prejudices which, in the opinions of some, hooped society about, and made it whole. We made, as we thought, a good fling at the brutality and ignorance of *The Morning Post* for its many sins against the tribe of Israel, (though we did not particularize its infamous support of that brutal madman of Russia[48] in his conduct towards the suffering Hebrew). Well, for this, our misunderstood satire, a "Jew" complains to the *Times*, the *Chronicle*, and lastly to ourselves; and that in serious condemnation of "the grossness of language" and "malice" of what, in the innocency of our heart, we thought a rap on the knuckles of by-gone bigotry and present uncharitableness. We beg of a "Jew" to read us again under the direction of some quick-witted friend; then, are we certain, he will be sorry for the bitter words with which he has bespattered us. In our sufferings, however, we have illustrious company. Great men, even before *Punch*, have been misunderstood and reviled by dulness for their best intentions. One Daniel Defoe wrote *A Short Way with the Dissenters*, satirically advocating their social rights; when his leathern-eared clients read him backwards, and would have sacrificed their champion. When Gulliver's Travels were first published, did not a certain Bishop condemn the work as a book of lies, avowing that "he didn't believe a word of it?"[49] Shall *Punch*, then, complain, even when in his "trumpery sphere," as Sidney Smith[50] would say, he advocates the

*Punch*, VI, 104.

[48] brutal madman of Russia, Czar Nicholas I (1796–1855).

[49] "A Bishop here said, that Book was full of improbable lies, and for his part, he hardly believed a word of it; and so much for Gulliver." Swift's letter to Pope, Nov. 27, 1726.

[50] Sidney Smith (1771–1845), famous nineteenth-century wit and the mainstay of the *Edinburgh Review* in its championship of a variety of reforms.

common rights and liberties of the Hebrew, and yet for such advocacy is arraigned of "malice, prejudice, and jealousy," even by "a Jew?"


## THE PRESIDENT AND THE NEGRO.*

THE LIFE OF PRESIDENT TYLER, we learn from the American papers, has been saved by a black man. The President was returning from the Congress Burial-ground, Washington, where he had attended the interment of the victims killed on board the Princeton, when his horses took fright, and would have precipitated him down a steep, but that they were arrested by the hand of a negro. We know not whether, according to American notions, we can courteously congratulate the President on his escape,—seeing that it makes him a debtor for his life to a black—a mere human chattel—a thing of sale and barter. The accident brought the first magistrate of the first republic into such close dependence on the compassion and sympathy of probably a black slave, that we know not how he can well cleanse himself of the humiliating annoyance. Heroes of the olden day have gladly preferred death rather than owe their lives to acts or persons mean or infamous; and animated by the like ennobling spirit, we must believe that President Tyler would have earned for himself a higher reputation with his countrymen, had he loudly and sternly rejected the succour of the black, and suffered himself to be whirled down the mortal precipice before him. He would, then, like Curtius taking the leap,[51] have vindicated the nobility of his soul for the honour and glory of his country. He would, by his last mighty act, have proved to the sneering world that Americans sell black men like beasts really for the reasons that Americans give; that the negro is a creature only a little above the ape, a piece of mechanism of human seeming, but in no manner touched by the same sympathies, solemnized by the same affections, as the white man! Thus considered, it would have been a sublime spectacle to behold President Tyler prepared for death, and loudly forbidding the approach of the negro, as a creature with whom he had nothing in common—an outcast of God and man, whose compassionate help brought odium on the assisted. Thus dying, the President would have as-

*Punch, VI, 155.

51 Marcus Curtius, in Roman mythology, a soldier who leaped, armed and on his horse, into a chasm which had opened in the Forum. The soothsayers had declared that, before the chasm would close, the chief strength of Rome must be sacrificed. In the opinion of Curtius, Rome's power lay in arms and valor.

serted a great principle, and left a memory sweet and balmy to man-selling Americans. As it is, the life of President Tyler is damnified, soiled, blotted; for he holds it only from the compassion of a black, who is most probably a slave.

However, President Tyler, in the overflow of his gratitude, may wish to reward his deliverer. May we suggest the mode? A white man is to be hanged in Louisiana for aiding and abetting the escape of a black woman; let the negro who has saved the white President have a place at his execution, that he may see the punishment of the white who, touched by humanity, would save a black.


# THE MAY-DAY OF STEAM.*

No LONGER milkmaids dance along the Strand[52] on May-morning—even the leaves of Jack-in-the-Green are withered[53]—and the chimney-sweepers, who were wont to summon our halfpence, by the rattling broom and shovel, no longer call on May-day for the yearly dole. True it is, that impostors, men lost to the sweetness of self-respect, do on May-day caper in the streets, and with ghastly merriment strive to make us smile and pay. But, reader, put no faith in such forlorn merry-makers; they are not sweepers. They never made soot their daily bread. They know no more of the inside of a chimney, than did Falstaff in his days of sack and sin know of the inside of a church. They are hapless creatures, wanting the dignity of a fixed profession; they are the gipsies of London, now boiling their kettle in one alley, now in another; to-night sleeping in an eastern door-way, to-morrow slumbering in St. James's Park.[54] Sometimes, too, to pay the belly-tax, to eke out feverish life, sometimes they pick a pocket. Sometimes, too, they become halfpenny panders to lying rumour, and sell apocryphal deaths of foreign kings—declarations of war—and particular accounts of the elopement of some unborn wife, who has gone off "with her husband's footman." And on May-morning the deceivers take the characters of sweeps, and dance the unwary out of halfpence. As for

*Punch, VI, 196.

52 the Strand, a famous street in London, full of hotels, theaters, and office buildings.

53 Jack-in-the-Green, in the English custom a man or boy is enclosed in a framework covered with leaves and boughs as part of the May Day games.

54 St. James's Park, a public park in Westminster, London, surrounding the richly historical St. James's Palace, established by Henry VIII.

the real sweeps, they have advanced in luxury, and dine at Copenhagen-house.[55] They dance, too, but then it is to the sounds of hireling minstrels; they have become respectable, and have left the streets to cheats and impostors, falsely calling themselves "my lord" and "my lady." Thus, the London man of thrift, hurrying to business, is only reminded of May-day by rogues and vagabonds! The May-day of the milkmaids is passed away—the May-day of hawthorn, garlands, and pipe and tabor is departed; and in their place we have now the May-day of Steam!

Many of our readers will, we doubt not, be gladdened to learn that the day in all the manufacturing districts was rung in by merry peals from every church-steeple. All Manchester made a holiday. Birmingham and Leeds washed the smoke and soot from their faces, and donned garlands. We have voluminous accounts of the May-Day of Steam, and all authentic—all from "our own reporters"—writing from fifty different places in the kingdom. From this mass of information, *Punch* will extract its essence in a few satisfactory paragraphs.

It seems that the master-manufacturers—the mill-owners—the lords of the steam-engine, who realise our fairy visions of Genii and Magi, doing all things by their potency over elemental power—making fire and water their tremendous, yet subservient vassals,—it seems that these excellent men, their hearts gushing with gratitude towards the bounty of Steam that has made them kings, that has heaped up wealth, hitherto thinly scattered, into a few mountains of gold, making the poor poorer, and the rich richer,—it appears that they resolved to make holiday on May-Day, in thankfulness to their thousands of workmen, and in gratitude to steam. Wherefore, early on May morning—(in giving an account of the ceremony at one place, be it observed that we describe the doings at all) —all the men, women, and little children employed at the factory, arrived at their place of labour, some carrying hawthorn boughs—some having wreaths of flowers about their heads—some gay ribands. A band of music was assembled at the doors of the factory; and when all the people had arrived, they formed in procession; and entering the building, with the masters at their head, they marched round the engines, hushed and resting for that day, and laid reverent hand upon them—and flung flowers over them—and stuck them all over with green boughs; and cheered and huzzaed the giant power which, though with might to rend a rock, is yet made tractable to a child's finger.

And when the engines had been duly decorated, all the people de-

---

[55] Copenhagen House, a tavern in the parish of Islington, noted for political mob meetings.

parted where they listed, until noon. And then they met again, and sat down to a feast in the factory; and the memory of James Watt was drunk, not in solemn silence, but with loud, heart-grateful shouts to the Giver of all Good, who had vouchsafed so great a benefactor to man.

After this, one of the workmen rose, and for a long time talked of the said James Watt. His words, put in brief, were simply these. He said that if steam had been called the ruthless destroyer of the poor man's happiness, it was because its ultimate beneficence was unheeded. True it was, that its first operations—and society was then in such a crisis—created great misery by the monstrous inequalities of fortune it produced: it placed the riches of the world in the hands of a favoured few. Nevertheless, its onward progress must produce unmitigated good to the human race; for say that all human labour could to-morrow be performed by the elements, would the large family of man be content to wither piecemeal from the earth, whilst a few elder sons of Luck and Mammon possessed all? Oh, no; then would cease the gross, the wicked inequalities of the world; then would men divide more in "conscience and tender heart;" then the solemn needs of human life would be more respected, and all men claim their fair share of the labours of the elements—all men eat sufficingly of the fruits thereof. Meanwhile the problem must be worked out in patience, in tolerance, in the earnest cheerfulness of hope!

After this the people joined in dances—then some sang in chorus—then again they feasted; and in the evening all departed for their homes, merry and comforted.

And in this way—though the circumstance has remained unnoticed by the newspapers—passed the May-Day of Steam!

## THE IOWAYS—"THE LOST TRIBE" —AND YOUNG ENGLAND.*

FRIDAY LAST an agreeable incident powerfully tended to prove the truth of Mr. George Jones's[56] theory—a theory so ingeniously, so eloquently supported in his *Ancient History of America*,—that the Red Men are no other than the descendants of the lost tribe of Israel. Young England[57]

*Punch*, VII, 95.

56 George Jones (1804–1896), a nineteenth-century pioneer miner, merchant, and legislator, who was a striking figure in the early history of Iowa and Wisconsin; was surveyor general and later a senator of Iowa.

57 Young England, a group of politicians including George Smythe (1818–1857), author of *Historic Fancies*, and Lord John Manners (1818–1906), led by Benjamin

—it is proved by Young Ben—is also a section of the wandered race. Well, the Ioway Indians—the last marketable imports from the Back-Woods— with an instinctive feeling of their remote origin, did, on Friday last, visit Grosvenor Gate, Park Lane,[58] and then and there did, in the most affectionate manner, fraternise with the magnificent host, Benjamin D'Israeli, Esq., M.P. The superficial newspapers stated, that "the immediate object of the visit was to give these children of the forest an idea of an English gentleman's residence, and of the style of living of *our aristocracy*." No such thing; we grant, that such may have been the ostensible purpose of the Indians' visit to Benjamin's wigwam, but the real object was, as we have said, to fraternise, as the remnant of the tribe of Israel, with Young England, and in due ceremony, to admit Mr. D'Israeli, Lord Manners, Mr. George Smythe, and other illustrious spirits of the regenerating party, as brothers of the tribe. This ceremony was performed in the library. A suitable oration was delivered by Se-non-ty-yah, the Medicine Man; and was responded to by the author of *Historic Fancies,* who chaunted an appropriate stave (to appear in the forthcoming new edition of his work.)

The Indians were then conducted over the mansion, and expressed themselves prodigiously delighted with all they beheld. The kitchen appointments wrought them into a state of high enthusiasm; and when they were shown that very complex piece of machinery, the ball-cock, which regulates the supply of water into the butt, they were roused into a state of inconceivable excitement. Hereupon, the host, with his fine knowledge of human nature, read "these children of the forest" a couple of pages of *Coningsby,* and the lowering effect was marvellous. They were immediately cooled down to their ordinary temperament.

The party was next conducted into the bath-room. Whereupon, the Medicine Man observed, that he cured most of *his* patients by immersion in cold water, and by vapouring. Mr. D'Israeli, with one of his slaughtering smiles observed, "*He* had tried vapouring, especially in Parliament; and all things considered, it had done wonderfully."

The house being thoroughly inspected, the party returned to the dining-room, where—the Young England Members joining—the dance of brotherly love was executed. A "*déjeûner*" was then served up, and duly

---

Disraeli (1804–1881). Romantic in spirit, they opposed the utilitarianism and worship of wealth of the time and believed social revolution could be avoided if the upper and lower classes united to resist the radicals and the capitalists. The upper class would thus become the leaders in a neofeudalistic society.

58 Grosvenor Gate, Park Lane, a fashionable residential section in Mayfair, London.

honoured. At four o'clock, the guests departed, Mr. D'Israeli having with his own hand fixed the pen with which he wrote the last chapter of *Coningsby*, in the head of the Medicine-Man. (It may be viewed by the curious at Egyptian Hall.[59])

If, however, there be *any truth* in the report that the Ioways were invited to Grosvenor Gate that they might see, and for a time share in, "the way of living of our aristocracy," we beg to inform Mr. D'Israeli that there are thousands of darkened souls in London, equally ignorant of that Paradise, Grosvenor-Gate, as his guests the Red Indians. Therefore, we have now no doubt, that Mr. D'Israeli will upon this knowledge instantly issue cards of invitation to the dwellers of Shoreditch, Whitechapel, Kent Street, Seven Dials,[60] and to other remote fastnesses of savage, pauper existence.

## WANTED,—A FEW BOLD SMUGGLERS!*

PUNCH, being within this past fortnight denied admittance into France, by an order expressly issued to that effect in Paris; an order, carried out with all characteristic zeal and fidelity by Douaniers and Postmasters, by which means every number of *Punch's* inimitable and cosmopolite journal found in the possession of a steam-boat passenger has been seized and impounded, as though it were another Infernal Machine in handsome type—by which means every copy has been stopped at the French Post Office (to the all but irreparable loss and most poignant grief of the defrauded subscriber),—

*Punch* is hereupon determined to engage at any cost,

### A FEW BOLD SMUGGLERS,

that this Journal may continue to disseminate civilisation throughout benighted France; and, if possible, to touch the hearts of the natives with a true sense of human glory, converting them from the false worship of blood and fire, and gathering them into a brotherhood of peaceful men. Hence, smuggling—at the worst, a venial eccentricity—exercised in the cause of benevolence and *Punch*, becomes an occupation for the Philanthropist and the Philosopher; and the man who successfully introduces

---

[59] Egyptian Hall, in Piccadilly, used for public performances and shows, such as Barnum's exhibition of Tom Thumb.

[60] Shoreditch, . . . Seven Dials, the slum areas of London. See also p. 370, n. 23.

*Punch*, VII, 106.

our sheet into France, may, for all time forward, consider himself a human benefactor. He is the missionary of peace among the drum-beating
heathen.

It would ill-become the character of *Punch*—now, happily, known to
the universe for his plain outspeaking—to effect an ignorance of the cause
which has made him distasteful to that fortifying monarch, Louis Philippe. No, no; *Punch* is fully aware that his well-meant epistle to Joinville[61]—that letter, written with a dove's-quill dipped in attar of roses—
was vitriolic acid to the royal palate. He knows, too, that his exposure of
the Royal Beggarman, who talks of his sons and daughters as a mendi-
cant talks of his sores, that he may gull and pillage the unwary, the while
he is padded with greasy bank notes beneath his rags and tatters,—*Punch*
knows that his exposure of royal avarice has called down upon him the
prohibitory vegeance of King Dives, detected, as *Punch* detected him,
mumming as Louis Philippe Lazarus.

And, therefore, is the weekly sheet of *Punch* prohibited throughout
free and sunny France! *And*, therefore, does *Punch* appeal to the gallantry and magnanimity of the smuggler, that, by the beneficent aid of the
wiles of contraband, he may still, in despite of Louis Philippe, exercise a
high Moral Influence over his unhappy subjects. He, it has been said, is
a benefactor to man, who makes two ears of wheat grow where one only
grew before. What, then, will be his reputation, who, by the genius of
smuggling, causes two numbers of *Punch* to circulate in France, in places
where one has been prohibited? Who shall enter into the sublimating
feelings of that man? Not *Punch:* no—it would be presumptuous.

Ladies and Gentlemen desirous of acting as smugglers to *Punch* are
requested to apply at his office from Monday next to Saturday inclusive,
between the hours of 8 and 8; or to the Editor, who, with two of his
agents, is now residing in the *Rue St. Honoré*, Paris. A preference will be
given to ladies; *Punch* having, in his various continental trips, observed
that the softer and more innocent sex smuggle with an ease, a graceful
audacity, far beyond the power of that sophisticated creature—Man.

Handsome terms will be given to Members of Parliament—also to a
few members of the Dramatic Authors' Society.[62]

No Bishop need apply.

---

61 Prince de Joinville (1818–1900), Louis Philippe's third son, who gained notoriety through his bellicose pamphleteering. *Punch* responded with satire and invective
to many of his essays.

62 In his other writings Jerrold complained bitterly about England's hack writers
translating and adapting French plays for the English stage, thereby making it unprofitable for theater managers to cater to the native drama.

# THE QUEEN IN SCOTLAND.*

Sir Andrew Agnew[63] has written a letter to the Earl of Aberdeen,[64] though intended as a sort of side-wind epistle to Her Majesty. This letter is, on the face of it, meant as a lecture to Queen Victoria on her better keeping of the Sabbath. Sir Andrew is grievously afraid that the Queen will introduce the sinful levities of Sunday-breaking England among the patent pious folk of sweetly austere Caledonia. He trembles lest the Sabbath revelry of Windsor should startle and confound the kilted proprieties of Blair Athol. Certainly, if we wanted to pick out a man of pattern impudence, we would go neither to the court or camp, but to the conventicle. Your self-thought saint is ever a fellow of imperturbable brass. One *Mawworm*, in such material, outweighs a hundred *Bobadils*.[65] Take an example:—

> Scotland has, since the Reformation, [says Sir Andrew,] been distinguished amongst the nations of Christendom as a strict Sabbath-observing country, in the true Scriptural sense of that word; and it is this important fact which, with all imaginable respect, and deference, and dutifulness, and loyalty, it is humbly prayed *may be brought under the notice, at this time*, of Her Most Gracious Majesty the Queen, not doubting that in this, as in all other respects, it is the gracious desire of the Royal mind to recognise, *to respect, and to gratify the religious habits, the peculiar characteristics, and the best principles of Her Majesty's most loyal and devoted subjects in this her ancient kingdom.*

That is, Sir Andrew, in plain English, hints that the Queen will behave herself better on Sundays in Scotland than is her wont on the Sabbath-day in England. As her Scotch subjects are in every respect a nobler, purer, more generous, and really and truly more religious people than the English—in fact as, past dispute, they are the chosen vessels of all created flesh—so should the Queen pay to them that studious observance only due to the elect of heaven. Thus, Sir Andrew hopes that, on the Sabbath, the Queen will encourage no quadrille parties; that Prince Albert will

*Punch*, VII, 146.

63 Sir Andrew Agnew (1793–1849), baronet of Lochnaw and promoter of Sabbatarian legislation. As a member of parliament he took charge of a movement called the Lord's Day Society to institute measures prohibiting all but necessary labor on Sundays, but he failed to see his proposed bill translated into law.

64 George Gordon, Earl of Aberdeen (1784–1860), secretary for foreign affairs under Peel from 1841 to 1846, was known for his cautious and conciliatory foreign policy.

65 Mawworm, the vulgar copy of Dr. Cantwell, the hypocrite, in Bickerstaff's *The Hypocrite*. Bobadil, the braggart captain in Ben Jonson's *Every Man in His Humour*.

not whistle "My heart's in the Highlands;" and that the little Princess will especially not play at "Beggar my Neighbour"[66] with Lady Caroline Cocks.[67] It is evident that Sir Andrew fears licence of this sort, or why, with such tremulous sanctity, should he give warning to the Queen? The saintly baronet continues:—

> It would be the highest presumption to suggest to your Lordship's consideration the extent of the overwhelming moral influence which the example of the court is calculated to produce upon the religious habits of Scotland on this auspicious occasion.

Her Majesty's visit will extend to a few days; yet may such brief time be fraught with mortal danger to the habits of the most moral people on the face of the earth! For that the Scotch are the most moral people of the universe, who shall be bold enough to doubt, seeing that they themselves never lose the remotest chance of declaring it? Well, let us hope the best for Scotland in her present peril; but had *Punch* been born north of the Tweed (think of a Scotch *Punch!*), he would not feel at ease for the surpassing purity of his native land until Queen Victoria's court was once more fast at Windsor.

The amount of nonsense from those folks "whose heads do grow"[68] heaven above knows where—those mysterious diurnal scribes called "Our own Correspondents," "Our own Reporter," "Our own Special Reporter," and such like magii—has been of average quantity and quality. The *Morning Post's* "special," of course, carries the day. Hence, the "rude hand of health," which, according to the same authority, has its "established dwelling-place in the hills and glens of Scotland," (making lodgings preposterously dear, no doubt,)—well, this rude Cribb-like[69] hand of health has made very free with the Queen's complexion; "for," says the "special,"—and we are half-inclined to think that Jenkins has recovered from his trance,[70] and wears a kilt—for

> Her Majesty left the shores of England like a second *Galatea*—
> 'Candidior nivei folio, *Galatea*, ligustri';[71]—

[66] Beggar my Neighbour, a card game.

[67] Lady Caroline Cocks, one of the maids-of-honor at Victoria's coronation.

[68] "The Anthropophagi, and men whose heads / Do grow beneath their shoulders." (*Othello*, I, iii, 144–145.)

[69] Tom Cribb (1781–1848), champion prizefighter.

[70] Jenkins, a satiric personification of the *Morning Post*. See "Jenkins!"

[71] "Candidior folio nivei Galatea ligustri." (Ovid, *Metamorphoses*, Bk. xiii, l. 789.) "O Galatea, whiter than the petals of the snowy columbine." Galatea, a sea nymph, falls in love with Acis and is wooed by the Cyclops. The line quoted is from the Cyclops' seductive bid to win Galatea from the arms of Acis.

but constant exposure to the weather *and* the fresh air, which *streams* through 'the land of mountain and of *flood*,' *have* substituted a healthful ruddiness for the pale cast of thought with which her Majesty's countenance has been sicklied over, &c. &c.

Her Majesty as Galatea! Well, we hope no man doubts our loyalty— but for the moment, charmed by the picture of the special Jenkins, we could not help associating Her Majesty with the Opera glories of Drury Lane!

The Princess Royal, mounted on a Shetland pony, and attended by a groom and servant, always accompanies her Majesty and the Prince in their morning walk through the grounds, and the Royal parents are frequently seen to stop and listen with alternations of interest and amusement to the *naifs* observations of the youthful Princess on the novelty of the objects which meet her view at every instant.

How extraordinary! that a father and mother should be pleased and interested with the simple prattle (that is, with "the *naifs* observations") of their own babe! Is it possible that a woman, become Queen, can condescend to laugh and talk with the child of her blood? Well, we only hope that such eccentricities will not bring royalty into contempt.

We suspect there will be a great run for Gaelic masters at the West-end,[72] the Queen having become so intensely Scotch.

Her Majesty appears to have a great taste for things *peculiarly Scottish*. At Dunkeld, Moulinearn, and Blair, she tasted, and not only so, *but as the report goes, highly relished*, the Athol brose which was proffered her; and oaten cake is an established and especial favourite. 'Scotch broth,' as Englishmen term it, is also in daily requisition at the royal table.

The most astounding part is to come:—

*It is even whispered* that her Majesty is not altogether unacquainted with the mysteries of Scotch 'haggis.' The English cooks are puzzled.

And therefore, we are informed, Her Majesty has appointed two new officers to her kitchen, to be called the Serjeant of Brose, and the Grand Master of Cockaleekie![73]

And then as to dress, both her Majesty and the Prince, when at the Falls of Bruar *appeared in tartan plaids*, and, but that they are now in mourning, they would, it is said, wear tartan dresses.

72 West End, a fashionable section of London noted for its theaters.

73 Scottish dishes: brose, an oatmeal mixed with a boiling liquid; haggis, the heart, liver, and lungs of a sheep or calf, minced with suet and oatmeal, seasoned, and boiled in the stomach of the animal; cockaleekie, chicken broth flavored with chopped leeks.

However, the Prince has promised—when out of mourning—to wear nothing but the kilt at Windsor. One incident, shamefully unnoticed by the Scotch papers, shows the intense admiration of the Queen for all things Scottish. Walking to the Falls of Bruar, Her Majesty suddenly paused—and out of compliment to the custom of the country—pulled off her shoes and stockings, and walked an hour and more barefoot!

> The Princess Royal, young though she be, *is not slow in these things* to imitate her royal mother. Not a child in all broad Scotland likes better to lunch on milk and oaten cake, or dine on broth. Meeting the young son of Lord Glenlyon, the other day, in the Castle avenue, she told him how much *she liked his tartan dress,* and how it was the same as was worn by the Prince of Wales.

The Princess has also refused to wear shoes and stockings, and, in imitation of the peasantry, runs about the grounds of Blair Athol "bare leggit."

Her Majesty, however, has learned a new pleasure from her visit to Scotland. She now knows what water really is; for, according to a Scotch paper (*The Witness*), she takes a copious draught from a stream in Glen Tilt, "declaring that never in England did she taste of such a stream!"

Her Majesty will, however, have left many marks of her condescension behind her, which will be duly prized, for we are told that—

> The good folks at the Falls [of Tummel] are delighted with the smallness of the Royal foot. From the prints *left in the sand* they have measured the exact length, and they keep the trophy as a *great* treasure.

Silver slippers will, we understand, be made according to the dimensions of the impression. Since *Robinson Crusoe* started at the foot-mark "left in the sand," there has been no such astonishment.

The royal party are accompanied by Scotch bards who point out different historical localities, at the same time narrating their legends. The field in which Claverhouse was shot,[74] was shown to Her Majesty.

> According to tradition, Claverhouse was shot with a sixpence, the superstition being that he bore a life that was charmed against ordinary modes of attack, and a body bulletproof.

This is, of course, a poetic fabrication. Shot with a sixpence! We should like to know who supplied the money?

---

[74] John Graham, of Claverhouse, first Viscount Dundee (1649[?]–1689), fought and died in the Highlanders' defense of Scotland against the English at Killiecrankie.

# A DAINTY DISH TO SET BEFORE A QUEEN.*

Sing a song of Gotha[75]—a pocket-full of rye,
Eight-and-forty timid deer driven in to die;
When the sport was open'd, all bleeding they were seen—
Wasn't that a dainty dish to set before a Queen?

The QUEEN sat in her easy chair, and look'd as sweet as honey;
The PRINCE was shooting at the deer, in weather bright and sunny;
The bands were playing Polkas, dress'd in green and golden clothes;
The Nobles cut the poor deer's throats, and that is all *Punch* knows!

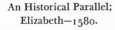

An Historical Parallel;    Or,    Court Pastimes.
Elizabeth—1580.              Victoria—1845.

*Punch,* IX, 135.
75 Gotha, a city in the former state of Thuringia, central Germany. In 1640 it became the capital of the duchy of Saxe-Coburg-Gotha. Prince Albert's father, Ernest I,
was duke of Saxe-Coburg-Gotha.

# ⫷UNCH'S LETTERS TO HIS SON.*

## DEDICATION
## TO
## THE RIGHT HON. THE LORD CHAMBERLAIN,
### (WHOEVER HE MAY BE.)

Punch reading to Lord Chamberlain.

*The Writings of Douglas Jerrold (8 vols.; London, 1851–1858), 1–145.

My Lord,—Take my word for it, you have greater reason to be proud of this Dedication than of your wand of office. Having read it, you may, for the remainder of your official life, walk in the eyes of all men, at least half an inch higher. As, however, persons in your exalted rank are not always inevitably promoted to the eminence by the invincibility of their reasoning powers, or the subtlety of their wit, it may perhaps be necessary for me to explain to you why, from this day forward, you should enjoy an increase of official altitude. Few things irk a man more, than to know he has inflicted the heaviest, yet withal the sweetest, obligation on another, who nevertheless obstinately remains in the most Stygian ignorance of the fact. Fancy, my lord, a pearl-diver—your lordship may possibly guess the perils of the trade—having plunged to the bottom of the oozy deep; strange, horrid monsters about him; the ocean booming and rolling over him; fearful thoughts of his wife and little ones stirring in his breast; imagine him groping for the treasure which, it may be, is destined to repose upon the palpitating bosom of an Eastern queen. He rises to the surface of the deep—he is on dry land. Happy diver! he hath fished up a union—

> Richer than that which four successive kings
> In Denmark's crown have worn![1]

He believes his fortune made; the precious pearl has enriched him, his wife, and little ones for life. Alas, no! the waywardness of fate denies to his pearl the asylum of a crown—refuses to it the ear of a queen. No: that pearl, by the very wilfulness of destiny, is flung among the wash of pigs, and is swallowed with a grunt by that bacon hog, altogether unconscious of the treasure to be dissolved into nothing by his porcine chyle. Now he must be a hardhearted man—a lout, a churl—who would deny to the poor pearl-diver the barren satisfaction of pinching the pig's tail, to assure the beast, as well and as reasonably as a beast can be assured of anything, that he has swallowed the jewel—that he has the worth of I know not how many bars of gold in his ignorant bowels. No: justice—who though she may not choose to use them, yet keeps her scales and weights in every man's breast— justice declares that the man shall have the rightful privilege of pinching the pig's tail; or, in familiar phrase, that he shall not lose his pearl without—as the vulgar hath it—having a squeak for it!

Now, my lord, hold me not guilty, of any unseemly parallels. It is true,

---

[1] *Hamlet*, V, ii, 252–253.

in the following Letters you will, I know, meet with as many pearls as you ordinarily see at a royal drawing-room: nevertheless do not for an instant believe that I libel you as a hog. No, my lord, repress, annihilate the nascent thought. Yet, consider, that as this Dedication, like a patent iron coffin, is expressly hammered out to last until doom's day—consider, my lord, how many chamberlains, and how various their capacities, may exist between this time and the world's end! It is to meet all possible accidents that may occur to all future Lords Chamberlain, that I here insist on dwelling upon the obligation I have laid them under, by dedicating to them these adamantine Letters.

Having resolved to publish, I looked serenely round the world for a nominal patron. At first I thought the Lord Chancellor, as legal guardian of the defenceless rich—for there is not one of these Letters that may not be considered as the orphan inheritor of invaluable wealth, that is, if wisdom always went as at the trunkmaker's, by avoirdupois weight,— yes, I thought the genius of the woolsack[2] might fitly protect these costly epistles; but reflecting upon the many orphans, the many lunatics, too, still upon his lordship's hands, I instantly resolved not to swell the number of his responsibilities, and, therefore, thought again.

Next, the rattle of the Prince of Wales fell upon my ear. "These Letters," said I, "shall be dedicated to the Prince: they will especially serve to commemorate the day on which his Royal Highness was taken out of long frocks—the brevity of every epistle will touchingly illustrate the shortness of his coats." My wife exulted at the idea. "The very thing," said she; "for, isn't there our last boy, Ugolino?[3] he'll want something as he grows up; and the Prince can't do less than make him a tidewaiter."[4] The mercenary speculation—for all women are not mothers of Gracchi[5] —determined me to give up the Prince of Wales. "No," said I, "the dirty motive-makers of the world will be sure to misconstrue the act; they will swear that Punch was only loyal that he might be prosperous; they will say that he only worshipped the rising pap-spoon that his own brat might catch the fragments that fell from it." My heart swelled at the suspicion, like a new-blown bladder, and I struck off from my list the Prince of Wales.

[2] woolsack, the Lord Chancellor's office.
[3] The name possibly suggested by Dante's story in *The Inferno* of Count Ugolino, who was shut in a tower to starve to death with his sons and grandsons.
[4] tidewaiter, a customs inspector working at dockside or aboard ship.
[5] Cornelia, the mother of the Gracchi (two Roman statesmen and social reformers), presented her sons when asked for her jewels.

I next looked into the Houses of Parliament. Here, I thought, are people whom the world sometimes persist in taking for my blood relations; and, it must be confessed, that both in the Upper and Lower Senate words are spoken and capers cut, that—were I to be impeached for either—it would, I fear, be very difficult for me to prove an *alibi*. "Why, there's fifty of 'em, at least," said my wife, "that you can't persuade the world ar'n't your own kith and kin." "And for that reason, wife," I replied, "I will have none of 'em. No; I am fully aware of the relationship myself; but it's their dirty pride that chokes me—their arrogance that makes them sometimes pass me, even in Parliament-street, as if I was to them an alien in blood, in manners, and religion. And why? I get my living in the open air. Well; didn't Julius Cæsar, the Duke of Marlborough, do the same? And when Wellington and Wagstaff were on service, didn't they labour, too, *sub dio?* Can you gather laurels in a back parlour—can you grow bays upon a hearth-rug?"

It was then, my lord, I resolved to dedicate these Letters to you. The reason is obvious:—

THE LORD CHAMBERLAIN NEVER DID ANYTHING FOR PUNCH!

You have graciously let me alone; and I have flourished under the benignity of your neglect. I pitch my stage wheresoever I will, in Westminster or not, without your warrant: I act my plays without your license.[6] I discourse upon the world as it is, on the life that is moving about us, and on the invisible emotions of the heart of man, and pay no penny to your deputy. I increase in social importance; for I am not withered by your patronage.

Had fate made me, for these last two hundred years, the master of a play-house, how different might have been my condition! Had I, since the Act which made you protector and censor of the dramatic sisters, Melpomene and Thalia—poor girls: there are people who swear you have treated 'em worse than Mrs. Brownrigg used her apprentices[7]—had I felt your

---

[6] One of the duties of the lord chamberlain was to license plays. During the first half of Jerrold's career as a dramatist he had to have his plays performed at unlicensed theaters.

[7] Elizabeth Brownrigg (d. 1767), notorious English murderess; midwife to the poor women of the parish workhouse, she was hanged at Tyburn for the murder of one of her apprentices; her skeleton was exhibited in the Old Bailey as a lesson to potential criminals.

patronage, how often had I been *banco rotto*; how often had I played—understand me, not paid—a "doleful dump"[8] in Portugal-street![9]

Wherefore, then, do I dedicate to you these Letters?—From an exalted spirit of independence. I owe you nothing, my lord, and have flourished upon the obligation.

PUNCH.

## INTRODUCTION.

IN HUMANE compliance with the incessant and affecting supplication of many hundred bosom friends, these epistles are for the first time submitted to print. Yes, I swear it: and to solemnise the oath, I am ready to kiss a bank-note of any amount above fifty pounds,—I am wholly won to type by the entreaties of sundry fathers, for whose children I have—as, indeed, I feel I ought to have yearnings of peculiar affection.

These letters were originally addressed to, I verily believe, my own son. In them, I have endeavoured to enshrine the wisdom of my life. In them, I have sought to paint men as they are—to sketch the scenes of the world as they have presented themselves to my observation—to show the spring of human motives—to exhibit to the opening mind of youth the vulgar wires that, because unseen, make a mystery of common-place.

I am prepared to be much abused for these epistles. They are written in lemon-juice. Nay, the little sacs in the jaws of the rattle-snake, wherein the reptile elaborates its poison to strike with sudden death the beautiful and harmless guinea-pigs and coneys of the earth,—these venomous bags have supplied the quill that traced the mortal sentences. Or if it be not really so, it is no matter; the worthy, amiable souls, who would have even a Sawney Bean painted upon a rose-leaf, will say as much; so let me for once be beforehand, and say it for them.

The child for whose instruction and guidance through life these letters were especially composed, has passed from this valley of shadows—he is dead. Death, in its various modes of approach, is an accordant mys-

8 Possibly from Richard Sheale's "Ballad of Chevy Chase": "For Witherington needs must I wail, / As one in doleful dumps."

9 Portugal Street, in Lincoln's Inn Field, and the location of the Court of Justice in Bankruptcy; Portugal Row is associated with various playhouses.

tery with the mystery of life. To one man it comes in the guise of a grape-stone—to another in the aspect of a jackass eating figs. To my dear son death appeared in the tempting shape of a fine South-down wether. Yes, mutton was his fate.

Had it pleased fortune to make me a man of bank-paper, the life of my darling child might have been spared. Then had I shown that the dear boy acted only in obedience to an irresistible impulse born with him—strengthened by maternal milk—made invincible by oft indulgence. Then had I proved that the child in what he did was but the innocent accessary of his unconscious mother.

I have dried my eyes and will endeavour to explain myself.

Three months, to a day, before the birth of my child, we had not for the previous eight-and-forty hours rejoiced our loyalty with the sight of his majesty's head even upon copper; and yet—be Mercury my judge!—we worked most gallantly—handed round the hat most perseveringly—laughed most jocosely, and all with bleeding hearts and a slow fire burning in our bowels. Nathless, halfpence came not. At that time, I remember, we were terribly run upon by Parliament. The madness of politics took away the people's brains; and literature, and art, and Punch, while the mania lasted, were—strange infatuation of men!—neglected for the House of Commons.

Four-and-twenty times in four-and-twenty streets had we acted that day, and yet no coin fell in the oft-presented hat. With thoughts of an empty garret, a supperless destiny if money came not—of my unrepining, much-enduring wife—of all her wants in that her time of weakness,—with all these horrid memories blazing in my brain I rattled away, and laughed, and cried and crowed *roo-tooit-roo-tooit* in every key and cadence, and heard myself bruited by the mob as a merciless, unfeeling rascal, without one touch of humanity for aught that breathed. Alas! at that moment I had an ulcer in my heart big as a rat-hole.

Evening came on, and with it cold and drizzling rain. We were preparing for our twenty-fifth representation, when a delicious odour suddenly steamed through the canvas, and on the instant, a voice—to my foolish ear sweet as the multitudinous voices of cherubim—cried—

*Hot, hot—all hot—mutton pies all hot!*

My dear wife placed her hand upon her heart—she knew I had not a penny—softly sighed, then fell in a dead swoon into my arms. There she lay, and still the retreating voice rang through the night—

*Hot, hot—all hot—mutton pies all hot!*

At length my spouse returned to life. With the fine delicacy, the mighty self-denial of her sex, she breathed not her wish. But I looked in her eyes, and read—*Mutton pies—all hot—hot, hot!*

And who, after this, can wonder at—much more blame—my darling, blighted son for his uncontrollable affection for Southdown, or in fact any other, wethers?

Oh, ye thousands of philosophers, dozing, dreaming, yawning in garrets—oh, ye broad-brimmed, long-skirted, ankle-jacked sages, who look into men's skulls as men look into glass hives—who untwist the cords of the human heart carefully yet surely as the huswife untangles a skein of silk—could not twelve of ye be found to go into a box to discuss, and by your verdict dignify, as pretty a case of morals and metaphysics as ever came from the Press-yard?[10] But no; drysalters, hardwaremen, yea, ropemakers (for my innocent boy never thought to challenge the last juryman as peculiarly interested in the verdict), judged him, and of course he was lost.

As a further illustration of the benighted intellect of the jury, it was argued against my boy—my doomed one from the womb!—that he had on a previous occasion shown a violent love for a bale of Welsh flannel, the property of a hosier on Ludgate-hill. Of course, he had. It was the inevitable result of his constitution. The flannel was part of the sheep. What he did, he did from necessity. He was organised for the act. The jury—asses!—called it a second offence. Why, it was one and the same thing. Nay, had my child made off with a gross or two of lamb's-wool socks, and half-a-dozen Witney blankets, a philosophic jury would have considered the collective acts as but an individual emanation of pre-organised temperament; and, pitying the mother in the son, have returned a triumphant acquittal. But what knew the jury of affinities?

Had I been rich I could have proved all this, and my boy had been saved upon a constitutional eccentricity. As it was—but I will no longer dwell upon the theme. Enough for the curious. My boy's fate may be found in the archives of Seven Dials.

These letters will, I trust, testify my paternal solicitude. It is my pride, that they were treasured by my son, and were bequeathed by him, with other effects, to the individual whose adroit attention to my boy in his last moments was witnessed by hundreds, and commented upon in the handsomest way by various distinguished writers of the English press. It is to the liberality of this individual I am indebted for the original docu-

---

10 Press-yard, the court of old Newgate Prison, from which point prisoners charged with capital punishment started for the place of execution.

ments; for, elevated far above the petty spirit of huckstering, he at a word took a pot of porter for the treasure, and with a significant wink and a light-hearted laugh, wished me joy of my bargain.


## LETTER I.

### THE BRIGHT POKER.

MY DEAR LITTLE BOY,—So early as cock-crow this morning, your dear mother reminded me that you were this day nine years old. The intelligence delighted, yea, and saddened me. My sweet little pet, you will think this strange: I will explain myself. When I remembered that I was the author of a rational being, of a creature destined, it might be, to have a great stake in this world, and a still greater in the next, my heart rose within me, and I was in a transport of happiness. When, again, I reflected that I had given to the earth an intelligent animal, doomed, perhaps, to continual fisticuffs with fortune; marked, branded with poverty; sentenced to all the varieties of the elements; a cold, hungry, houseless, haggard, squalid piece of human offal; a thing with the hopes and aspirations of man, now hardened by the injustice of the world to callous, calculating insensibility, now stung into the activity of craft;—when I saw you ragged and despairing, an outcast in this life, and hopeless for ——but then I banished the picture from my brain. "Things," I thus communed with myself, "must not be thought of after this melancholy fashion; otherwise little boys will become extinct."

You are now, however, called upon to remember—for you are sufficiently old to understand the obligation, and I shall therefore no longer address you as a mere child—that to me you owe your life. It now nine years (metaphysicians would say something more,) since you opened a debtor account with me: an account never to be payed off by laying down the principal, but to be duly acknowledged by the punctual payment of interest in the shape of love, duty, and obedience. Understand, you owe me your life: whether you were, or were not, a party to the debt at the time it was contracted—whether at my own whim and caprice I fixed upon you an obligation, never in reality thinking of you at all, matters not: you are my debtor, up to the present period, for nine springs, as many summers, the like number of autumns, and not one less winter. Consider the hold I have upon you—remember the debt that will be every year increasing, and be docile, be obedient.

It is related of St. Francis, that, being destitute of children, he made to himself a family of snow-balls; and, that, when made, he gave to them pretty and endearing names, and took them in his arms, and hugged them to his bosom, and doubtless thought himself quite a family man. Now, my dear child, I am not a St. Francis—(though I think I have at least patrons under other names in the Calendar,)—and am therefore incapable of begetting a snow-ball for my heir; but shall I feel less for my own flesh and blood than the first of the grey coats cared for congealed water?

My affection, then, speaks for you in this, and shall be audible in many, letters. The world is opening upon you. In a few years you will enter upon that fearful struggle for the daily shoulder of mutton—that terrible fight which every day shakes the earth to its foundations—that never-ceasing squabble which, when Jove is melancholy—for who shall say that Jove himself has not his megrims?—makes laughter for his majesty and his court assembled. How, then, to get the best of the fray—how to secure the best cut of the shoulder? My son, give heed to a short story.

The widow Muggeridge was the cleanliest of huswives. You might, in vulgar phrase, have eaten your dinner off her floor; the more especially as plates for two were never known upon her table. Her household gods were a scrubbing-brush and scouring paper. She fairly washed the world from under the feet of her husband. She insisted, as she worded it, upon his being nice and comfortable; and therefore plentifully sluicing the sick man's chamber, as he lay, knocked down by a fever, Muggeridge died of cold water and a clean helpmate. When assured of her husband's death, it was the touching regret of the new-made widow that he had not staid to change his shirt. If any man ever took pleasure in his grave, it must have been Muggeridge; for never since his marriage had he known what it was to enjoy a piece of wholesome dirt.

And here, my dear child, let me advise you, if it should be your destiny to wed, and live in humble state, to avoid by all means what is called a clean wife. You will be made to endure the extreme of misery, under the base, the invidious pretext of being rendered comfortable. Your house will be an ark tossed by continual floods. You will never know what it is to properly accommodate your shoulders to a shirt, so brief will be its visit to your back ere it again go to the wash-tub. And then for spiders, fleas, and other household insects, sent especially into our homesteads to awaken the inquiring spirit of man, to at once humble his individual pride by the contemplation of their sagacity, and to elevate him by the frequent evidence of the marvels of animal life,—all these calls upon your higher faculties will be wanting; and, lacking them, your immortal part will be dizzied, stunned, by the monotony of the scrubbing-brush, and poisoned, past the remedy of perfume, by yellow soap. Your wife and children, too, will have their faces continually shining like the holiday saucers on the mantel-piece. Now, consider the conceit, the worse than arrogance of this: the studied callous forgetfulness of the beginning of man. Did he not spring from the earth?—from clay—dirt—mould—mud —garden soil, or compost of some sort; for theological geology (you must look into the dictionary for these words) has not precisely defined what; and is it not, the basest impudence of pride to seek to wash and scrub and rub away the original spot? Is he not the most natural man who, in vulgar meaning, is the dirtiest? Depend upon it, there is a fine natural religion in dirt: and yet we see men and women strive to appear as if they were compounded of the roses and lilies of Paradise, instead of the fine rich loam that fed their roots. Be assured of it, there is great piety in what the ignorant foolishly call filth. Take some of the saints for an example. Off with their coats, and away with their hair-shirts; and even then, my son, so intently have they considered, and been influenced by the lowly origin of man, that with the most curious eye, and most delicate finger, you shall not be able to tell where either saint or dirt begins or ends.

I have, however, been led from my promised narrative.

The widow Muggeridge, in her best room, had two pokers. The one was black and somewhat bent: the other shone like a ray of summer light —it was effulgent, speckless steel.

Both pokers stood at the same fire-place. "What!" you ask, "and did the widow Muggeridge stir her fire with both?" Certainly not. Was a coal to be cracked—the black poker cracked it; was the lower bar to be cleared —the black poker cleared it; did she want a rousing fire—the black poker was plunged relentlessly into the burning mass, to stir up the sleeping heart of Vulcan; was a tea-kettle to be accommodated to the coals—the black poker supported it. "And what," methinks you ask, "did the bright poker?" I answer nothing—nothing save to stand and glisten at the fireside; its black, begrimed companion, stoking, roking, burning, banging, doing all the sweating work. As for the bright poker, that was a consecrated thing. Never did Mrs. Muggeridge go to Hackney for a week to visit her relations, that the bright poker was not removed from the grate; and, carefully swathed in oiled flannel, awaited in greasy repose the return of its mistress. Then, once more in glistening idleness, would it lounge among shovel and tongs; the jetty slave, the black poker, working until it was worked to the stump, at last to be flung aside for vile old iron!

One dozen black pokers did the bright poker see out; and to this day—doing nothing—it stands lustrous and inactive!

My son, such is life. When you enter the world, make up all your energies to become—A Bright Poker.

# LETTER II.

WORDS AND THEIR COUNTERFEITS—HOW TO RECEIVE AND PASS
OFF THE SAME, WITH OTHER USEFUL COUNSEL.

MY DEAR BOY—I am much pleased with your last letter. Your remarks on the copies set you by your excellent master, Dr. Birchbud, convince me that schooling has not been lost upon you. However, beware lest you look too closely into the significance and meaning of words. This is an unprofitable custom, and has spoilt the fortunes of many a man. You may have observed a team of horses yoked to a heavy waggon; may have heard the bells hanging about their head-gear tinkle, tinkle, tinkle. The bells are of no use—none, save to keep up a monotonous jingle; although, doubtless, Giles the waggoner will assure you that the music cheers the horses on the dusty road, and, under the burning sun, makes them pull blithely and all together. Now, there is a certain lot of sentences in use among men, precisely like these bells. They mean nothing—are not intended to mean anything—but custom requires the jingle. Thus, when you meet a man whom you have seen, perhaps thrice before—and he declares that "he is delighted to see you," albeit it would give him no concern whatever if you were decorating the next gibbet—you must not, for a moment, look a doubt of his joy, but take his rapture as a thing of course. If he squeeze your hand until your knuckles crack—squeeze again. If he declare that "you're looking the picture of health," asseverate upon your honour that "he has the advantage of you, for you never saw him look better." He may at the time be in the last stage of a consumption—you may have a hectic fever in your cheek; no matter for that; you have both jingled your bells, and with lightened consciences may take your separate way.

I could, my dear child, enlarge upon this subject. It is enough that I caution you in your intercourse with the world, not to take words as so much genuine coin of standard metal, but merely as counters that people play with. If you estimate them at anything above this, you will be in the hapless condition of the wretch who takes so many gilt pocket-pieces for real Mint guineas: contempt and beggary will be your portion. Thinking yourself rich beyond the wealth of Abraham Newland[11] in the golden promises of men, you will risk a kicking from the threshold of the first verbal friend whom you seek for small change.

Your last copy, you tell me, was—

Command you may your mind from play.

You object to this as an unreasonable dogma. You say, you cannot command your mind from play; and insinuate it to be an impertinence of your master to assume any such likelihood on your part. In fact, you deny it *in toto*. More than this; you had the hardihood to contest the propriety of the text with your worthy master, who, you further inform me, appealed to your moral sense through your fleshly tabernacle, and—for some minutes—left you not a leg to stand upon.

I cannot, my dear boy, regret this last incident. It will, I hope, impress upon your mind the necessity of taking certain sentences current in the world for precisely what they are worth, without hallooing and calling a crowd about you to show their cracked and counterfeit condition. Dr. Birchbud, when a boy, had written—

Command you may your mind from play,

a hundred and a hundred times in fine large text. Well, did he believe in the saw any more for that? Did he, think you, expect you to believe in it? "Then, wherefore"—you may ask in your ignorance—"did he scourge me, for not believing?" Foolish boy! it was for not seeming to believe. This is precisely the treatment you will meet with in the world, if, with courageous conceit, you attempt to test the alloy in so much of its verbal coinage—coinage that is worn thin with handling; which wise men know the true value of, and pocket for what it's worth, and which only fools (and the worst of fools they call martyrs) ring, and rub, and look at, and having done so, screech out,—"Bad money!"

Now, my dear boy, the next time the worthy Doctor Birchbud gives you the copy—

Command you may your mind from play,

look at it with sudden reverence, square your elbow with determined energy, take up your pen as though you were about to book the text "in

[11] Abraham Newland (1730–1807), chief cashier of the Bank of England during the eighteenth century; amassed a fortune of £2,000,000 in stock and £1,000 a year from estates by economy in his expenditure and by speculation.

the red-leaved tablet of your heart,"—and having, in solemn silence, made the required number of copies, take the book up to your master,— and, as you give it in, let your countenance appear at once informed and dignified with the beautiful truth you have consigned to paper,—nay, let your whole anatomy seem at that moment absorbing the grand lesson you have inscribed in the copy-book. This done, you may return to your seat, and—whenever the master's head is turned aside—you may go on with your game of "odd or even" under the desk with Jack Rogers, play at "soldiers" on your slate, or any other pastime that may take your fancy. It is sufficient that you have gravely registered your belief, that—

Command you may your mind from play.

The registration is enough; whether you can, or will, is altogether another matter.

This subject reminds me of an inquiry you once made, at a time when you were too young to comprehend the matter. On the paper covering a square of Windsor soap were printed the Royal Arms. I recollect your charming smile at the lion and unicorn; and the childish curiosity which prompted you to inquire the meaning of the royal legend—

*Dieu et mon droit.*

That, my child, it is now proper for you to learn, means, "God and my right." When you shall have mastered something more of the History of England, and shall have read all that certain kings have done under that motto, you will then more fully understand what I have written to you upon taking words as counters, not as real things; of the necessity of always seeming to believe them the true coin, and the danger of crying counterfeit. "God and my right!" Ha, my dear boy, there have been men, who because they would stand out from the rest of the world, and would not believe in the divine origin of these syllables, have had their heads sliced like turnips from their shoulders, and their quarters hung up like sides of bacon over city gates; whilst other men, not one jot more believing, have, with a knowing wink at their fellows, and thrusting their tongues in their cheeks, bowed like willow wands to the words, and found their reward in beef, ale, and, in fulness of years, death in a goose-bed.

You say you employed the last half-holiday in birds'-nesting. This was very right. I would have you train your mind to manly sports. In due season, with the grace of fortune, you will be able to hunt hares, those pestilent and dangerous creatures having been especially provided to exercise the muscles and the intellects of man. Should you obtain that position in the world, which it is my fervent prayer you will arrive at, you may also be permitted to join in a royal hunt, a pastime of the highest dignity, utility, and humanity. For instance, you will chase a stag, for the express and only purpose of terrifying it; and having put it to an hour or two of serviceable agony, you will have it caught and conducted back to the pasture, to be left for future enjoyment. As, however, these must be the sports of your manhood, you are quite right now to begin with linnets and sparrows. You, my dear son, will one day have to quit the paternal roof for the great world. By reflecting on what the parent linnets and sparrows suffer, deprived of their young, you will have some wholesome idea of the anxiety of your loving parents under a like affliction.

You ask me to send you some corking-pins that you may spin cockchafers upon them. Your mother sends them, with her blessing and her best love. I trust, however, you will turn this amusement to your profit. As, under the blessing of heaven, I may probably article you to Mr. Abednego, the attorney and money-lender of Jewish prejudice, I would counsel you to take particular notice of the conduct of the cockchafer, when buzzing and spinning with the pin through its bowels—that you may know exactly how long it will live, and how much pin it will bear. This knowledge, for wisdom comes to us from so many channels, will be of great use to you as a disciple of Abednego, when making out your costs.

## OBJECTS WORTHY OF DISCOVERY—SHORT STORY OF MAN
## AND HIS DUCK.

MY DEAR BOY,—You tell me you have been reading *Captain Cook's Voyages,* and are so much pleased with them, that you would start round the world on a voyage of discovery to-morrow morning. You will seriously offend me by any repetition of this folly. Leave such mad adventures to fools and zealots. Stay you, and make greater discoveries, at home.

Do you know the reward of the simpletons who peril life, and forego all the comforts of the fleshly man—for what? To give, it may be, their name to an iceberg, and their carcases to the sharks. Columbus discovered America, and was at last rewarded with fetters for his pains. Who can point out the two yards of dust that cover Cabot the mariner, who found a home and a retreat for tens of thousands? Ask of the sea, in which of is multitudinous caves repose the bones of Hudson?

The known world is quite large enough for you; let fools, if they will, leave their snug arm-chairs, and sea-coal fires, to extend its boundaries. What matters it to you where the Niger begins or ends? Have you not the pleasant banks of Thames, the tens of thousands of unsophisticated natives thronging its shores; all of them ready to exchange their gold-dust for any glass-beads you may bring for barter, if, by your confidence and swagger, you can pass off the glass for veritable diamonds? If you can, great and sufficient will be your reward. If you cannot, you will undergo the rightful penalty of your ignorance. But the thing is done every day. Do not imagine they are the only savages whose skins are soot-colour, who wear rings through their noses, stick parrots' feathers in their woolly hair, and bow to Mumbo Jumbo as their only deity. My dear boy, you will find amongst the whitest, the most carefully-dressed, and most pious of London, absolute children of nature; men, as it would seem, expressly made for the support of their fellow-creatures, as shoals of herrings are every season spawned expressly for the nutriment of whales. Therefore, trust yourself to no canoe on the Senegal, but prosper on the banks of your paternal river.

You would like to be a discoverer? Very well. London is a boundless region for the exercise of the greatest sagacity. Leave to dreamers the solution of the shortest cut to India—find you the north-west passage to the pockets of your fellow-creatures. Discover the weaknesses of men; they will be to you more than the mines of Potoso,[12] bring you richer merchandise than cargoes of gold-dust and ivory.

If, however, forgetful of my paternal lessons and unworthy of your progenitor, you address yourself solely to what is absurdly termed the dignity of human nature and the amelioration of the condition of mankind,—if you choose to make one of the fools who have lost their labour and their soap in the vain attempt to wash the negro white,—why, starvation, obloquy, and wretchedness in every shape attend you! Your heart's blood may dry up in a garret, and—if your carcass be not arrested by the bailiff—you may rot in the pauper's corner of the parish churchyard. To be sure, after some hundred years or so, it may be some comfort for your ghost to slip from your forgotten grave, and make midnight visits to the statue that may be at length erected to the genius that died, the debtor of a twopenny loaf to a benevolent baker. If you will be contented with such reward, try of course to elevate your species. If, however, you would rather enjoy present sixpences, why then spin pewter plates on a balanced sword, or poise a donkey. My dear boy, work for ready money. Take no bill upon posterity: in the first place, there are many chances against its being paid; and in the next, if it be duly honoured, the cash may be laid out on some piece of bronze or marble of not the slightest value to the original. Sure I am, that no statue or monument is erected to the memory of one who is at length called the benefactor of his race, that the ceremony is not a holiday for famine and all the household furies. They behold in the thing an irresistible temptation to other fools. One late-rewarded martyr inevitably raises a new regiment to bleed and suffer.

It is upon this truth—for truth is not always to be disregarded—that I would have you stand: it is upon this principle I would have you eschew all romantic notions of travels to Abyssinia, and voyages to the Pole, for the more profitable discovery of the weaknesses of your fellow-creatures. Are you fond of wild countries, curious plants, rare animals, strange adventures? Plunge into the heart of man. There you will find deserts, poisonous weeds, snakes, and a host of iniquities arrayed against a host. You will also find streams gushing with health, amaranthine flowers, cooing doves, and things of divine aspect and heavenly utterance: with these, however, meddle not. No; turn from them, and, spite of yourself, convince yourself that they exist not, that they are the mere phantasma of the brain—the mere offspring of the imagination, that, sickened with

12 Potosí, a city in southern Bolivia at the foot of one of the world's richest ore mountains.

arid, burning tracts, sees in its sweet disease palms and silver springs, and in the tinkling of the camel's bell hears the heart-delighting nightingale. Not so with the dreary places and the venomous things. Learn every nook of these; catalogue every object. It is in such spots you are to drive a prosperous trade; it is such articles you are to use in barter. Does not the wise tradesman put on his comeliest looks, and bow lowest to his best customer? Virtue is a poor, paltry creature, buying her miserable penn'-orths at miserable chandlers'. Now Vice, Weakness, and Co., are large, burly traders, and "come smug upon the mart." Therefore, make yourself master of their tempers—find your way to their hearts; for they have hearts, even as blocks of marble sometimes contain within them the torpid, sweating toad, "ugly and venomous."[13]

However, in opening an account with this firm, be sure you never apply to them the names spat upon them by clean-mouthed Virtue. Oh, no! although you know them to be leprous to the bones, you must treat them, must speak of them, as though they were the very incarnation of health. Though their corrupt practices are to the nostril like the foulness of a new battle-field, snuff them as though you inhaled the odours of myrrh and frankincense burning in the temple.

When you have become a scholar in the weaknesses of the human heart, you may then lay them under what impost you will. You may—but I will tell you a little story in illustration of the truth of this.

You must know that the greater number of the inhabitants of Ceylon have it, as their firm belief, that, when dead, their souls will take up their habitation in the bodies of various animals. A wise fellow—too wise to work, and sage enough to be determined to enjoy himself without labour—turned the superstition of his neighbours to constant profit. Whenever his pockets were empty he would rush into the streets, and carrying a live duck in one hand, and brandishing a knife with the other, he would exclaim to the terrified people—

"Wretches, this duck may be your grandfather—your grandmother—your father—your mother—your brother—your sister—your son—your daughter! Wretches! I'll kill the duck!"

Whereupon, men, women, and children would throw themselves upon their knees, and offering what money they had, beg of the man not to kill their grandfather, their grandmother, their son, their daughter, but in the depths of his mercy, and for the sake of ready money, to touch not a feather of the duck!

[13] "Which, like the toad, ugly and venomous, / Wears yet a precious jewel in his head . . . ." (*As You Like It*, II, i, 13–14.)

And the man, pocketing the cash, would walk away, for that time spar-
ing the duck.

My son, you are not an inhabitant of Ceylon, but a denizen of enlightened London; nevertheless, in every city every man has some sort of a
grandmother in some sort of a duck.


## LETTER IV.

### ON THE CHOICE OF A PROFESSION.

MY DEAR CHILD,—You say you are anxious to select for yourself an agreeable and profitable profession, and solicit my paternal counsel to assist
you in your choice. This brings to my recollection, that your darling
mother once begged that I would accompany her to a mercer's, to choose
a gown. We entered the shop, and desired an inspection of the ware-
houseman's commodities. Velvets—cut, flowered, and plain; satins of all
colours; sarsnets; silks, shot with thunder and lightning; muslins, pop-
lins, bombazeens, pompadours; all the beautiful products of the loom
were graciously taken from the shelves, and displayed upon the counter
before us. Some two to three hours were agreeably passed in this way;
when your dear mother, with one of her sweetest smiles, thanked the
shopmen for their trouble, then said, "she thought she could only afford
a tenpenny gingham."

My dear boy,—I fear it will be thus with you in your choice of a profession. I may, it is true, unroll an archbishop's lawn before you—may
call your earnest attention to a Lord Chancellor's ermine—may request
you to feel the weighty bullion of a commander-in-chief's epaulets—to
weigh in your hand the gold-headed cane of a court physician,—and
when all this is done, you may be compelled to call for the leather apron
of a cobbler, or the goose and needle of a tailor.

I wish—and Heaven witness the aspiration—that at your birth the law
of primogeniture had bound you apprentice to 15,000£ per annum, besides my good-will, when I slept beneath a slab of marble. Such a calling
must be a very pretty business, and, believe me, I should have mightily
liked to be your master. As fortune has ordered it otherwise, let us look
at the professions.

Will you enter the church? Alas! what a prospect lies before you. Can
you discipline your mind and body to fulfill the functions of your office?
I will at once suppose you a bishop. Can you, I ask it, satisfy your appe-

tite with merely locusts and wild honey? Will you be content with raiment of sack-cloth, or at the best, linsey-woolsey; and can you answer for
your conscience that you will, at all times and in all weathers, be ready
to make a pilgrimage to the hovels of the poor: to give comfort to the
wretched; to pray beside the straw of the repentant guilty; to show, by
your own contempt of the creature blessings of this world, that you look
upon the earth as a mere temporary tarrying-place,—a caravanserai,
where you are awaiting until called beyond the clouds? Consider it; as a
bishop, you will be expected to take your seat in the House of Lords.
When there, shall you be prepared, with the rest of your brethren, to set
a continual pattern of piety and self-denial to the lay-nobles? Will you be
ever prompt—as bishops always are—to plead the cause of the wretched;
to stand between the sinking poor and the arrogant rich; and with a
voice of almost divine thunder, wake in the callous hearts of worldlings a
slumbering conscience for their fellow-men? Will you be in the House
of Lords, a lump of episcopal camphor—a bundle of spikenard—a pot of
honey? Can you—as all bishops always do—abstain from the lusts of
Mammon, and keep your lawn, white and candid as the wings of angels,
from the yellow soil of filthy Plutus? Thinking only of the broadest, the
shortest, and the best way to heaven,—will you (like all bishops) never
meddle with turnpike acts, or job with wooden pavements? Eschewing
the vanity of coach and footman (as John the Baptist did, and all bishops
do,) will you think only of the carriage of Elisha; and turning from the
pomps and vanities of an episcopal palace, can you (as all bishops do)
feed humbly, lodge lowly,—hungering only for immortal manna,—waiting only to be called to that home—

Whose glory is the light of setting suns.[14]

My dear boy, examine yourself, and say, are you equal to all this? I
think you are my own flesh and blood, and thinking so, doubt your con-
stancy in this matter. Hence, I would advise you to eschew the church;
for unless you could live a life apostolical, as all bishops always do, what
disgrace would you bring upon the bench—what slander and a by-word
would you be in the mouths of the heathen!

Let us now consider the law, and suppose you called to the bar. Have
you the fortune to support your dignity?—Have you, for this is more, that
gentleness of spirit, that philanthropy of soul, which would make all men
brothers, which would pluck from the hearts of your fellow-creatures,
malice and dissent, the foul hemlock and nightshade that poison the

14 "Whose dwelling is the light of setting suns." (Wordsworth, "Tintern Abbey," l.
97.)

sweet sources of human love? Consider the change that has come upon the law and its guileless professors. There was, indeed, a golden time, when you might have amassed a fortune by playing bo-peep with Truth; by abusing, reviling her; by showing her virgin innocence to be strumpet infamy; by plucking every pinion from her sky-cleaving wing, and making her a wretch of sordid earth: by causing Truth herself to blush for her nakedness.—More, you might have successfully "moved the court" to punish her for the indecent exposure; and thus Truth, by the potency of your eloquence, might have been handed over to the scourging arm of the beadle, whilst Falsehood, your successful client, should have gone triumphant home, in a carriage-and-four, with white favours. These golden times are past. Then, you might have walked the Hall,[15] gowned and wigged, with a harlot tongue to let for hire, carrying any suit into court, as a porter carries any load; then at the Old Bailey you might even have shaken hands with avowed murder in his cell, and fresh from the blood-shot eye, and charnel breath of homicide, have called Heaven, and its angels, to bear witness to the purity of the cut-throat who had paid you so many golden pieces for your exordium, your metaphors, your peroration; your spattering of witnesses, your fierce knocking at the startled hearts of half-bewildered jurymen; threatening the trembling twelve with midnight visits from the ghost of the innocent creature in the dock, if the verdict went for hemp. This you *might* have done, but this is past. Now, Conscience wigs itself, and sits with open door, giving advice gratis. Therefore, can you afford it in purse? And more; have you the necessary milkiness of humanity—for such is the term simpletons give it—to play the peace-maker between man and man, giving advice, allaying feuds, reconciling neighbour to neighbour, weighing out justice in her golden scales, and charging not one maravedi for the trouble? Can you, as barrister, write over your door—as may now be seen in thousands of places,—"*Advice given against going to law, gratis?*"

In the olden time, I should have advised you to make an effort for the bar; but with the present romantic notions—for I can give them no worthier name—operating on the profession, you can afford it neither in pocket nor in spirit. To such an extent have barristers carried their peace-making quixotisms (of course, considerably assisted by their worthier brethren, the attorneys), that the judges have nothing to do. Already the moth is eating up the official ermine!

Will you be a soldier? Well, I will presume you are a Field-Marshal. A war breaks out: a wicked, unjust war. It may be thought necessary

15 the Hall, that is, the Guildhall, containing the various municipal courts.

(such a case occurred about a century ago, and may occur again,) to cut the throats of a few thousands of Chinese, for no other reason than that the Celestial Emperor hath, with his "vermilion pencil," written an edict against the swallowing of British opium. You are ordered for the Chinese waters, to blow up, burn, slay, sink—in a word, to commit all the beautiful varieties of mischief invented by the devil's toy-woman, Madame Bellona.[16] Well, with the spirit that is now growing in the army—a spirit that has lately developed itself in so many bright examples—you are compelled to throw up in "sublime disgust," your Marshal's baton, and, like Cincinnatus, retire to Battersea to cultivate cress and mustard; philosophically preferring those pungent vegetables to laurels stained with the blood of the innocent, defiled with the tears of the orphan. You may then send your epaulettes to Holywell-street,[17] to be burnt for the gold—or sell your uniform to be used, on masquerade nights, at the Lowther Arcade.[18] My dear boy, military glory is not what it used to be. Once people thought it a jewel—a solid ruby. But philosophy has touched what seemed a gem, and has proved it to be only congealed blood.

No, you shall be neither Bishop, Chancellor, nor Generalissimo; but, my boy, you shall be—

But that I'll tell you in my next.

## LETTER V.

### THE ADVANTAGES OF BEING "NOTHING."

IN MY LAST, my dear boy, I promised to advise you on the choice of a profession. I hasten to redeem that promise. Then I say to you, strive to be neither bishop, chancellor, generalissimo, nor court physician; but, my beloved child,—be Nothing.

By not trammelling your mind with the subtleties of divinity or law—by maintaining a perfect freedom from the prejudices of a military or medical life,—you will be able to take a more dispassionate view of the world about you; will be the more ready to accommodate yourself to any

16 Bellona, in Roman mythology, the goddess of war and wife of Mars.

17 Holywell Street, in the Strand, occupied chiefly by secondhand booksellers and disreputable vendors.

18 Lowther Arcade, a covered walk surmounted with glass domes, leading from West Strand to St. Martin's Churchyard; chiefly inhabited by dealers in children's toys and cheap jewelry.

profitable circumstance that may present itself. Consider how many cur-
ates who devote their lives to divinity shiver in a brown-black coat; fight
a daily fight with the meanest necessities; and with wife, and it may be
half-a-dozen children ill-clothed and ill-fed at home, are paid forty
pounds a-year to be pattern pieces of holiness and benevolence to all the
country round. The clerk, who to his Sunday duties, unites the profitable trade of soleing and heeling dilapidated shoes, is a nabob; the clerk
is not cursed with the brand of a gentleman; he may ply with wax-end
and awl—may vend soap, brick-dust, and candles—run errands, beat
carpets,—do any servile work to make up his income; *his* Sabbath "amen"
being in no way vulgarised by the labour of the week. But the curate—
alas, poor man!—he has been to college, and is a gentleman. Thus, by
virtue of his gentility, he must be content with beggary, nor soil his or-
bread in its very literalness, nor dare to hope the luxury of butter. You
are not my own flesh and blood, if you would stand this.
are not my own flesh and blood, if you would stand this.

Next for the law. I should have no objection to your being called to
the bar, as a sort of genteel thing. A wig and gown may often prove a
tolerable bait for decently endowed heiresses. They give you the nominal
standing of a gentleman, under which character you may make various
practical speculations on the innocence of mankind; but for living upon
your business, you might as soon hope to make a daily dinner on the
flag-stones of Pump-court. Consider, my son, what a thing is a briefless
barrister! A cockatrice, that cannot lay eggs—a spider, without an inch
of web!

I have no vote for any borough or county; and though in my time I
have served multitudes of politicians with votes when in and out of office, there is not one of them who has the gratitude to own the obligation.
Hence, what will be your fate if you go into the army? I might—with assistance from a few loan societies—be able to purchase you a pair of colours; but as neither myself nor your mother has any interest with anybody at the Horse Guards, what would be your fate, if unhappily alive,
at seventy? Why, still the pair of colours; and, if you have served long in
India, a face of orange-peel, and a piece of liver no bigger than your
thumb. Glory, my boy, is a beautiful thing in the Battle of Waterloo at
Astley's;[19] and there, if you have military yearnings, take your shilling's-
worth of it.

[19] Astley's Amphitheatre featured extravanganzas, burlettas, and pantomimes; converted into the Theatre Royal in 1862.

As for medicine, if you set up in what is called an honourable manner, to kill by diploma,—you will find the game so beaten and hunted, that 'tis ten to one you bag a patient once a twelvemonth. If, indeed, fortified by your own unauthorised opinion,—you can persuade people into patent remedies against disease and death, disarming the destroyer by a learned name attached to bread-pills or coloured Thames water,—take my blessing, and straightway—having entered into a sleeping partnership with a confidential undertaker—found a College of Health. There is no such golden walk to fortune as through the bowels of the credulous; and when sick, all men are credulous. Pain is a great leveller, alike hurling down scepticism, philosophy, and mere prosaic common-sense. The man, who before his friends will sneer at a vaunted specific, will sneak out by himself to seek the quack vendor of the despised anodyne: in the same way, the fine ladies who profess to laugh at astrology, will disguise themselves in old shawls and bonnets, and venture up dirty lanes and into foul garrets, to consult bedridden fortune-tellers, on the whereabout and when-coming of their future husbands. If you have any feeling for medicine, and have face and nerve to cry "Quack" lustily—away with you into the market-place, and begin. But if, with the unprofitable pride of science, you would only physic, bleed, and blister on the strength of a diploma, the boy who carries out your medicine shall be happier than his master, and—when he gets his wages—better paid.

Again, then, I say it, my son, be Nothing! Look at the flourishing examples of Nothing about you! Consider the men in this vast metropolis whose faces shine with the very marrow of the land, and all for doing and being Nothing! Then, what ease—what unconcern—what perfect dignity in the profession! Why, dull-brained, horn-handed labour, sweats and grows thin, and dies worn out, whilst Nothing gets a redder tinge upon its cheek, a thicker wattle to its chin, and a larger compass of abdomen. There are hundreds of the goodly profession of Nothing who have walked upon three-piled velvet from their nurses' arms to the grave: men who in the most triumphant manner vindicate the ingenuity of the human mind; for enjoying and possessing every creature comfort of existence, not even a conjuror, nay, sometimes not even a police magistrate, can discover how they get it.

Consider man as Nothing, and what a glorious spectacle! A man following an allowed, a known profession, is a vulgar object, let his incomings be ever so great: we know his whole mystery—we can tell whence flows his tide of wealth. The Thames is a gorgeous river, but knowing its name, we talk little of its magnificence. 'Tis otherwise with the Niger.

The man who with nothing, has all things, is to us a sort of Friar Bacon.[20] We approach him with a feeling deeper than respect. He is the Cornelius Agrippa[21] of our times. We know not that some familiar spirit does not act his bidding. He may, on the contrary, be a king's son by a left-handed marriage. He moves in a cloud of mystery—he is away, apart from the common. We know that if other men were to cease from their ordinary occupations, the whole train of human wants would immediately set in upon them; whilst the man professing Nothing lives, independent, *tabooed*, from all the annoyances of life. Oh, my son! I grant the secret may be difficult to compass; but study for it—search it out, though your brain become dry and rattle in your skull like a withered hazel-nut—still, once discover how to live with Nothing, and you may snap your fingers at all mortal accident. Nothing, when a successful Nothing, is the nabob of the world!

You will, in your progress through life, be called upon to wonder at the discoveries of Galileo, who swore that the world moved round the sun—and then, or I mistake, that the sun moved round the world; you will hear a great deal of Homer and Shakspere, who shaped out worlds upon paper, and begot men and women with drops of ink: folks will talk to you upon the discovery of the circulation of the blood, and other gossip of the like sort, demanding your admiration, your homage, for what they will call the triumph of human genius. Fiddle-de-dee! What should you care how the world moves, or whether it moves at all, so you move well in it? As for Homer and Shakspere, the first was a beggar, and for the second—for the great magician, who as people will cant to you, has left immortal company for the spirit of man in its weary journey through this briary world—has bequeathed scenes of immortal loveliness for the human fancy to delight in—founts of eternal truth for the lip of man to drink, and drink—and for aye be renovated with every draught,—he, this benefactor to the world, could not secure a comfortable roof from the affections and gratitude of men, for the female descendant of his flesh, who withered from the world, almost an outcast and a pauper! Now, the man who can live a long and jovial life upon Nothing, has often (by some strange wizard craft) the wherewithal to bequeath to his heirs. As for literature and science,—tales of fairy-land, and the circulation of the blood,—be it your care to make nothing your Ariel; and for your blood,

20 Friar Bacon, the wise necromancer of Brasenose College in Robert Greene's play, *Friar Bacon and Friar Bungay.*

21 Cornelius Agrippa (1486–1535), German writer, soldier, and physician whose works on occult subjects gained him a reputation as a magician.

heed not how it passes through your heart, so that as it flows, it be enriched with the brightest and strengthened with the best.

Be a successful Nothing, my son, and be blessed!

## LETTER VI.

PUNCH INTRODUCES HIS SON TO "HERMETICAL" PHILOSOPHY.

WHAT! my dear boy, my last letter has thrown you into a fit of melancholy? You look hopelessly, recklessly, on the prospects of human life, and would fain flee into a hermitage, there to ponder on the mysteries of social humbug—of life and death; the toils and the trifles of mankind? This resolution on your part reminded me that I was the fortunate possessor of a few fragmentary thoughts on the vast subjects you would contemplate—of thoughts born in solitude of a restless brain that has long since mingled with the earth. Take them—ponder on them—and for the present be content to know them as—

FRAGMENTS ON HUMBUG, SOLITUDE, LIFE, DEATH, AND
SELF-KNOWLEDGE, BY THE HERMIT OF CONEY-HATCH.

I have thought it wise and pleasant in my solitude, having no ready-money market for my time, to devote my hours on hand to the intellectual wants of my fellow-man. The reader, affected by the beauty of my subject, may haply feel a generous curiosity, may yearn to know the condition of the sage who seeks to discourse upon the most vital, the most profound, the most mysterious principle of human society,—for such is humbug. It is the cement of the social fabric. It is the golden cord tying together, and making strong, the sticks and twigs of the world. It is the dulcet bell, whose ravishing sound calls the great family of man to eat, drink, and be merry! Hapless are they, whose leathern ears list not the music; for if they feed at all, at best they feed on draff, and are to the revellers even as swine are to bipeds.

Let not the reader seek to know more of me than, with a most white conscience, I am permitted to tell him. The great events of my life are not my own. I speak without any oracular quibble; I mean this, and no other. The great accidents of my mortal travail have been sold; yea, bartered by me for so many Mint medals, and a stamp receipt given for the payment. Thus it was. In a moment of pecuniary impatience, I offered a choice of the events of my life to a gentleman in want of materials for a popular novel. With a frankness that has been of singular loss to me throughout my existence, I opened the goods unreservedly before him. As market-wives say, I let him have the pick and choose of the lot; kept nothing back for a second huckstering. Well, the buyer left me without a decent event in my basket. Every picturesque accident, from exaggerated homicide to the forgery of a will in a moment of vinous intoxication, was bought, and I confess as much, honestly paid for by the novelist 'fore-mentioned; and, if there be truth in human bargains, as indeed there must be when solemnised by a stamp, for otherwise, casuists have their opinions,—the incidental property of my life belongs to the purchaser. I have this consolation: my mundane struggles have affected, delighted, and instructed the world, though labelled with the name of another. Though I have remained, and must remain unknown, my deeds, dressed to the best advantage, have enraptured thousands. Like the ostrich plume waving above the whiter brow of lovely peeress, my life has found its way among the richest, and by consequence, the noblest of the earth,—whilst I, the liver, the poor plucked bird, have wandered over barren sand and fed on iron. But this is a story older than quills.

I have nothing, then, of my life at the service of the reader, but that part of it, the poor remnant following the bargain narrated above. This being my own property, I shall invest it in the present volume. My birth and parentage I have sold, and, I honestly believe, at their full value. There, however, remain to me a few fragments which, like sweepings of a spicery, though not good enough to season a holiday dish, may give an enduring sweetness to a cold body of philosophy. The cloves and cinnamon which the clean-handed huswife would reject for her pudding or custard, may serve for the dead belly of an embalmed Plato. In these days, philosophy itself must be spiced and sweetened, and have its eyes taken out, lest it become noisome in the nostrils of society. That too shall sometimes be the most acceptable body of philosophy, which retains the least hint of bowels.

I know not what business women have with goose-quills, beyond that of plucking them from the bird of mischief that the animal may become the better companion for apple-sauce. The later prejudices of the world have, however, concluded otherwise; hence, my maiden aunt, Abishag Jones, excelled all the family in her writing; perhaps it was, that she was the only one of her tribe who wrote bank cheques. My poor father was never so happy as when he could get a pen between the fingers of Aunt Abishag. We grew up, it may be said, with an instinctive reverence, an increasing admiration, of the handwriting of Aunt Jones. Now, I believe it is an acknowledged principle of human action, that what we greatly admire, we often seek to imitate. At all events, it happened so to me. With untiring energy, I laboured to emulate the flowing delicacy of Aunt Abishag's pen: and at length succeeded to such a nicety, that a gentleman, a perfect stranger, handed over to me fifty pounds as a reward for my zealous ingenuity.

Women are fantastic animals. I make no flourish of this discovery; indeed, I almost fear that others, it may be in the dark, have stumbled on the hidden truth. My Aunt Abishag was, however, a living and most energetic illustration of the fact; for it was to be reasonably supposed that she would have felt a flutter of pride at the successful genius of her nephew; that she would have considered his delicate imitation of her calligraphic powers as an elaborate homage to her best endowment. It was otherwise. Vindicating the prerogative of her sex, she became so capriciously obstreperous, that, respecting even her most violent whimsies, I renounced the world and all its selfishness, and became that which I now am.

"What is that?" asks the reader.

With a brevity, which I hope will distinguish the small-talk of my future life, I will endeavour to answer the query.

My Aunt Abishag confined not her inquiries of the whereabout of her ingenious nephew to her personal exertions. Hence, availing herself of the bounteous powers of the press, she caused my portrait to be typographically delineated, and as a most touching proof of her regard for me, offered the princely sum of twenty pounds to whosoever should snatch me from the wily temptations of liberty, and hold me in safe keeping.

I will not attempt to describe the emotions which stirred within my breast, and rose to my throat, as I perused this last affecting evidence of my aunt's regard. Happily, I was diverted from a too intense contemplation of woman's tenderness, by a notice, that, in the same gazette, somewhat irreverently shouldered the manifesto of Aunt Abishag. From that notice I take these words:—

> A Hermit wanted.—To philosophers, misanthropes, or gentlemen in difficulties, a singularly eligible opportunity presents itself. A nobleman of enlarged social views is desirous of engaging an individual for the term of three years in the capacity of hermit. The party engaging will be required to conform to the most rigid discipline of eremite life. No Irishman need apply; and as the nobleman is desirous of assuring to himself every prob-

able guarantee for the due performance of the contract, married men only will be treated with.

I looked from my Aunt Abishag to the nobleman of enlarged social views—I wavered but for a moment between my affection, my duty to my aunt, and a new-born, romantic desire to let my beard and nails grow. In brief, for it is in the result only that the reader is interested, here I am, at this moment, in my hermitage—a snug, weatherproof box, eighteen feet by ten—with an oak table, one stool, one platter, one maple cup, a bed of dried rushes, one blanket, one gown, one hat, one staff. Here I am, on the night of this —— day of ——, in the year of Christian hopes ——, with the bell of Coney-hatch Church jerking twelve. Here have I been these twelve months; and if a neighbouring fountain reflect truly, then am I as reverend and venerable an anchorite, especially about the chin, as any nobleman could desire to spend his cash upon. I have more than once thought—and strange to say, there has been a fearful pleasure in the errant notion—that if in this drear solitude I should be made the subject of a popular murder, my locks and beard worked in brooches, earrings, and bracelets, would realise sufficient from the romantic and the curious to endow sundry anxious persons with becoming fortitude for my untimely loss. I have, however, as speedily banished this vanity as unworthy of my new self—as unworthy of a cell, that, according to a very stringent agreement drawn up by the attorney of Coney-hatch, is to be a shrine for unselfish contemplation; a retreat, wherein the highest powers of intellectual man are, by daily exercise, by nightly discipline, to climb the golden chain of necessity, and strike delicious music from every link.

# LETTER VII.

### THE HERMIT'S "PHILOSOPHY"—CONTINUED.

How PURE this atmosphere! How sweet, with opening lungs and indrawn chest, to take a long, deep, bacchanal draught of midnight air, cool from the stars and odorous with May! With not a taint of urban smoke—with not the fever-heat of corroding mortal life—to infect the soul with maladies of which men daily die, albeit doctors dream not of the true disease! How grand at this moment to hear, in the profound of night, the heart of the earth beat—beat towards eternity! To feel a new affection, as we recognise a new life—closer sympathies with all that presses upon us! To lose our old habitual eyes, that blink dreamily at common-place; with true vision to see spirits ascending and descending from every blade and leaf; and with ears tuned to the most secret melody of nature—that like a happy huswife, sings as she toils—list the working of that vast laboratory compassed in yon giant oak!

We can do more. Drop through the earth, and, with strengthening heart and health-obtaining brain, look face to face at death, and see a new-found beauty in his barren bones. We can scan him, talk to him, and see a thousand curious beauties—odd, grave blandishments, in the abused wight; the worthy creature, wronged in our half-knowledge, slandered in the malice of our ignorance. What filthy names—when the broad sun was shining upon us, and we were laughing in the glory of a new doublet and jerkin—have we spat upon him! How have we mauled him, when we have thought of his wicked will with cousin Bridget—a red-lipped creature with the breath of a heifer! How did we rate him for a wretch, a beast, a monster dining upon heartstrings—an ogre that blotted out the beauty of the sun—that put a poison into the violet's leaf—that turned all gracious and all lovely things to hideous, ghastly masquerade!—How did we clench our fist, and stamp at him, as, with reeling brain and bursting heart, we stood at thy grave, O Admetus![22] and wished ourselves a clod of the valley, to mingle with thy bones!

Fortune is called harlot every hour of the day, and that, too, by grave gentlemen who only abuse the wench before company because they have never known her private favours. Bad as she is, however, let sour-faced Seneca and all the other philosophers of the vinegar-cruet stalk with paper lanterns before her door, they will never bring the romping hoyden into ill repute. No; she will still be visited, prayed to, cajoled, flattered; and when she plays a jilt's trick, will be abused as lustily as ever. Yet, what is this universal abuse—this polyglot reviling—for fortune is damned by all colours and in all tongues,—to the foul, ungrateful, scandalous, mean-spirited, shabby—aye, and hypocritical, abuse of death!

Oh, no! do not believe what is said of death. All folks abuse him, and therefore, if for nothing else, out of the very chivalry of your nature—shake hands with him. No—not hands; that, for a few years at least, is a little too near. But there—give him the end of your walking-stick, and let him shake that. Well done! Now, look at him. Hath he not been

---

[22] Admetus, in Greek mythology, king of Pharae and husband of Alcestis. When Admetus was dying Apollo persuaded the gods to spare him if someone would consent to die in his place. Alcestis willingly gave her life but was later rescued from the dead.

scurvily limned? The dirty portrait-painters of the world, learning that
the good fellow had so many enemies, have villainously libelled him.
Should you recognise, in the fine benevolence now smiling upon you—
and surely no chamberlain, with finger on his golden key, ever looked a
visitor a sweeter welcome—should you see, in the frank hospitality before you, the sneaking, haggard, noiseless stabber, painted by a million
brushes? Is he not all over—gentleman! Behold his face—his frame! Hath
he not the countenance of Adonis, with perhaps a somewhat downward
look? The outline of an Apollo? He carries a dart. It is no vulgar imple-
ment—no piece of torturing cold iron, to pierce and grope in human
bowels, but an arrow from the quiver of Eternal Day. It has been used
so much in this thick-dew world, that, to the filthy eyes of men, it has
lost its brightness; but it is not so: the immortal ray is under the rust.
The meanest, the scurviest abuse has been cast upon all-suffering death.
Not one fair gift has been left him. Even the sweetness of his breath has
been traduced. Now, madam—nay, put aside your smelling-bottle, and
fearlessly approach. There! Death breathes. Is it not an air from Ely-
sium? Amaranth, madam—amaranth!

   We are content to take up the abuse of the world as truthful censure
—to believe in the hard sayings flung in the teeth of death as well-earned
reproach. We condemn him by hearsay; and join in the halloo of an unthinking, ignorant mob. But invite death to a tête-à-tête: divesting yourself of vulgar prejudice, sit down in a place like this—for you are in my
hermitage, reader, and calmly and dispassionately chat with him, and
you will find the fine old fellow to have been villainously maligned—
shamefully scandalised. You will, to your own surprise, and no less comfort, discover in death the noblest benefactor—the staunchest, truest
friend. All the naughty things you have heard of him will seem to you
as the gossip of cowards—the malice of fools. All the foul paraphernalia
—the shroud, the winding-sheet—the wet heavy clay, the worm and corruption at which serious gentlemen shake their heads, and talk for an
hour upon, have no more to do with you than with the hare that may
nibble the grass above what once was yours: no more touch you than
they touch the red-faced urchins making chains of buttercups and daisies on a falsifying tombstone. When moralising wordmongers seize you
by the button, and holding up a skull or old earth-smelling tibia to your
eye, look straight down their noses, and tell you that in a short time you
will be no more than that they thrust in your face,—tell them, with all
reverence, they lie. What will your skull, your bones, be to you, more
than your corn that was cut out on Thursday—more than that vile dou-

ble-tooth which, having tortured you for a fortnight, was, a week since, lugged out of your jaw, and left at the dentist's? It is the vile literalness of people's brains that gives an unhandsomeness to the dead bones of men; that makes them in the grave a part and parcel of the sentient thing; that would make their foulness and disgrace a humiliation to the soaring man. You show me his lordship's cast-off court-suit of tarnished silver: that it is cast off, proves to me that he has possessed himself of a better. Show me the skull of a dead philosopher—nay, of a defunct pickpocket; commence a dumpish morality on the terrible change of head undergone by sage or thief, and I shall reply to you—It is excellent that it is so; for, depend upon it, the change is for the better; he has obtained a much handsomer article.

We libel the sanctity of death, when we dress it in artificial terrors. We profane it, when, applying a moral galvanism to its lineaments, we make it mope and mow at the weak and credulous.

The truth is, we have made too much a mystery of the commonplaces of death: we have made scarecrows of skeletons, instead of looking upon them with a sort of respect—as we look upon the hat, coat, and breeches of one we once loved,—of one who once wore the articles that were a necessary part of his dress for this world, but that in fact never made any portion of that thing, that essence, which we knew as he. You say, that was his thighbone: very well—this was his walking-stick. Bone or cane, one was as much of him as the other: he is alike independent of both. I deny that he is changed—that his dignity is in the remotest degree compromised, because his human furniture is nailed in a box, and crammed in a hole. You might as well preach upon the disgrace of walking-sticks, because our friend's bit of dragon's-blood, after sundry domestic revolutions, has been cut into a dibber. To make a death's-head horrible—to preach from its pretended loathsomeness a lesson to the pride of humanity—to extract from it terrors to the spirit of man, whilst yet consorted with flesh and blood,—the churchyard moralist should prove that the skull remains the ghastly, comfortless prison of the soul,—that, for a certain time, it is ordained its blank and hideous dungeon. Then, indeed, would a death's-head be horrible; then would it appall a heart of stone and ribs of steel. But, good sexton-preacher, when now you show me a skull, what do I look upon? The empty shell, through which the bird has risen to the day.

I have learned this in my hermitage—learned it, sitting cheek by jowl with death, talking over his doings, and deeply contemplating the loveliness of his attributes.

# LETTER VIII.

I HAVE LEARNED another trick in this solitude. I have learned to separate the twin natures with which, it is my belief, every man is born, and to sit in judgment upon the vices, the follies, the high feelings, and grovelling appetites, that make up the double *me*. Make a trial of the process, reader. Quit the world for a season. Look boldly into yourself; and however high may have been your notion of the cleanliness of your moral temple, you will, if you look with steady, courageous eyes, blush and marvel at its many dirty little holes and corners, the vile, unswept nooks —the crafty spiders and their noisome webs. And in this temple, to your surprise, you will behold two pulpits for two preachers. In the innocency of your knowledge you thought there was but one divine, and that a most respectable, orthodox, philanthropic creature; punctual in his discourses, exemplary in his discipline—indeed, the very pattern of a devout and cheerful man. You look, and behold, there is another preacher, a fellow with no more reverence in him than in Malay amuck; a pettifogging, mean-spirited, albeit quick-witted, shuffling scoundrel, whose voice, too, in the throng and press of the world has appeared to you so like the voice of the good, grave gentleman whom you deemed alone in his vocation, that you have a thousand times, without reflection, followed his bidding—unhesitatingly obeyed his behests, and only now, when you have set apart a season for consideration, only now perceive the imposture—recognise the counterfeit.

"What!" you exclaim, "and was it he who prompted me with that bitter answer to poor inoffensive Palemon?"[23] "Was it he who bade me button up my pocket and growl—'No,' to such a petitioner on such a day?" "Was it he who whispered me to cross the road, and cut to the heart the ruined, shabby-coated Damon?"[24] And still further considering the matter, you remember that the interloper monitor, the fellow whose very existence you never suspected, has had nearly all the talk to himself; the grave gentleman, whose voice has been so well imitated, and whom you thought your pastor and your master, having been silenced, outtalked, by the chattering of an unsuspected opponent. I say it, you are twin-souled. Step into my hermitage. Submit to wholesome discipline of

---

23 Palemon, in Chaucer's "Knight's Tale," and his Theban cousin Arcite fall in love with the same girl; dying after being injured in a joust, Arcite yields the girl to Palemon.

24 Damon, in Greek legend, the inseparable friend of Pythias, for whom he willingly offered to die.

thought, and, be assured of it, you will, in due season, be able to divorce self from self; to arraign your fallen moiety at the bar of conscience; to bring against it a thousand score of crimes, a thousand peccadilloes, all the doings of the scurvy rascal you bear within you, and whose misdeeds are for the first time made known to you.

Well, the court is open.

Who,—you cry,—is that beetle-browed, shuffling, cock-eyed knave at the bar? Is he a poacher, a smuggler, a suborner of false testimony, a swindler, a thief?

Gently, gently, sir: that unfortunate creature is your twin-soul. It was he who in the case of Mr. Suchathing advised you to—

God bless me! I remember—don't speak of it—shocking!—I'm very sorry.

And it was he who, when poor widow Soandso—

There, hold your tongue! I recollect all about it. How have I been deceived by that scoundrel! But then, how could I ever have believed that I carried such a rascal about me?

For my own part, I am firm in the faith that I should never have discovered my own twin varlet had I not shut the door upon the world and taken a good inside stare at myself. No; my hair would have grown grey and my nose wine-coloured—for it hath a purpureal weakness,—and as a distinguished statesman, whose name I forget, once said, I might have patted the back of my naughty twin soul, deeming him a remarkably fine sample of the article; and so gone on, working for a handsome epitaph, and dying with a Christian-like assurance that I had earned the same. I might have lived and died thus self-deluded, but for this retreat so happily opened to me by the illustrious nobleman aforesaid.

*A work of this nature is not to be performed upon one leg; and should smell of oil, if duly and deservedly handled.*

Such is the solemn avowal of a fantastically grave philosopher, on the completion of his *opus magnum*; but surely that vaunt hath a more fitting abiding-place in the present page. My subject, too, like that of my brother philosopher, from its innate dignity, its comprehensive usefulness, might employ the goose-quills of a whole college. It were easy to tell off at least five hundred men—many of them having the ears of kings, and what is more, the purse-strings of nations at their command—all of them, by nature and practice, admirably fitted for the work. From their very successes, the world has a claim upon them for the encyclopedic labour. However, until the time arrive when these men, touched by a sense of their ingratitude, shall repair the wrong, let the present little book receive the welcome due to good intentions. I am content, in the whirl and mutation of all mundane things, to be trumped by a minister, a cardinal, a philosopher, a commercial philanthropist, by any one or one hundred of these. When such men shall have grown sufficiently ingenuous to respond to the crying wants of their fellow-creatures, and shall publish Humbug *in extenso*, I shall sleep quietly beneath the marble monument which the gratitude of my country will erect to my memory, although this little volume, superseded by the larger work, shall be called in like an old coinage, and no longer be made the class-book of the young, the staff of the middle-aged, and the solacing chronicle of the old.

Imperfect as the work may be, it would, I feel, have been impossible to write at all upon Humbug amid the delicious distractions of a city. Is it asked,—wherefore? Alas! the writer would have been confounded by the quantity of his materials. Solitude—continued, profound solitude—was necessary to the gestation and safe delivery of this book. I have endeavoured to show that the true solemnities, the real sweetnesses of death—the mystery of our inner selves, which said mystery we walk about the world with, deeming it of no more complexity than the first mouse-trap,—are only to be approached and looked upon in their utter nakedness when safe from the elbows and the tongues of the world. Now, if life be a mystery, Humbug is at once the art and heart of life. A man may, indeed, get a smattering of moral philosophy in a garret within ear-shot of the hourly courtesies of hackney-coachmen; but Humbug, though she often ride in a coach of her own through the highways of the city, like a fine lady, suffers her pulse to be felt only in private. Humbug is the philosopher's Egeria,[25] and to be wooed and truly known in secret.

Think you, reader, there is no other reason for the sundry prorogations of Parliament, than that the excellent men (selected only for their wisdom and their virtue from their less wise and less virtuous fellows,) having generously presented so many pounds to the state, their services are for a time no longer required? Such is not the profound intent of prorogation. Its benevolent purpose is to send every senator into healthful solitude, that he may fortify himself with a frequent contemplation of his past votes; that he may call up and question his twin soul, and rejoice himself to know that the Dromios[26] within him have given their

25 Egeria, the mythical woman adviser of Numa Pompilius, legendary second king of Rome.
26 Dromios, the merry identical twins, Dromio of Ephesus and Dromio of Syracuse, who are the servants of identical twins in Shakespeare's *Comedy of Errors*.

voices in accordance—that one of the sneaking gemini, out of the baseness of expected gains, has not cried "Ay," when its nobler fellow stoutly intended "No!"

\*   \*   \*   \*   \*   \*   \*

CONCLUSION OF THE "HERMIT'S" FRAGMENTS.


# LETTER IX.

ON THE "BEAUTY" AND "LUXURY" OF TRUTH.—
THE UNALLOYED GUINEAS.

So, MY DEAR CHILD, you have had enough of philosophy—have read enough of the speculations of the Hermit of Coney-hatch, to feel that your yearnings for solitary contemplation were but a passing weakness; to know, that it is in the bustling world about you, true wisdom finds its best, its most enduring reward? Parchment, my dear child, though writ and illuminated with all the glories of the human brain, is a perishable commodity: now, gold in bars will last till the world crack.

I now come to the principal subject of your last letter,—"the beauty of Truth."

My dear boy, truth is, no doubt, a very beautiful object; so are diamonds, pearls, rubies, emeralds; but, like those sparkling, precious things, it is by no means necessary to your condition of life;—and if sported at all, is only to be enjoyed by way of luxury. Beware, lest a vain conceit should ruin you. The nobleman, the man of independence, may speak truth, as he may wear a brilliant in his breast, worth a hundred guineas. Now, as you must be content with at best a bit of Bristol-stone,[27] with a small imitation of the lustrous reality, so, in like way, can you not afford to utter the true sparkling commodity at all times. Do not suppose, however, that I would have you never speak the truth. Pray, do not misunderstand me. You may, as a man of the world, and a trader who would turn the prudent penny,—you may always speak the truth when it can be in no way to your advantage not to utter it.

At the same time, my beloved boy, take heed that you obtain not the evil reputation of a liar. "What!"—I think I hear you exclaim,—"your advice, papa, involves a contradiction." By no means. What I wish to impress upon you, is the necessity of so uttering your verbal coinage,

27 Bristol-stone, rock crystal found in the mountain limestone near Bristol, England, and used in making ornaments, vases, etc.

that to the superficial eye and careless ear, it may have all the appearance, all the ring of the true article. Herein consists the great wisdom of life. The thousands who have grown rich by its application to all their worldly concerns are incalculable. The world, as at present constituted, could not go on without lying. And, I am convinced, it is only the full conviction of this fact that enables so many worthy, excellent people to club their little modicum of daily falsehood together, for the benevolent purpose of keeping the world upon its axis.

For a moment, consider the effect produced in London alone, if from to-morrow morning, for one month only, every man, woman, and child were to speak the truth, the whole truth, and nothing but the truth. You have read of towns besieged, of cities sacked, of the unbridled fury of a sanguinary solidiery; but all this would be as sport to the horrors of this our most civilised metropolis. Gracious Plutus! Think of the bankruptcies! Imagine the confessions of statesmen! Consider the internal revelations of churchmen! Only reflect upon the thousands and thousands of —at present—most respectable, exemplary people, congregated in the highways and market-places, making a "clean breast" to one another,— each man shocking his neighbour with the confession of his social iniquity, of his daily hypocrisy, of his rascal vice that he now feeds and cockers like a pet snake in private! If all men were thus to turn themselves inside out, the majority of blacks would, I fear, be most alarming. We might have Hottentot chancellors, and even Ethiopian bishops!

A wise German, named Goethe, has observed—"There is something in every man, which, if known to his fellow, would make him hate him." How, then, could the world go on with this reciprocal passion of hatred? Philosophic statesmen, conscious of this fact, have therefore leavened every social institution with a necessary and most wholesome amount of falsehood. Hence, too, we have what are called legal fictions. Hence, Justice, the daughter of Truth, debauched by Law, gives, with a solemn smirk, short weight to the poor, and a lumping pen'orth to the rich.

What are the fees paid to hungry, hundred-handed office, but offerings exacted by falsehood? What is the costliness of Justice, but the wilful extravagance of lying—the practical mendacity of life? Truth, by a paradoxical fiction, is painted naked; and Justice is robed in plain, unspotted white. Why, the old harridan must have as many gew-gaws—as many big-beaded necklaces—brooches—pins—chains, and armlets, as the wife of a Jew bailiff. These things she must have, or what does she with the presents made to her—the fees exacted?

I tell you again and again, all truth will not do in this world. I will give you a short story, in illustration of the reality of this.

How, or by what accident, they escaped from the Mint, was never known, but certain it is, that one hundred guineas of pure gold, without the least alloy, were once upon a time issued to the world. Old Gregory Muckly, by chance, obtained half-a-dozen pieces of this coin, which, together with a few other pieces, were carefully hoarded in a worsted stocking: and when Gregory was safely deposited in churchyard clay, they became the rightful property of his son Hodge.

Hodge was a simple, honest creature; caring nothing for the pomps of the world;

> The sum of all his vanity, to deck
> With one bright bell some fav'rite heifer's neck.[28]

Business, however, brought him to London. Well, before he returned to Gammon Farm, he would purchase a London present—a bran new scarlet shawl for sister Suke. Two guineas did Hodge, with fraternal self-complacency, set apart for this gift. Caught by the truthful assurance exhibited in a mercer's window that the stock was "selling off under prime cost," Hodge thought he was sure of at least a three-guinea shawl for two. Hereupon, he entered the shop; rolled his eyes from side to side, seeking the radiant present for sister Suke.

"Have you a nice, bran new scarlet shawl for two guineas?" asked Hodge.

"Sir," replied the shopkeeper, "you come at a lucky moment: we have the most delicious article—the most wonderful scarlet. To anybody else, sir, it would be three guineas and a half; but as you have frequently been a customer to us"——

"Nay, nay," cried Hodge, "I was never here before."

"I beg your pardon, sir; humbly beg your pardon—another gentleman like you," said the tradesman.

"I'm no gentleman, neither," said Hodge; "and all I want is, you to show me the shawl."

"There, sir," said the mercer, throwing the shawl upon the counter; "there's a scarlet."

"Ha! ha! so it be—like a poppy," chuckled Hodge.

"A poppy, sir,—a poppy's brickdust to it," said the tradesman.

"Nay, nay, not so," cried Hodge; "and I think I've seen more poppies than thee."

"Ha! ha! no doubt, sir—very true. Well, I assure you, to anybody else this article would be three guineas and a half; but to you, we'll say two."

28 "The bound of all his vanity to deck / With one bright bell a favourite heifer's neck." (Wordsworth, "Descriptive Sketches," ll. 584–585.)

"There they be," said Hodge; and he laid down the two unalloyed guineas on the counter.

As the tradesman took up the coin, a shadow fell upon his face; and turning to his shopman, he whispered, "Run for a constable." Then addressing himself to Hodge, he said—"Walk this way, if you please."

In two minutes Hodge was in the mercer's back parlor; in five, in the custody of a constable; and in ten more, arraigned before a magistrate, being charged with an attempt to pass off bad money.

"Look at the things, you worship; look at their colour—feel 'em— they'll bend like pewter; and to attempt to pass such pocket-pieces upon an honest tradesman,—really!" and the mercer was bursting with indignation.

Hodge's defence was not listened to, and he was sent to gaol for two days, until a proper officer from the Mint could be in attendance to pronounce judgment on the suspected guineas.

"Indeed, this is curious," said Mr. Testem, the Mint functionary; "but I don't wonder at your suspicions: the fact is, these guineas are *too good*." Mr. Testem then narrated that a hundred pieces of coin, of pure, unalloyed gold, had been accidentally issued, and that Hodge's two guineas were of them.

My son—he who in this world resolves to speak only the truth, will speak only what is *too good* for the mass of mankind to understand, and, like Hodge, will be persecuted accordingly.

## LETTER X.

EVERY MAN HIS OWN APPRAISER.—LEGEND OF THE RIGHT LEG.

YOUR LAST LETTER, my dear son, annoyed, oppressed me. What! you wish you had been born an Esquimaux, a Chippewaw, a Hottentot, rather than a member of the most civilised, most generous nation (as every people modestly say of themselves) on the face of the earth. Ungrateful boy! is this the return you make me for the very handsome present of your existence,—is this your gratitude for being called out of nothing to become an eating, drinking, tax-paying animal?

Despondency, my child, is the slow suicide of the mind. Heaven knows what I have suffered at the hands of the world!—how, with my heart bleeding into my very shoes, I have still chirped and crowed *roo-tooit-*

*tooit,* despising while I laughed with and chattered to the reeking rascals, niggard of their pence, who still thronged and gaped about me.

> Alas! 'tis true, I have gone here and there,
> And made myself a motley to the view,
> Gored mine own thoughts, sold cheap what is most dear,
> Made old offences of affections new.[29]

Nevertheless, if now and then my heart has been a little slack, I have braced it up again with my drum, and looking upon life at the best as composed of just so many pleasurable sensations, I have enjoyed myself as often as I could, which I have thought the very wisest way of showing my gratitude for my existence. When I could not obtain large pleasures, I put together as many small ones as possible. Small pleasures, depend upon it, lie about as thick as daisies; and for that very reason are neglected, trodden under foot, instead of being worn in our button-holes. We cannot afford to buy moss-roses at Christmas, or camellias at any time: and so, all the year round we couple buttercups with vulgarity; and the lovely, odorous things that grow in the hedgeside, we let wither where they grow, for no other reason than that the king's highway is not a royal garden.

At the same time, my dear boy, I would not have you copy the contentment of your father. Contentment is very well in a pastoral; and I have seen something which called itself Contentment, sitting smugly at a small-coal fire, enjoying its crust and half-a-pint of beer in a tin mug on the hob,—only because it would not stir itself to get the port and olives, that with very little exertion were within its reach. Though I know this to be pusillanimity, and not contentment, nevertheless, my dear child, I cannot altogether acquit myself of it. Be warned by your sire. I might, with my genius, have trod the boards of a play-house,—have had my name upon the walls, in type that blacking-makers should have envied; I might have danced quadrilles in Cavendish square[30] on my off-nights, and been trundled about the town in my own air-cushioned carriage; for I have all the qualifications in the highest degree which lead to such a golden result.—Of this I am assured by their success as poorly and extravagantly copied by another; but no, I was doomed to be a street vagabond, and came into the world with a base taste for mud in my infant mouth, and an ear throbbing for drum and pandeans. Hence, I have—when doing my best—been scoffed at, and abused by fish-

---

[29] Shakespeare, Sonnet 110.
[30] Cavendish-Square, in London, surrounded by homes of fashionable physicians, surgeons, and dentists.

wives, when, with the sagacious application of the same powers, I might have been pelted by heiresses with nosegays from the boxes.

My child, know not diffidence: it is an acquaintance that hourly picks your pocket—that makes you hob-and-nob with fustian, when otherwise, you might jostle it with court ruffles. Receive this for an axiom: nineteen times out of twenty the world takes a man at his own valuation. A philosopher[31]—I forget his name—has called the human soul, on its first manifestation in this world, thickly veiled as it is in baby-flesh—a blank sheet of paper. Now I, my son, call every full-grown man at his outset in life, a piece, not of blank, but of *bank-paper*; in fact, a note, in all things perfect save that the amount is not written in. It is for the man himself to put down how many pounds it shall pass for; to snatch an eagle-quill, and, with a brow of bronze and eye of brass, to write down

£ ONE THOUSAND

or else, with shaking hand and lips of indigo, to scratch a miserable, pauper-stricken, squalid—

£ ONE

It is, I say, for the man himself to give value to his own moral paper: and though, I grant, now and then the prying and ill-natured may hold up the article to the light to search for the true water-mark, the owner of the note has only to swagger and put the face of a Cæsar on the transaction, to silence every scruple.

As an instance, my dear boy, of what perseverance will do—of what an inexorable advocacy of merit (or fancied merit, for that is the thing) will do for the professor,—I will give you a short story, drawn from a Dutch annalist of the sixteenth century.

Serene and balmy was the 9th of June morning, 1549, when three men dressed as heralds, and superbly mounted on piebald horses, appeared in the streets of Utrecht. Immediately behind them, mounted on a mule richly caparisoned, rode a man, or rather a human bundle—a hunchback, with his right leg less than a goose's over-roasted drumstick; the leg was, moreover, bowed like a pot-hook; and, as at first was thought, that its deformity might be fully seen, was without hose or shoe; in plain words—it was a naked leg. The dwarf was followed by six horsemen, handsomely arrayed, and strongly mounted.

[31] John Locke (1632–1704), in his *An Essay Concerning Human Understanding* (1690).

The procession halted before the burgomaster's door, when the heralds, putting their trumpets to their lips, blew so loud a blast that every man's money danced in his pocket. The crowd with gaping mouths and ears awaited the proclamation of the herald, who thus unburthened himself:

"Let it be known to all corners of the creation, that our most noble, most puissant master, now present, the right valorous and worthy Vandenhoppenlimpen, has the most perfect right leg of all the sons of earth! In token whereof, he now exhibiteth the limb; whereat, let all men shout and admire!"

On the instant, the dwarf cocked up his withered stump, self-complacently laying his hand upon his heart; and at the same moment the crowd screamed and roared, and abused and reviled the dwarf, whilst some market women discharged ancient eggs and withered apples at him,—until the procession, followed by the roaring populace, made their way back to their hostelry.

The next morning, at the same place and like hour, the same proclamation was made. Again the undaunted dwarf showed his limb, and again he was chased and pelted.

And every day for six months, the unwearied heralds proclaimed the surpassing beauty of Vandenhoppenlimpen's right leg, and every day the leg was exhibited. And after a time, every day the uproar of the mob decreased; and the leg was considered with new and growing deference.

"After all, we must have been mistaken—there surely *is* something in the leg," said one contemplative burgher.

"I have some time thought so," answered another.

"'Tisn't likely," said a third, "that the man would stand so to the excellence of his leg, unless there were something in it, not to be seen at once."

"It is my faith," said the burgomaster's grandmother—"a faith I'll die in, for I have heard the sweet man himself say as much a hundred-and-fifty times, that all other right legs are clumsy and ill-shaped, and that Vandenhoppenlimpen's leg is the only leg on the earth, made as a leg should be."

In a short season, this faith became the creed of the mob; and, oh, how the neighbouring cities, towns, and villages emptied themselves into Utrecht, to gaze and marvel at Vandenhoppenlimpen's leg! When he died, a model of the limb was taken, and cast in virgin gold, is now used as a tobacco-stopper on state occasions at the Stadt-house of Utrecht.

My child, there are at this moment many Vandenhoppenlimpens eating bread very thickly buttered, from having stoutly championed the
surpassing merits of their bowed and bucked right leg.


## LETTER XI.

ON THE NECESSITY OF HYPOCRISY—STORY OF
THE LEMON MERCHANT.

NO, I HAVE no sympathy, my son—none whatever, for you. What! to have
scraped a very promising acquaintance with a man of Alderman Bilberry's wealth—to have had him more than once nod to you; and then,
when fortune—a happy fortune! as it might have turned out—throws
you both together in the same Greenwich boat, to lose the alderman for
ever! You will say, the alderman acted meanly, dirtily, shabbily; will tell
me, that you saw him only five minutes before take twopence in change
for a glass of ginger-beer, when, at the same time, he regretted to the
trumpeter, who came round the deck to gather for himself and musical
companions, that "he had not a copper about him, or would give it with
the greatest pleasure." What devil, may I ask you, tempted you to jog
the alderman's memory on the ginger-beer and penny-pieces? You will
say to me, the alderman told a lie, the alderman acted shabbily; and,
therefore, you reproved him; and, what you doubtless think a splendid
peacock's feather in your cap, you reproved him with a joke! I shall certainly write no more to you, if I find my letters do you so little service.

My son, never see the meanness of mankind. Let men hedge, and
shirk, and shift, and lie, and with faces of unwrinkled adamant tell you
the most monstrous falsehoods, either in their self-glorification, or to
disguise some habitual paltriness, still, never detect the untruth; never
lay your finger on the patch they have so bunglingly sewed upon their
moral coat, but let them depart with the most religious persuasion that
they have triumphantly bamboozled you. By these means, although you
are most efficiently assisting in the hypocrisy of life, you will be deemed
a sociable, a most good-natured fellow. Be stone-blind, and you will be
benevolent; be deaf, and you will be all heart. To have an insight—or at
least to show you have it—into the dirty evasions of life, is to have a
moral squint. To lay your finger upon a plague-spot, is to be infected
with malice. No: though you meet with men scurfed with moral leprosy, see not the scales, but cry out lustily, "What perfect gentlemen!" To

discover meanness in men, is, in men's opinion, to be strongly tinctured with the iniquity.

Mr. Chaucer, in allusion to the devil, says of him,

> He hath in Jewè's heart his waspè's nest.[32]

Now, what we call the devil, has built—by the agency of his demon wasps, Pride, Avarice, Scorn, Oppression, Selfishness, and others—thousands of nests in the hearts both of Jews and Christians. Well, suppose you have the power of looking into their hearts as though they were so many crystal hives,—suppose you behold in them the rapacious insects—hear their buzzing—almost see their stings; if you cry "Wasps! wasps!" men will shake their heads at you for a malicious, evil-minded fellow; but, my dear boy, clap your hands, and cry, "What a honeycomb!" and you shall pass from mouth to mouth as the "best of creatures." When you have seen something more of the world, you will know that men rarely attribute an exposure of a social evil to an inherent indignation of the evil itself, but to an unhealthy appetite for moral foulness. Then, my boy, will they most virtuously defame you—then will they, in the name of outraged virtue, call you hard, high-sounding names. The wrestlers of old, says Plutarch, threw dirt on one another that they might get a better grasp, and more successfully trip up each other's heels. In the like way, does ignorance or hypocrisy, in the name of virtue, cast dirt upon him who would trip up a giant wrong. There were, doubtless, those among the Philistines—particular and most virtuous friends of Goliath—who called David a very sour-natured little fellow.

It is extraordinary, too, how this scandal will stick upon you; how it will be used to misinterpret all your motives—to give a twist to your most heroic, most benevolent actions. I will suppose that you are crossing a bridge, or walking by a river's side. Well, a nursery-maid—thinking, it may be, of Jack Robinson, whom she is to meet when the child is put to bed—is so far buried in her thoughts that she lets the baby tumble souse in the stream. You may not swim like a dolphin, yet without waiting to take off your coat, or lay your gold repeater on the grass, you leap into the water, and with no small personal risk manage to bring the baby safe to the bank. Well, you think yourself entitled to at least the good opinion of the world for your heroism. Alas! you have been such a bitter person all your life, you have told such disagreeable verities, you have so constantly refused to club in with that conventional hypocrisy that has neither eyes nor nose for social blotch or social taint, that De-

---

[32] "Our firste foo, the serpent Sathanas, / That hath in Jues herte his waspes nest." (Chaucer, "The Prioress's Tale," ll. 558–59.)

traction denies to you one word of praise for your ducking; but gravely insists that your sole reason for jumping into the river was this,—you *thought you saw* a silver spoon shining at the bottom.

Having obtained a name for ill-nature, or in reality having acquired a fatal reputation for using your eyes, it will be in vain for you to deal in praise of anything. No; the people who profess to know you will, like witches, read even your prayers backwards; will insist that there is some lurking mischief, some subtle abuse, in what appears to be unmixed and heartfelt eulogy. Offer what you will to the world, the world will declare you only deal in one commodity. You will be in the condition of the man who sold lemons. His history being very short, and at the same time touchingly illustrative of the evil I would warn you against, shall be set down in this letter.

There was, in a certain city, a man who sold lemons. From boyhood until forty, he had dealt in no other fruit; and with those who needed lemons, his stock was in good request. And so years passed away, and the man made a tolerable living of his merchandise, though a certain bluntness of manner, a resolution never to take one farthing less of a customer than he first asked, did somewhat keep down the profits of his calling. Throughout the city the man was known by no other title than the Lemon Merchant. At length, but how it came to pass I know not, lemons ceased to be in demand; no man, woman, or child, purchased a lemon— lemons seemed, henceforth, to be the forbidden fruit; crowds of passengers passed the man's basket but no one spent a single obolus. Want, starvation, threatened our lemon-merchant. What was he to do? It was plain, the fashion had turned from lemons, and had set in for nothing but oranges. Well, my son, you would think it was some good genius that whispered to the man, "Give up thy lemon basket; do not vainly strive to huckster with what is now the accursed fruit, but sell what little goods thou hast, and hieing to the market, there buy thee oranges; sweet, delicious oranges; oranges, luscious as the flesh of Venus." The lemon-merchant followed the advice of his counsellor, and selling up all he had in the world, invested the money in a box of magnificent oranges; they were the finest in the market; the mouths of emperors might have watered for them; they were a gladdening picture to the eye—a restorative perfume to the nose. Since the oranges that wooed the lip of Eve in Paradise, there never had been such oranges.

It was a grand holiday, when for the first time our henceforth orange-merchant took his customary stand at the steps of the Church of St. Angelica. His eye twinkled, and his heart swelled with honest pride as he looked at the passengers who thronged by him, and then again looked at the golden fruit piled in his basket at his foot. It was very strange; but though all the orange-dealers about him sold their stock in a trice, although he was left with the only oranges near the church, no one, albeit seeking oranges, offered to buy the fruit of him. At last, the man took heart, and cried to the people as they passed, "Oranges; sweet, sweet oranges! Buy my oranges!"

"Oranges, fellow!" cried the passengers, "what impudence is this? Isn't it clear that there isn't an orange in your basket—isn't it certain that you deal in nothing but lemons?"

It was in vain for the man to bawl "Oranges!" for there was no one who heard him, who did not laugh and sneer, and answer, "Pooh! pooh! Lemons!"

My dear son, once get a reputation (as you have done with Alderman Bilberry) for the acidity of truth, and though your lips, like the lips of the infant Plato, shall distill honey, the world will not believe in the sweetness. Offer what oranges you will, the world will repay the offering with the cry of—"Lemons."

## LETTER XII.

ON THE PHILOSOPHY OF BORROWING.—HOPKINS'S UMBRELLA.

YOU ASK ME to supply you with a list of books, that you may purchase the same for your private delectation. My dear boy, receive this, and treasure it for a truth: no wise man ever purchases a book. Fools buy books, and wise men—borrow them. By respecting, and acting upon this axiom, you may obtain a very handsome library for nothing.

Do you not perceive, too, that by merely borrowing a volume at every possible opportunity, you are obtaining for yourself the reputation of a reading man; you are interesting in your studies dozens of people who, otherwise, would care not whether you knew A, B, C, or not? With your shelves thronged with borrowed volumes, you have an assurance that your hours of literary meditation frequently engage the thoughts of, alike, intimate and casual acqaintance. To be a good borrower of books is to get a sort of halo of learning about you, not to be obtained by laying out money upon printed wisdom. For instance, you meet Huggins. He no sooner sees you than, pop, you are associated with all the Cæsars; he having—simple Huggins!—lent you his Roman History bound in best

historic calf. He never beholds you but he thinks of Romulus and Rem-
us, the Tarpeian Rock, the Rape of the Sabines, and ten thousand other
interesting and pleasurable events. Thus, you are doing a positive good
to Huggins by continually refreshing his mind with the studies of his
thoughtful youth; whilst, as I say, your appearance, your memory, is associated and embalmed by him with things that "will not die."

Consider the advantage of this. To one man you walk as Hamlet; why?
you have upon your shelves that man's best edition of Shakspere. To another, you come as the archangel Michael. His illustrated Paradise Lost
glitters amongst your borrowings. To this man, by the like magic, you
are Robinson Crusoe; to this, Telemachus. I will not multiply instances;
they must suggest themselves. Be sure, however, on stumbling upon what
seems a rare and curious volume, to lay your borrowing hands upon it.
The books may be Sanscrit, Coptic, Chinese; you may not understand a
single letter of it; for which reason, be more sternly resolved to carry it
away with you. The very act of borrowing such a mysterious volume implies that you are in some respects a deep fellow—invests you with a certain literary dignity in the eyes of the lending. Besides, if you know not
Sanscrit at the time you borrow, you may before you die. You cannot
promise yourself what you shall not learn; or, once having borrowed the
book, what you shall not forget.

There are three things that no man but a fool lends—or having lent,
is not in the most hopeless state of mental crassitude if he ever hope to
get back again. These three things, my son, are—BOOKS, UMBRELLAS, and
MONEY! I believe, a certain fiction of the law assumes a remedy to the
borrower; but I know no case in which any man, being sufficiently das-
tard to gibbet his reputation as plaintiff in such a suit, ever fairly succeeded against the wholesome prejudices of society.

In the first place, books being themselves but a combination of borrowed things, are not to be considered as vesting even their authors with
property. The best man who writes a book, borrows his materials from
the world about him, and therefore, as the phrase goes, cannot come into
court with clean hands. Such is the opinion of some of our wisest law-
makers; who, therefore, give to the mechanist of a mouse-trap, a more
lasting property in his invention than if he had made an Iliad. And
why? The mouse-trap is of wood and iron: trees, though springing from
the earth, are property; iron, dug from the bowels of the earth, is property: you can feel it, hammer it, weigh it: but what is called literary
genius is a thing not ponderable, an essence (if, indeed, it be an essence)
you can make nothing of, though put into a air-pump. The mast, that
falls from beech, to fatten hogs, is property; as the forest-laws will speed-

ily let you know, if you send in an alien pig to feed upon it: but it has been held, by wise, grave men in Parliament, that what falls from human brains to feed human souls, is no property whatever. Hence, private advantage counsels you to borrow all the books you can; whilst public opinion abundantly justifies you in never returning them.

I have now to speak of UMBRELLAS. Would you, my son, from what you have read of Arab hospitality—would you think of counting out so many penny-pieces, and laying them in the hand of your Arab host, in return for the dates and camel's milk that, when fainting, dying, with thirst, hunger, and fatigue, he hastened to bestow upon you? Would you, I say, chink the copper coin in the man's ear, in return for this kindly office, which the son of the desert thinks an "instrumental part of his religion?" If, with an ignorance of the proper usages of society, you would insult that high-souled Arab by any tender of money, then, my son—but no! I think you incapable of the sordidness of such an act,—then would you return a Borrowed Umbrella?

Consider it. What is an umbrella but a tent that a man carries about with him—in China, to guard him from the sun,—in England, to shelter him from the rain? Well, to return such a portable tent to the hospitable soul who lent it,—what is it but to offer the Arab payment for shelter? What is it but to chaffer with magnanimity, to reduce its greatness to a mercenary lodging-house-keeper? Umbrellas may be "hedged about" by cobweb statutes; I will not swear it is not so; there may exist laws that make such things property; but sure I am that the hissing contempt, the loud-mouthed indignation of all civilised society, would sibilate and roar at the bloodless poltron, who should engage law on his side to obtain for him the restitution of a—lent umbrella!

We now come to—MONEY. I have had, in my time, so little of it, that I am not very well informed on monetary history. I think, however, that the first Roman coin was impressed with a sheep. A touching and significant symbol, crying aloud to all men,—"Children, *fleece* one another." My son, beware of this prejudice; for it is the fruit of the vilest ignorance. it is good to respect ancient symbols: therefore, whatever the gold or silver may bear—whatever the potentate, whatever the arms upon the obverse—see with your imaginative eye nothing but the sheep; listen with your fancy's ear to nought but—"fleece"—"fleece!"

I am aware, that a prejudice exists amongst the half-educated, that borrowed money is as money obtained by nothing; that, in fact, it is not your own; but is only trusted in your hands for such and such a time. My son beware of this prejudice; for it is the fruit of the vilest ignorance. On the contrary, look upon all borrowed money, as money dearly, richly earned by your ingenuity in obtaining it. Put it to your account as the wages of your intellect, your address, your reasoning or seductive powers. Let this truth, my son, be engraven upon your very brain-pan. To borrow money is the very highest employment of the human intellect: to pay it back again, is to show yourself a traitor to the genius that has successfully worked within you.

You may, however, wish to know how to put off your creditor—how to dumbfound him, should the idiot be clamorous. One answer will serve for books, umbrellas, and money. As for books, by the way, you may always have left them in a hackney-coach. (This frequent accident of book-borrowers, doubtless, accounts for the literary turn of most hackney-coachmen.) Still, I will supply you with one catholic answer.

Hopkins once lent Simpson, his next-door neighbour, an umbrella. You will judge of the intellect of Hopkins, not so much from the act of lending an umbrella, but from his insane endeavour to get it back again.

It poured in torrents. Hopkins had an urgent call. Hopkins knocked at Simpson's door. "I want my umbrella." Now Simpson also had a call in a directly opposite way to Hopkins; and with the borrowed umbrella in his hand, was advancing to the threshold. "I tell you," roared Hopkins, "I want my umbrella."—"Can't have it," said Simpson. "Why, I want to go to the East-end, it rains in torrents; what"—screamed Hopkins—"what am I to do for an umbrella?"

"Do!" answered Simpson, darting from the door—"do as I did; BORROW ONE!"

## LETTER XIII.

### HOW LEARNING MAY BE OBTAINED—BY SHAVING: AND OTHER MEANS.

YOU TELL ME, I have not answered your request. You say, you feel—and I hope you do—the full force of my arguments on the beauty of borrowing: nevertheless, I have not forwarded to you the list of books that, of all others, are the first to be borrowed. You say you wish to become a reader. It is a laudable aspiration.

Readers, my dear son, are of two sorts. There is a reader who carefully goes through a book; and there is a reader who as carefully lets the book go through him. Which do you desire to be?

Whilst it is necessary that you should have the mere cant phrases of literature, I would, as your affectionate father, counsel you against any unseemly pedantry. You may, without sacrificing any of the time due to the serious purposes of life, obtain a sufficient knowledge of books, whereby to pass for a man of very considerable information; and, in this world, a successful seeming is every bit as good as the real thing. Look around upon men; behold the stations they fill, and tell me if it be not so.

You shave once a day. Well, purchase a cheap copy of Blackstone's Commentaries on the Laws of England. You will perceive that in his Preface, Sir William speaks of the necessity of every gentleman knowing something of the statutes he lives under. Now, my dear boy, I would have you learn the laws of your country, as I would have you, ere you entered an orchard to pluck the best fruit growing there, know the whereabout of the man-traps and the wires of the spring-guns. Having such knowledge, you may here pluck a pippin, here gather a plum; and cramming your pockets full of the juiciest produce of the place, return over the wall whence you came without a single scratch, and altogether shot-free. Now, you have only to consider the whole world an orchard guarded by the man-traps and spring-guns of laws: and have only to know *where* the laws are laid, that though you intrude upon them ever so closely, you are never caught or hit by them. Do this, and who is to charge you with having pilfered a single codlin? You have never been caught in the trap, the law has never fired upon you, and you have therefore your action for libel against any man who shall dare so much as to wink at you and whisper "Codlins!"

To return. You shave once a day.[33] Well, tear off a leaf of Blackstone, and whilst you are stropping your razor, carefully read it. This is so much time saved; and by this daily practice, you will in due season digest the whole of the Commentaries. Sometimes you will go over your beard a second or a third time,—whereupon, strop your razor again and again, and go through two or three pages. I knew a Lord Chancellor who, like Lord Chesterfield's friend, was "such an economist of time," that he went through all the statutes only in this manner. Being happily blessed with a very stubborn beard, he lathered himself at least thrice a morning; on each occasion getting by heart three leaves of legal wisdom. I have known him declare that as a lawyer, he was confident he owed all his prosperity in life to close shaving.

You are to consider that the operation of shaving is singularly auspicious to study. The soul seems retired from the surrounding vanities of the world, and takes refuge in itself. A great novelist has declared that

---

[33] [*Jerrold's note*] Punch confesses that he owes the idea of this process to the Earl of Chesterfield, who in his "Letter CI." to his son, suggests even a more ingenious mode of absorbing the essence of "all the Latin Poets."

if, when he rose from his desk, he left a pair of lovers in a quandary, had his hero or heoine at a dead lock, wanted a lucky escape, or an ingenious discovery,—he went to bed serenely certain that the whole difficulty would be solved with the shaving soap of the next morning.[34] Hence, his novels may be considered as much the offspring of the razor as of the goose-quill. I much question whether the lack of imaginative works among the modern Jewish Rabbis may not be attributed to their copiousness of beard; they never shave; hence, in a lofty, dignifying sense, they never think.

Having gone through Blackstone, razor in hand, you may then in like manner address yourself to ancient and modern history.

You will know quite as much of the Medes and Persians, the builders of the Pyramids, Magna Charta, and all such shadowy matters, after a month's good stropping,—as if you had sat with your brow between your thumbs, pondering and dreaming for a twelvemonth. You will have got by heart a pretty catalogue of names; and names, not things, are quite sufficient for a man, if he will but troll them boldly over his tongue, as though he had the most intimate acquaintance with all that belonged to them. "Virtue and learning," says Philip Lord Chesterfield, "like gold, have their intrinsic value; but if they are not polished, they certainly lose a great deal of their lustre: and even polished brass will pass upon more people than rough gold."[35] Lord Chesterfield knew what was due to life and—the peerage.

There is also another way of obtaining the wisdom of books. You have doubtless seen the advertisements of benevolent sages who profess to cure disease by simply smelling certain drugs and simples. Nothing need be swallowed, nothing need be administered. These doctors owe nothing to the natural teaching of the ibis, to whom, if history speak truly, Esculapius was so much indebted. All they require is, that a patient shall have a nose; and that organ granted, they guarantee a cure. In like manner, do many very clever people obtain learning: they smell the volumes—nothing more. They take a good sniff of a book, and history, politics, poetry, polemics, all fly up their nose in particles, like so much hartshorn; nor is such a mode of education, in the words of the Rev. Dr. Busby,[36] to be sneezed at.

If this were not the fact, do you think so many persons would purchase

---

34 [*Jerrold's note*] See Lockhart's "Life of Scott."
35 *Letters*, March 6, 1747.
36 Richard Busby (1606–1695), headmaster of Westminster School, where he was noted for his strict discipline; among his illustrious pupils were John Locke and John Dryden.

libraries? Do you suppose they buy the books to pore over them? Certainly not. It is sufficient that they have the volumes on the shelves; an aroma of learning arises from them; it is received into the system of the owner, and he is, and cannot help it, learned. If this were not the case, think you so many human asses would lay out so much money on russia-bindings? No: they carefully shelve the books, and catch learning, as they sometimes catch cold, by coming down the staircase.

Having said thus much, it is, I think, unnecessary for me to give you a list of books for your private study. All that is necessary, is to borrow the volumes, and those as handsome as possible, and having once secured the books, the learning in them is, of course, your own. I would, however, advise you to carefully study *The Newgate Calendar*, a work enshrining so many instances of human ingenuity, courage and suffering; a mine of gold from which philosophic novelists have cast pocket-heroes for ladies, and mantel-piece ornaments for boarding-schools. You will find in the literary off-shoots of the records of the gallows, that the human soul is in its composition, very like a ball of India-rubber; the lower it falls, the higher it bounds. Or it may be likened to the Greek fire, that burns the brightest in a common sewer.

I would advise you also to take a peep into the Grecian mythology; there are some pretty names there with which you may sometimes spangle your discourse, not unprofitably. There is also much moral instruction to be gathered from the stories. Let me particularly recommend to you the tale of the abduction of Proserpine by Pluto. Proserpine has been promised a full divorce from the king of hell, if she have tasted nothing in his dominions. Unable to control herself, she has taken a pomegranate seed, and the divorce does not stand good. I have no doubt (if it could be discovered) that this case has been considered in many nice judgments of the Ecclesiastical Court.

History has been called "philosophy teaching by example." You may, if you will, consult it in this spirit; but the truest philosophy teaching by example that ever came under my notice, was in a little town in France, at a bookseller's shop.

The beautiful national song *Malbrough s'en va-t-en guerre*, words and music, lay open in the window; and there stood an old Frenchwoman, holding in her hand a little Gaul of some six years old, whom like a young starling she was at once teaching words and song . What a labour of love she made of her task! How she crowded forth the air, jigging, as it does, with contempt for England, and how the child chirruped after her!

Malbrough s'en va-t-en guerre,
Mironton, mironton, mirontaine,
Malbrough s'en va-t-en guerre,
Ne sait quand reviendra![37]

"There, indeed," said I to myself, gazing on the old woman and her
pupil; "there, indeed, is History—there is Philosophy teaching by example!"

## LETTER XIV.

### THE EVIL OF SENSIBILITY.—STORY OF THE BANKER'S CLERK.

A MAN who would thrive in the world has no such enemy as what is
known by the term—sensibility. It is to walk barefooted in a mob: at
every other step your toes are crushed by the iron-shod shoon of crowding vagabonds, who grin from ear to ear at the wry faces you make, at the
cries that may escape you. "Why didn't you stay at home?" asks one; "Put
your toes in your pocket," counsels another; quite unconscious of the
deep philosophy enriching his advice. Yes, my son; difficult as it may appear, the only thing for the man to do—that is, the poor man born with
sensibility—is to put his toes into his pocket; in plain words, to smother
his sensibility in the place where he hopes some day to carry his money.

Many are the martyrs, my son, whose lives will never be penned. Many
the victims who, in garrets and in cellars, have vindicated what is called
the heroism of human nature, and by the awful magnanimity of suffering, given assurance of the ethereal temper of the human spirit. How
many, even with earthly famine whitening their lips, have smiled in
lovely patience, thinking of immortal tables! How many, in the tatters
of beggary, reeking in the nostrils of their fellow-man, have apparelled
themselves for God! The looks of angels have made bright the darkness
of a dungeon; and the odours of seraphic wings sweetened the vapours
of a vault.

But no, my son, I must not pursue this theme. Who would think that
I could talk thus? I! a mountebank—a mummer—the buffoon for halfpence? Oh, my son, it was shallow philosophy; it was worse; it was a
wicked want of charity in Dr. Johnson to exclaim, "PUNCH has no feelings!" The world, I grant, gives me but little credit for such possessions;

[37] "Marlborough is going to war, / *Mironton, mironton, mirontaine,* / Marlborough
is going to war, / No one knows when he'll return!"

and, therefore, I am prone to wrap myself up in the pride of mystery, and to affect insensibility, that I may escape the charge of hypocrisy. Who would believe in the tears of PUNCH? Who, though he saw them trickling down my nose, would believe they came hot and bitter from my heart? A heart! Said I a heart? Who would believe I had such an organ? Albeit I were laid upon the surgeon's table, the crucial incision made in my breast—nay, the heart itself plucked out—who would believe in its ventricles? A heart! A cushion—a thing stuffed with bran, to stick pins in: for so the world has used it. My son, PUNCH is not the only creature thus libelled, because inwardly unknown. The Poverty of the world is but a pale-faced, melancholy Punch; a creature denied sensibility, that it may be made to bear the harder buffets. Allow to Poverty all the fine moral organisation—the same susceptibility that makes the system of the rich man delicately melodious as a musical snuff-box,—and we should give ear to the utterance of human wants as to a flood of holy song; as to the most plaintive, yet most sacred music of the habitable earth. But no; the organisation is disallowed, and therefore such music is impossible. Thus is it with Poverty in the ears of Worldly Pride; and thus to Worldly Ignorance is—PUNCH!

However, the purpose of these letters is to fit you for a prosperous career in life; and therefore, I charge you, by all your hopes of larder, wine-cellar, banker's account, and carriage—I charge you put down, smother every rising of sensibility. You might as well take a voyage to the North Pole in your shirt, as hope to live comfortably in the world, if endowed with sensibility. Had you been born to a golden pap-spoon, it might have been otherwise; but you, a child of the gutter, the spawn of the highway—you to talk of sensibility—you might as well talk of the family jewels.

Beware of sensibility. If it become morbidly affected, the result is—

But I will narrate to you a history, my son, illustrative of its perils: a true history—true as my hunch. How I came by it, matters not. Suffice it to say, it is as true as the sunbeams.

STEPHEN GLADSTONE—for that shall be his name—in his seventeenth year, was placed at a banker's desk. His gentleness, his almost feminine tenderness of manner, made him the favourite of all who knew him. He was endowed with a most fatal sensibility. His cheeks would redden at the sudden accost of a stranger; and when his employer, as would often happen, spoke in commendation of his labours, the tears would gush from his eyes, and he would tremble from head to foot, like a detected culprit. For three years Stephen remained in the employ of Messrs. ——; and every year, such was his assiduity, such his exemplary conduct, his salary was increased. Already the oldest clerks began to predict that "Stephen Gladstone would soon be a junior partner."

When Stephen had attained his twentieth year, a sudden alteration was visible in his features—his manner. Day by day, he became haggard —careworn. His face was pale and juiceless; and his eyes, ordinarily dull and filmed, would suddenly flash with lustrous brightness. The slightest sound would make him start as at a thunder-crash. His employers speed- ily noticed the change; and again and again desired Stephen to forego his duties for a month or two, to have change of air and scene; but every such desire seemed to inflict inexpressible torture upon the clerk. He would declare he was very well; if he looked ill, he knew not why he should do so, for he was in excellent health; never—never better. And still day by day he seemed to waste and wither; and day by day the weight upon his spirits grew the heavier.

At length, Stephen's employers resolved to address themselves to a physician; who, having heard their story, managed to obtain what seemed an accidental meeting with the clerk.

"Why, Mr. Gladstone, you are not well. Come, come! I see what this is."

"Indeed, sir, you mistake: I am well—quite well. Surely, sir, I should know best," said Stephen, a little irritated.

"Never tell me," said the physician, whose cordial tone and benevo- lent manner would have gained the confidence of a misanthrope; "I see your case plainly; it's love—nothing but love."

Stephen looked a look of misery in the physician's face, suppressed a groan, and broke from him.

A week elapsed, and Stephen suddenly appeared before the doctor. His face was distorted with anguish; he reeled, and fell into a chair; and sat gasping with the brain's agony. Instantly the physician was at his side—soothing, comforting him.

"I can endure it no longer: you shall know all, doctor,—all, though the hangman be at the door. Listen! you know not, for these six months, what scorpions have been stinging me. To-day again—this very day—my employers raised my income: they reward me—*me!* Doctor, look at that hand! It is a thief's—I tell you it is a thief's! But I said you should know all. My masters—kind souls! have praised me for my zeal—have desired me to seek recreation—to absent myself from the house! Oh, God, if late and early I was at the desk, it was that my books might escape detection! And they call this zeal, and they reward me for it—me, who have robbed, have pillaged them!"

Long and kind was the speech of the physician, who at length charged himself to break the business to the masters of the wretched youth, and with heavy heart departed on his mission. His tale was soon told.

"Ha! ha! ha! Impossible," cried the bankers. "Gladstone embezzle money! why, he couldn't take a farthing—not a farthing: all his books have been regularly balanced." It was indeed so. His morbid sensibility, worked upon by the possibility of the act, had, in his fantastic terrors, made him a criminal.

"This is a mistake, quite a mistake": and the physician sought to soothe the mind of the excited clerk.

"Then I am no thief?" asked Stephen, as if awakened from a horrid trance.

"You've been unwell—nothing more; a little unwell," said the physician.

The discovery of his innocence was, however, too much for the young man's reason: from that moment it was utterly shattered. The banker's clerk—alas! poor human nature!—died a maniac.


# LETTER XV.

### WEALTH AND ITS USES. STORY OF THE SLIPPERS. "JUST ENOUGH."

ONE OF THE BEST and most satisfactory uses of wealth, my dear boy, is to dazzle with our riches the eyes of our neighbours. Your dear mother once hit this point to a nicety. We had long expected the payment of a small legacy bequeathed to her by a distant relation, whose exact degree of kindred I cared not much to inquire into. It was enough for us that your dear mother's name was down in the will; and that the executors promised some day to faithfully perform the injunctions of the dear deceased. "And when we get this money," said your mother to me in a moment of connubial confidence, "I tell you what we'll do with it—I tell you, my love, what we'll do with it." As I knew she would proceed no further until I begged to know her intentions, I at once put the question. "What, my dearest, what will you do with it?" "Why, my love," answered your parent, her eyes sparkling with pleasure, "we'll take the plate out of pawn, and give a party." Yes; the great gratification to be gathered from the legacy was, that we might flash our four teaspoons and pair of tongs in the eyes of people for whom we had not the slightest esteem; and to one of whom your mother had, I know, on three occasions captiously refused the loan of her bellows.

You will find, as you know more of the world, that your mother's tea-spoons and tongs are, albeit the humble, yet the true representatives of whole buffets of plate. You will possibly find yourself invited to feast with a man who cares not a tithe whether you have a dinner or not; his only object is to show you your envious face in his golden salvers, to make your mouth water with his Dutch fruit pieces; in a word, not to fill your belly with his turtle and venison, but to abase your mind with a prostrating sense of his wealth. He takes possession of your admiration, as a feudal chief receives the homage of his vassal. And this you are to consider the true use—the real dignity of wealth.

There are some enthusiasts—that is, the generous mob of philanthro-pists with empty pockets—who vow that wealth is only given to the rich in trust for the poor. Whilst you remain a pauper, remain of this religion—when you obtain money, read your recantation before Midas.

Philosophers have held that the *aurum potabile*,[38] if taken into the human system, tends to refine mortal clay of its inherent grossness, and by degrees to assimiliate the flesh of earthly man to the flesh of the gods. Whether gold be swallowed, or a sufficient quantity of it be merely car-ried in the pocket, the grateful result is precisely the same. Consider hundreds of the heavy purse-bearers of the world, and tell me if it be otherwise with them. They have the lineaments of men; they are bipeds like the poorest beggar: but their moral and physical systems are so col-oured, so permeated with the precious metal, that they are creatures quite apart from the ordinary race of mortals. Do their daily acts betray their affinity with them? Are they not as far above the pauper who quenches his thirst at the brook, as the pauper above the frog he dis-turbs there?

I think I have heard you say, you love the face of Nature? The open sky—the fields, the trees, the shining river, all are glorious to you! My dear boy, whatever may be your present delight in contemplating these objects, as yet you know nothing of their value. Look upon them with the eye of a proprietor, and what a bloom will come upon the picture! Every bit of turf will be an emerald to you; every grasshopper will chir-rup—a very angel to your self-complacency; every tree, moved by the wind, will blow to you as you pass by it; the very fish in the river will

Show to the sun their wav'd coats dropp'd with gold,[39]

38 aurum potabile, a cordial or medicine consisting of some volatile oil in which minute particles of gold were suspended.

39 Probably a corruption of Pope's "The yellow carp, in scales bedropp'd with gold." ("Windsor Forest," l. 144.)

reflecting there *your* wealth, and not *their* beauty. Nay, that portion of the sky which rains and shines its blessings upon your land, you will behold as yours; yea, human pride, strong in its faith of property, will read upon the face of heaven itself— "Meum!" Every sunbeam will be to you as tangible as if it were an ingot. How delicious and how entrancing must have been the feelings of Adam when he awoke in Eden, to find himself—a landed proprietor!

If you can walk the fields and look upon the sky with these ennobling emotions, then, my son, you will know the real merits—the true uses of wealth. You will then own that it is only the man of money who can worship Nature as she ought to be worshipped; inasmuch as it is only he who can truly estimate her thousand beauties; who can feel his heart rise and glow as he surveys her charms; and, putting his hands in his pockets, can love her with a lover's tenderness.

This man, rejoicing on his own land, meets something in shape like himself plodding the sod. This two-legged animal envies the squirrel in the wood—the hare he has startled from its form: he has nothing; his very hands are useless to him: he is denied a spade to delve with, a plough to guide. Poor wretch! he is incrusted with ignorance; covered like a tortoise. What eyes, what thoughts has he for the loveliness of Nature? Let the gracious gentleman who owns the soil and the pauper encumbering it, sit with him upon two hillocks and discourse on the loveliness of life.

Well, they have talked there three hours; for see, the sun is blazing in the west. What have your heard from the man of wealth? Has he not spoken of Nature as a benignant goddess—has he not painted life with the bloom of Paradise still upon it? His whole speech has been a thanksgiving! What have you heard from the pauper!—evidence of grossest ignorance.

> A primrose by a river's brim,
> A yellow primrose is to him—
> And it is nothing more.[40]

He looks upon the meads, pranked with a thousand flowers, with a heavy, leaden look; they are, he says, to him a blank—a nothing.—And for life, he feels it most when it is gnawing at his bowels.

Will you, after this, my son, say that one of the highest uses of wealth is not to quicken our apprehension to the thousand beauties showered about us? Hence, my child, the inevitable intelligence and superiority

40 "A primrose by a river's brim / A yellow primrose was to him, / And it was nothing more." (Wordsworth, "Peter Bell," ll. 248–250.)

of the rich—hence, the gloom and crassitude of the poor. If you love nature, you must obtain wealth for the true—the lawful enjoyment of her. You must wed her with a golden ring.

Having obtained wealth, you are only to consider your own gratification in its outlay. There are foolish people who stint their appetites of many pleasant fillips, that when the worm is wriggling in their shrouds their thankful children may be sure of dinners. Leave your children to shift for themselves—Destitution is a fine whetstone to ingenuity.

In the course of my travels, I once entered a church in Amsterdam. I was attracted to a monument by a pair of slippers, cut in marble; and underneath was written, as I was told, in Flemish,—

JUST ENOUGH.

I found upon inquiry that this was the monument of a wise, rich man, who resolved to make his living appetites the tomb of his wealth; and so nicely adjusted his outlay, that when he died nought was left of his magnificent fortune but his pair of old slippers. "It is just enough," he said, and expired.

There are rich men who live and die in the spirit of the Flemish spend-thrift: for to them, this world—and this world only is—"JUST ENOUGH."

## LETTER XVI.

### HOW TO CHOOSE A FRIEND: THE PURPOSES OF FRIENDSHIP.
### A STORY OF "FRIENDS."

MY DEAR BOY,— Choose your friend as you would choose an orange; for his golden outside and the promise of yielding much, when well squeezed.

Lord Chesterfield has beautifully and truly remarked: "whatever is worth *doing* at all, is worth *doing well*."[41] This axiom applies admirably to the treatment of a friend.

There is no surer evidence of a contented meanness of spirit in a young man, than a disposition to club a friendship with merely his equals in life: whilst, on the other hand, the ardent, speculative mind, that, looking abroad for a communion of feeling, selects his Pylades[42] from the rich and powerful, indicates a just knowledge of the whole and

---

41 *Letters*, Oct. 9, 1746.
42 Pylades, in Greek mythology, the constant friend of Orestes.

sole purposes of human friendship. What is its object? Is it not to succour and assist the man elected for its twin brother? And how are you,
poor and powerless, to expect aid and practical consolation from one as
helpless as yourself? Can the naked clothe the naked? Can the beggar bestow alms upon the beggar? No; be assured of this truth; it is to defeat
the purpose of all friendship, it is to frustrate its most beneficent and humanising end, to ally yourself with any companion, who cannot better
your fortunes: to whom you cannot on all occasions resort, either for the
interest of his word, or for what must be indisputably acceded to be the
purest, the noblest offering of the human soul,—ready money.

For a poor man to boast of a poor man for his friend, is to flourish in
the face of the world an empty purse. To such a man a poor friend is a
clog, an incumbrance; a reduplication of his own wants; an exaggeration of his own squalor. What should Lazarus do but burden Lazarus?
To enter into such a compact is to make friendship a bubble—the echo
of a name—an empty sound!

How different your condition with Gloriosus for your friend! The
jewel on your finger is a brilliant evidence of the value of friendship.
The horse you sometimes ride proves to yourself and all the world that
amity is a substantial matter; the burgundy that at Gloriosus's table
beams in your eyes, and circulates in your system, makes your bosom
glow with the sweetest feelings; and you lay your hand upon your heart,
and feel friendship to be a lovely, a most sufficing thing! Thus, you build
an altar to friendship in your very self. You are a breathing, moving,
satin-cheeked evidence that friendship is not, what cynics and misan-
thropes call it, a thing of air—the dream of fools.

Can you do this if you hang upon the skirts of your fellow-poor? No,
my son. Therefore, if you have a nature capable of friendship,—if you
would prove to the world the surpassing beauties of the feeling which
poets have sung, and sages melodiously discoursed of,—hang on the rich,
select the man of wealth, and him only for your friend; dwell and glitter
in his bosom like his diamond shirt-stud.

Possibly there may be ill-mannered people who for this will call you
a toad-eater. Let them: I will in few words, and from truthful history,
teach you how to answer them.

The ill-natured antiquaries of the Netherlands, with bile against the
politest nation upon earth—of course, I mean the French—have declared
that what are now quartered as the lilies of France, were originally toads.
The Abbé Dubos[43] gives a reasonable excuse for this; an excuse that

---

[43] Abbé Dubos, Jean Baptiste Dubos (1670–1742), French critic, historian, and diplomat.

ought to disarm malignity of its sneer: the French could not help it. The Germanic nations—the French then being a part of them—having engaged all the courageous and terrible birds and beasts, such as eagles, lions, griffins, dragons, and the like, left nothing whatever for the poor Franks; who were therefore compelled to go to the puddles for their bearings, and so contented themselves with a toad. This toad, in process of time, became metamorphosed into a bee, for on the 27th of May, 1655, the Curé of St. Brie, at Tournay, wishing to enlarge his wine-cellar, the workmen he had employed upon that benevolent object, came plump upon the coffin of King Childeric I. It was then discovered that upon his Majesty's royal robe were sewed innumerable golden bees. These were subsequently removed to the royal cabinet of France. Whether, however, they took flight at the revolution, I know not. "I do not doubt," says the Abbé Dubos, "that our *bees*, by the ignorance of painters and sculptors, have become *lilies*." Lilies, that, according to Malherbe, were once especially fragrant in the nostrils of John Bull.

> A leur odeur l'Anglais se relâchant,
> Notre amitié va recherchant.
> Et l'Espagnol, prodige merveilleux,
> Cesse d'être orgueilleux.[44]

You may ask me, my son, what has this antiquarian rigmarole about the toads, the bees, and the lilies of France, to do with the lesson I would propound on the beauty of friendship? My son, be instructed.

Let the envious call you toad-eater; make you of that toad a golden bee, still gathering honey from your friend, and turning it to your private advantage. And then, if detraction accuse you of hoarding from the treasures of your Pylades, declare your friendship to have no bee-like propensity whatever, but that it grows in your heart, pure and odorous as—

> The lily, lady of the flowering field.

Thus, when the world throws the toad in your face, take a lesson of the Frenchmen, and declare there was never aught toad-like in the matter; but always, always a lily! Toads you never eat; you only snuff lilies.

Friendship, like love, may, I know, have very odd beginnings. I speak, however, of the friendship of simpletons and penniless enthusiasts. I

---

[44] By François de Malherbe (1555–1628), French critic and official poet of Henry IV and Louis XIII: "At their smell the English relax / And court our friendship once more / And the Spanish, wonderful to say, / Cease to be haughty." ("Stances a la Reine Marie de Medicis pendant sa régence 1611," ll. 17–20.)

will narrate to you what I think a very comical incident, illustrative of the mysterious working of friendship.

Lieutenant Montgomery had seen much military service. However, the wars were over, and he had nought to do, but to lounge as best he could through life upon half-pay. He was one day taking his ease at his tavern, when he observed a stranger, evidently a foreigner, gazing intently at him. The lieutenant appeared not to notice the intrusion, but shifted his position. A short time, and the stranger shifted too, and still with unblenched gaze he stared. This was too much for Montgomery, who rose and approached his scrutinising intruder.

"Do you know me, sir?" asked the lieutenant.

"I think I do," answered the foreigner. He was a Frenchman.

"Have we ever met before?" continued Montgomery.

"I will not swear for it; but if we have—and I am almost sure we have," said the stranger, "you have a sabre cut, a deep one, on your right wrist."

"I have," cried Montgomery, turning back his sleeve, and displaying a very broad and ugly scar. "I didn't get this for nothing, for the brave fellow who made me a present of it, I repaid with a gash across the skull."

The Frenchman bent down his head, parted his hair with his hands, and said—"You did: you may look at the receipt."

The next moment they were in each other's arms. They became bosom friends for life.

## LETTER XVII.

### ON POLITICAL FLATTERY.—THE SKULL GOBLET.

ONE GEMELLI CARRERI, a travelled Italian, has preserved the following story. Ponder on it, my son; for, duly considered, 'twill be found to enshrine the noblest worldly wisdom.

You have doubtless heard of Shah-Abas, called the Great? If not, it is no matter. A good story is just as good, and what may seem strange to your unripe reflection, *is just as true*, whether the hero of it ever lived or not. To the philosophic mind, Tom Thumb is as real a thing as Alexander. The wise man is as well taught by a shadow, as by Cæsar at the head of his legions.—However, to get back to Shah-Abas. He was a great man, for he killed a certain king of the Usbecks; and having killed him, did not ingloriously thrust all his carcass into a hole, but preserved the royal skull from worms and darkness, and made it the companion of his carousals and his merry night. Briefly, the great Shah-Abas had the king's skull set in gold, for a drinking cup. Well had it been for the world, had all kingly skulls been ever as socially employed! The Shah died; and for what we know, had a merry laugh in the shades with the king of the Usbecks, when he met and told him of the late hours his skull still kept on the earth, of the wine that sparkled in it, or the free talk that passed about it, of the jokes that were cracked, of the songs that were chirrupped! The Shah's descendant much treasured the skull; and feeling death to be the great teacher, never slept, without taking copious advice from the king of the Usbecks. It happened that the Usbeck people sent an ambassador to the Shah's descendant, to permit and ratify a treaty of commerce. In those days, commercial principles were in the bud; and therefore, the prejudice of the Usbecks is not to be considered in the strong light of present wisdom. The Usbecks prayed that they might be permitted to export their fleas free of duty into the realm of the Shah; offering as an equivalent, to admit the Shah's blue-bottle flies on the same enlightened footing. The question, as you may conceive, was of great national importance: many of the oldest Usbecks declaring they were a lost folk from the moment they admitted blue-bottles duty free: whilst some of the Shah's people maintained the exclusive privilege of their fleas, as though they were creatures of their own flesh; and loudly clamoured for stringent restrictions, for the sharpest scrutiny. Every Usbeck should be searched to the skin, to prevent the smuggling of fleas: whilst the Usbecks, firing at this, threatened to throw up a line of observatories on the frontiers to prevent the entry of a single blue-bottle into their kingdom. The Shah's people were not behindhand; for albeit they had all along admitted the Usbecks' sheep, they prayed the Shah that he would henceforth have every beast shaved bare as his hand, fleas having been known—it had been proved upon committee—to be conveyed into the kingdom by means of the wool. The people also called for an army of inspection on the annual flight of the swallows from the Usbecks to the country of the Shah: they, too, had brought fleas into the country, to the manifest injury of the home-breeder.

Matters were at the height, when the Shah gave a handsome banquet to the ambassador of the Usbecks. In the midst of the jollity, the Shah called, in the irony of his heart, for the loving-cup. The cup-bearer approached, and on bended knee presented the skull of the Usbeck king; the ambassador started at the indignity; and felt a nervous contraction of his fingers that suddenly seemed to hunger for the handle of his scim-

itar. Another second, and he had certainly made a cut at the throat of
the Shah, when his eye falling on the goblet-skull of his late revered
monarch, he thought he saw the bony cavity, wherein was wont to roll
and flash the burning eye of fiery despotism, quickly and most significantly contract as with a wink, and the jaw-bone slightly move, as much
as to look and say—"Don't make a noodle of yourself." Happily, too, at
the same moment, the Usbeck ambassador felt the fleas of his native
country close at his bosom. The ambassador smiled.

"What think you of the goblet?" asked the Shah, with a very ungentle-
manly leer.

"I think," said the ambassador, "my monarch was most happy, most
honoured, in falling by the hands of a great king: but he is still happier,
still more honoured, in having his skull preserved by a greater."

The king was mollified: from that moment the Usbeck fleas hopped
without any fiscal restriction into the Shah's dominions, and the blue-
bottles of the Shah, without let or hindrance on the part of custom-house
mercenaries, sang their household music in the parlours of the Usbecks,
and in their hospital larders made provisions for their oviparous little
ones.

I trust, my son, you can apply the moral of this veracious story? If the
ambassador had given vent to his rising imagination—if on the introduction of the royal skull, he had delivered himself of some red-hot sentence or two,—why, the anti-flea-law bigots had triumphed. Until this
day, perhaps, fleas had been smuggled into the lands of the Shah; and
blue-bottles, save as pets for the rich, been unknown in the land of the
Usbecks. But the ambassador rightly taking the wink from the royal
skull, the lowest subject of the Shah has the luxury of fleas; whilst fly-
blown mutton—allowing he can get mutton at all—is within the reach
of the meanest Usbeck.

Here, my son, you perceive the beauty, the utility of political flattery!
If Fortune, determining to show a great example to men, resolve to make
you a cabinet minister, engrave this story on your heart. Never do any
political act by straightforward means. Always go round about your purpose. And for this reason; straightforward honesty is the last resource of
a fool—mere honesty is the white chicken's feather in the cap of the
simpleton.

You were six years old when I took you to see my friend Mr. Polito's
elephant, and gave you a halfpenny. With a nascent generosity, which
nearly brought tears to my paternal eyes, you flung down the copper
coin at the feet of the majestic animal. Remember you not your first

wonder, when the elephant took the halfpenny up? What a curve he gave his trunk! How many bendings and turnings he employed ere he placed the halfpenny cake, purchased with Christian-like sagacity of the tradesman near his den, in his capacious mouth! The same action employed by that elephant to pick up a halfpenny, would be applied to the tearing up of the forest plane. My son, the elephant is a practical politician: remember him, and if you get exalted, do nothing great or small unless you do it with a twist.

As the remainder of the sheet is not sufficient for us to discuss a new subject, let me fill up the blank that remains with a few thoughts on the drinking goblet of the Shah. In the matter of kings, you must acknowledge, from what I narrated, that their influence passes not from the earth with their death. Though they are nothing, for good or ill, their skulls— so to speak—remain. What a great lesson does Napoleon offer to those Frenchmen who every morning wash themselves! Understand me.

The French are, above all nations of the earth, a people of practical wisdom—of practical morality. They make the glory of their great men a household thing.

Napoleon is on his death-bed, his eagles flee upon their golden wings to darkness—the trumpet wails in his ear—the last flutter of his heart rises with the muttering drum—and *"téte d'armée!"* is his death-sob. Napoleon is dead. A few minutes—the plaster is poured above the face of imperial clay, and posterity is insured the *vera effigies* of that thunderbolt of a man, just as the bolt was spent.

Now that face, in its dreadful calmness, is mutiplied in silver—in bronze—in marble—in richest metal and in purest stone! And now, to teach a daily lesson to the common mind, that awful countenance, with the weight of death upon it, is sold modelled in—soap!

Thus, have we not moral reflections brought to the very fingers' ends of the people? As the mechanic cleanses his palms, and feels his emperor's nose wasting away in his fingers, he thinks of Marengo and Austerlitz! With the imperial face the pickpocket makes his hands clean from last night's work, thinking the while of the rifled halls and galleries of Italy: the butcher, new from his morning's killing, washes his hands with the countenance of the emperor, the while he muses on Waterloo, and whistles the "Downfall of Paris:" and the philosopher peeps into the tub, and sees the type and memory of the warrior's deeds in bubbles floating upon dirty water.

ON SOCIAL FLATTERY: STORY OF THE DOG PONTO—
PIG AND PRUNE SAUCE.

MY DEAR SON,—Having in my last dwelt upon flattery, as necessary to the success of a politician, I dedicate this letter to a consideration of its utility to every man who would, by the exercise of his wits, make his way in the world. There is a negative flattery, as there is a positive flattery. A knowledge of the one is equally vital with the practice of the other. For instance:—You would conciliate the good graces of a man of wealth or interest? You hang and flutter about him for the bounty of his purse, or the magic of his good word in high places. This man may be a fool: I do not, understand me, fall in with the vulgar cry of paupers, that every man who is born rich is therefore born brainless; but your patron, or the man you would make your patron, may be a fool; and, consequently, is the more frequently tempted, like the climbing ape, to show his natural destitution. I think it is Mr. Addison who says, "He who is injured, and having brought his enemy on his knees, declines to punish him, was born for a conqueror." This is the sentiment, though not perhaps the exact words; for I have long since put aside *The Spectator* with your mother's cracked china. Mark, my son, a higher, a severer test of magnanimity. He who hears the abortive jest of a rich fool, yet refuses to turn his folly inside out, is born to finger ready money. This, my son, is flattery by negative. Have what wit you will, but carry it—as courtiers carry swords in the royal presence—in the scabbard. Suffer your patron to run you, as he thinks, through and through with his wooden dagger of a joke; but never let yourself be tempted to draw. Flattery has its martyrdom, the same as religion—and this is of it. Bear all the wounds inflicted upon you by wealth with a merry face; join in the laugh that's raised against you; but as you value success in life, never show an inch of steel in self-defence. Men who do otherwise may be chronicled for brave, expert wits; but they die beggars.

Come we now to positive flattery. Whatever dirty-shirted philosophers may say to the contrary, flattery is a fine social thing; the beautiful handmaid of life, casting flowers and odoriferous herbs in the paths of men, who, crushing out the sweets, curl up their noses as they snuff the odour, and walk half an inch higher to heaven by what they tread upon.

Your patron is an ass: you hear his braying—you see his ears: *asinus* is written all over him in Nature's boldest round-hand. Well, by delicately

dwelling upon the melodious wisdom of his words—by adroitly touching
on the intellectual beauty with which fate has endowed him, you make
him for the time love wisdom because he thinks it a part of himself—you
draw his admiration towards the expression of the intellectual every
time he looks in a mirror. You are thus, in an indirect way, serving the
cause of wisdom and intellect by juggling a fool into a worshipper. Let
it be granted, that you have your reward for this—that, in fact, you undertake the labour for the wages of life: what of it? Is not the task worthy
of payment? When men, in the highest places too, are so well paid for
fooling common sense, shall there be no fee for him who elevates a nin-
compoop?

You can see an ass browsing upon thistles. On this you fall into raptures at his exquisite taste for roses; the ass, with great complacency,
avers that he always had a peculiar relish for them. The ass brays.
Whereupon you make a happy allusion to the vibrations of the Æolian
harp. The ass declares it is an instrument above all others he is most inclined to. Are not roses and Æolian harps thus honoured, even by the
hyprocrisy of admiration?

Believe whatever the rich and powerful say; that is, seem to believe it.
Albeit they narrate histories wilder than ever Ariosto fabled, averring
themselves to have been eye and ear witnesses to what they tell, yet,
without a smile upon your face, gulp it all. Though the stories be long
and nauseous as tape-worms, yet swallow them as though they were
delicate as macaroni. You recollect Sir Peter Bullhead? He owed all his
fortune to a dog. I will tell you the story.

In early life, Sir Peter became footboy to Lord Tamarind; a man who
returned from the East Indies with a million of money, and his liver no
bigger than the roasted liver of a capon. Lord Tamarind was a liar of
the very finest courage. There was no story he would not undertake, and
make his own. Had he resolved upon it, he would have been present at
the siege of Troy, and more, have shown you the knee-buckles he had, in
single combat, won of Nestor.

Lord Tamarind had a favourite story of a dog: which story he would
drag in upon all occasions. His Lordship, go where he would, never went
without his dog. "Very curious, indeed, very; and talking of that, reminds me of an extraordinary anecdote of a dog. You never heard it, I
know; a remarkable case of conscience,—very remarkable;" and then his
Lordship proceeded—his hearers meekly resigning themselves to the too
familiar tale.

"You must know that in Batavia—it was when I was there—there was a certain Dutch merchant; I mention no names, for I respect his family. Well, this merchant—a shocking thing!—he was a married man: sweet little woman—five or seven children, and all that. Well, this merchant—very dreadful!—kept a mistress, country-house, and all things proper. Well, every evening he used to leave his lawful home to pass an hour or two with the fatal syren. He had a dog, a faithful, humble dog, that always followed him;—that was, moreover, greatly petted by the illegal enchantress. The dog, being particularly fond of his lawful mistress, became, day by day, very melancholy, sad, heavy-eyed and moping.[45] Then arose suspicions of hydrophobia—talk of poison, double-barrelled gun, and all that. Still the dog followed his master on his evening call. One evening, however—all day long it had been remarked that Ponto was more than usually meditative—the dog paused at the Dalilah's door. 'Ponto, Ponto,' cried the merchant, gaily entering the abode of wickedness, and whistling his dog to follow him—'Ponto, Ponto!'—But the dog stood with his fore-feet on the door-step, and wouldn't budge. 'Ponto, Ponto—sweet Ponto—good Ponto,' cried the wicked woman herself, coming to the door, and offering from her white hand the whitest cake. Ponto was immovable. Then looking at his master, the dog shook his

---

45 [*Jerrold's note*] The sagacity of Ponto is nothing to the sensibility of the race of King Charles's spaniels, that ever since the martyrdom of Charles the First have betrayed an inconsolable melancholy. The spaniels lost their liveliness when Charles lost his head. We take this assurance from a French author. In the *Journal des Chasseurs, ou Sporting Magazine Français*, for March 1842, will be found the story as related by the Comte de St. P——. The Count in the autumn of 1841, is shooting with a spaniel, when he falls in with an Englishman, who enlarges in this way (as told by the Count) on the merits of spaniels generally:—

"Ce sont des quêteurs infatigables," me dit-il; "excellens pour les fourrés, dont ils fouillent les moindres buissons: nous les employons beaucoup en Angleterre, où le prix de tel individu est, suivant sa généalogie, fort élevé. *Il n'ya qu'un seul reproche à leur faire*"; mais, ajoute-il, "ce défaut s'applique *malheureusement* à l'espèce entière."

—"Et quel est-il?" demandai-je à mon interlocuteur.

—"ILS SONT TRISTES"—reprit *gravement celui-ci*—"DEPUIS LA MORT DU ROI CHARLES!"

— (Upon this the Count observes, as well he may) —

"Superstition naïve et touchante!"

[*Editor's note*] "They are indefatigable hunters," he said to me; "excellent in the thickets, where they examine the smallest bush: we often employ them in England, where the value of such dogs, according to their pedigree, is very high. *There is only one reproach to make in their regard*"; but, he added, "that flaw applies unfortunately to the entire species."

"And what is it?" I ask my acquaintance.

"THEY ARE SAD"—he gravely replied—"SINCE THE DEATH OF KING CHARLES!"
(Upon this the Count observes, as well he may)—
"Naïve and touching superstition!"

head four or five times, as much as to say, 'Ar'n't you ashamed of your-self?'—sighed very deeply, and dropping his tail, walked solemnly home. The merchant was so affected by the dog's reproof,—(all this happened while I was in Batavia,) that he followed Ponto back to his lawful hearth, and for the rest of his natural life was never known to make an evening call again."

Lord Tamarind had three nephews; he cut every one off with a shil-ling for having boisterously expressed a doubt of the truth of what had occurred whilst he was in Batavia; but Peter Bullhead, who never failed to ask for the story of the dog—Peter, who had risen from footboy to his Lordship's secretary—inherited all the personal property of the Eastern story-teller. My son, every rich man has some sort of Ponto.

There will be occasions when it may be necessary for you to use con-siderable address. You must not flatter one at the expense of another; that is, when you have equal hopes of each. A friend of mine, who had lived all his life at court, told me a story that will illustrate what I mean. It happened that the king and queen were in the garden, and some of the courtiers with them. My friend was called by the king. Now it hap-pened that their majesties were so placed that my friend could not go to the king without turning his back—an act at court only little less than high treason—upon the queen. Here was a dilemma! "And how did you get out of the scrape?" I asked my friend. "In this way," he answered, "I *walked sideways.*" I have known many men in life get to the golden gate of fortune by walking every inch of the path—sideways.

In your flattery of mankind, you must also discriminate character, lest you throw away a valuable commodity. I have known men so unprin-cipled, that they have received the incense of adulation half their lives, and, dying, have left the man who burnt his myrrh and frankincense for them, nothing in reward but a miserable jest in the codicil.

There was my poor friend Sniffton. He hated pig and prune-sauce as he hated a poor relative. Nevertheless, for twenty years did he consent to eat it at his uncle's table; nor could he find words rich enough where-with to do honour to uncle's pig and prune-sauce. Uncle died. "Thank heaven!" cried Sniffton, "I shall now receive my reward in hard cash for my sacrifice to that damned pig and prune-sauce." The will was read, and thus was Sniffton rewarded:

"And I hereby give and bequeath to my dearly beloved nephew, Peter Sniffton, in consideration of his peculiar love of my pig and prune-sauce, the whole and sole—recipe whereby he may cook it."

My son, be wary, and avoid such wretches.

# LETTER XIX.

### THE PHILOSOPHY OF DRUNKENNESS: THE GENIUS OF THE CORK.

MY DEAR BOY,—I know few things that tell so fatally against a young man, when entering the world, as a weak stomach. I therefore most earnestly entreat you to fortify it by every means that may present themselves. It is true, that the increasing effeminacy of the world requires of the ingenuous youth a less capacity for the bottle than when I was young; nevertheless, there are occasions, when a man's previous habits and education will be tested by vintner's measure. Can there be anything more disgusting than to see a young man after, say, the third bottle, in a state of maudlin drunkenness? What tricks he perpetrates! How he lets all the world peep through the loop-holes of his soul; and how they who spy, grin at him and chuckle over the exhibition! What, too, is the end of this? I have known an otherwise promising young fellow so forget himself, as to render back in the most ungracious manner the hospitality of the host, who—suppressing his indignation by contempt—has ordered the servants to take off the gentleman's cravat, and lay him upon the mat for recovery. Then what running to and fro for vinegar—what wet towels for the temples—what hints, in desperate cases, of the lancet—until at length the wretched victim rolls from side to side, and gargles his throat with—"Better—better—m-uch better!" This is not only disgusting,—it is unprofitable.

No, my son; never get drunk—that is, in company,—above the girdle. There is a thermometer of drunkenness which every wise young man who has to elbow his way through the world would do well to consider. A man may be knee-drunk—hip-drunk—shoulder-drunk—nay, chin-drunk; but the wine should be allowed to rise no higher. Then he sits with a fine fluency of speech—his countenance brightened, his wit irradiated by what he has swallowed. And, perhaps, there is no situation in mortal life which so magnificently vindicates the ethereal nature of man, as that which presents him to us triumphing with rosy face above the mists and clouds of wine that roll around him! He is like the peak described by the poet: although vapours obscure him midway—

Eternal sunshine settles on his head.[46]

There he sits! His toes, it is true, may be of clay—but his head is of lustrous gold. Like the oracles of the ancient day, he speaks wisdom through the clouds that circle him!

[46] Oliver Goldsmith, "The Deserted Village," l. 192.

My son, by all means labour to arrive at this blessed, this most profitable condition. Then, though you stumble a little on going away, your stumbling will never be seen; for the potency of your head and stomach has survived the observation of your co-drinkers; and thus, though you are helped to your hackney-coach, a wine-skin, a very Silenus[47] up to the shoulders, you have the unclouded head of Socrates to adorn them! How many a worthy gentleman lives and dies with an undeniable character for sobriety, from only having kept his head above the port! A character is to be saved like a life, by merely keeping the chin above the fluid it swims in.

To obtain this power requires, I allow it, great practice: therefore, as a scholar, make your bottle your private companion. Take your liquor, as you would take your book, in profoundest solitude. "Try conclusions" with yourself in your own garret, that you may achieve victories in other men's dining-rooms.

I know that shallow, inexperienced moralists declaim against what they are pleased to call the vice of solitary drinking. Why, there is no such thing. A man can no more drink alone, than he can drink without his shadow.

Pop! There—the cork's drawn. *Gurgle—gurgle—gurgle—good—good—good*—No! it is in vain; there is no type—there are no printed sounds (allow me the *concetto*)—to describe the melody, the cadence of the outpouring bottle. Well, the bottle has rendered its virgin soul. You have resolved to sate yourself upon its sweetness. You think yourself alone. Oh, the vanity of ignorance! Why, the cork of what is called a solitary drinker, drawn from the bottle, is an audible charm that calls up a spirit —(angel or devil, according to contending moralists)—to come and sit with the toper. You have, therefore, only to retire with a full bottle to your own garret to be sure of company—and of the most profitable sort too; for your companion carries away no drop of your liquor; but there he sits with a jocund, leering look, on that three-legged stool; and there he tells stories to you—and sings to your rapturous spirit—and now hangs your white-washed walls with Sidonian tapestries—and now fills your gaping pockets with ideal gold!

What a world are you in! How your heart grows and grows! How, with frantic benevolence you rend aside your waistcoat (how you'll hunt for the two dropt buttons in the morning!) to give the creature room for its

47 Silenus, in Greek mythology, part bestial and part human creature of the forests and mountains, tutor of Dionysus.

uttermost expansion! What a figure you resolve to make in the world! What woman—nay, what women—you will marry! Now, you are gathering roses with dallying houris,—and now (with old Ronsard)—

> Peschant ne sçay quelles pierres,
> Au bord de l'Indique mer![48]

And whilst you take your flight here and there, how the spirit evoked by the cork hugs himself, and grins at you!

It is by such discipline, my son, that you will be enabled when in society to maintain the look and something of the reasoning powers of a man, when your whole carcass is throbbing with alcohol. You will also find a bottle the handmaid (bottles are, evidently, feminine) of philosophy. After every night's good set in with the genius of the cork, you will be the better able to judge of the true value of all worldly endowments. You will also have a finer, a deeper, a more enlarged comprehension of the weakness of human nature. If, before, you were not sufficiently impressed with the utility of money, you will, shortly after every visit of the genius of the cork, know its increasing beauty. It may be, too, you have not paid sufficient attention to that wondrous machinery—that complex

[48] Pierre de Ronsard (1524[?]–1585): "Fishing I do not know which kinds of stones, / On the banks of the Indian Sea." ("A Son Lut," ll. 19–20.)

simplicity of the human animal,—that you have not essentially considered your immortal essence to be what it really is—

> A soul, hung up as 'twere in chains,
> Of nerves, and arteries, and veins![49]

This inattention will be remedied—this ignorance informed—by frequent appeals to the bottle. You will, in a short time, acknowledge the
exquisite sensibility of the nerves; for you shall not be able to lift your
morning tea-cup without marvelling at the wondrous machinery vibrat-
ing before you. And the tongue, too,—that delicate instrument of silver
sound,—that shall lie like dry dirt in your mouth, heavy, hot, and voice-
less! And from this you will learn and feel that man is clay, and he at
once raised and humbled by the knowledge.

Depend upon it, the bottle is the spring, the true source of all human
inspiration—the fountain from which all philosophers, all sages, have
drunk their best wisdom.

What would have been Newton without a bottle? Do you think he
would ever have made his grand discovery unless he had dined first? Sitting in his orchard he saw an apple fall, (what a part have apples played
in human history!) and as it fell it *turned and turned.* Do you imagine
that Newton would have been so delicately susceptible of the turning of
a pippin, if he had not that day drawn a cork? Struck with the nascent
idea, he called for another bottle,—and then for another; and when the
philosopher had pondered upon the apple, had worked his analogies,
and had drunk a third bottle,—he was convinced, that not only had the
apple spun as it fell, but that the whole world turned round. If you
would prove the centre of gravity—get drunk.

My son, in conclusion, it is well to drink from your own bottle; but it
is still better to drink from another man's.


# LETTER XX.

## ON THE PHILOSOPHY OF GAMING.

MY DEAR SON,—You will, I trust, after these many fond and anxious epistles, look upon all men as divided into two classes—the men who eat men,
and the men who are eaten. With this conviction, it will, I hope, be your
determination always to obtain a good sufficing bellyful of your fellow

---

[49] Andrew Marvell, "A Dialogue between the Soul and Body," ll. 7–8.

creatures; and never to contribute in your own person a single mouthful to the banquet of the anthropophagi.

It is a vulgar mistake, the very crassitude of ignorance, to look upon only those men as man-eaters, who dispatch their victims with a club or tomahawk, and lighting the festive fire make their own man an honourable tomb for their enemies. This mode of eating only distinguishes the savage from his more refined brother, who disguises and sophisticates his cookery, and by the aid of certain social sauce, makes even himself forgetful of the horror which—to use the cook's phrase—is the *stock* of the feast.

In your boyhood, you were, I know, a most active taker of birds' nests. It was your delight to possess yourself of the eggs, ere the process of incubation had commenced, and having very adroitly sucked out the contents, you would thread the mere shell on a piece of grass, as a trophy of your success and good fortune. My dear boy, it is quite possible—indeed, it is every day accomplished—to treat the substance of men, as you have treated the eggs of larks and sparrows. How many successful egg-suckers could I point out to you, who applying the thousand means with which law and social chicanery supply every man, wise and adroit enough to use them, have so sucked and sucked that they have left nothing but the mere outside—the fragile shells of men! There is my old acquaintance, Barabbas Moses, with his sixty in a hundred. Twenty years ago he lived by putting off pencils, with apocryphal lead in them. How has he grown thus rich—how has he become thus treble-gilt? My son, he has been a most enterprising egg-sucker. How many birds of fine feather has he destroyed in the egg—how many shells of men might he wear about him! It is a poor thing to scalp a man; a coarse, rough, operation: but to feast upon his vitals, nay, to abstract his very marrow from him, to leave no blood-mark there, yet leave him with sufficient vitality to crawl about and look like a man, that, my son, is the master-piece of civilisation, the genius of refined life.

There is, however, a more open, a more generous mode of living upon men; a mode, dignified by fashion, exalted by authority—I mean gaming.

The gamester is, indeed, a privileged person; a creature, who merges all the petty, wearying anxieties of life into one sublime passion. Become a gamester, and you are fortified, nay, exempt from the assaults of divers other feelings that distract and worry less happy men. Gaming is a moral Aaron's rod, and swallows up all meaner passions.[50]

[50] Suggested by Pope's couplet: "And hence one Master-passion in the breast, / Like Aaron's serpent, swallows up the rest." (*An Essay on Man*, Epistle II, ll. 131–132.)

Consider, my son, the vigilance, the self-concentration, the judgment, the quickness of wit, and at times, the dexterity of finger, necessary to a successful gamester; and you will look upon the character with still-increasing veneration. Did you ever know a gamester fall madly in love? Did you ever know him, if a married man, waste his profitable time, his profitable thoughts, upon the woman he has buckled himself to? If he be a father, what is the laughter of his children to the melody of the dice? What, human hearts to the ace and king of the same suit, when trumps? He is exalted far above the weakening influences that pull down other men, and from his elevation looks with a cold eye of dignity upon the pettiness of human affections. You will hear other men rave about the beauties of nature; of hill and dale, mountain and flood. To the gamester, how small the space that bounds his imagination—but then how rich, how fertile—those half-dozen yards of bright green cloth!

You will hear men talk about the sweets of industry; of the dignity of labour; the more especially those men who never yet set their foot to a spade, or their hand to a plough. The sweets of industry! what are they to the sweets of fortune? And for the dignity of labour, give me, say I, the dignity of luck!

Observe what is called the industrious man. Mark his daily martyrdom. He rises early; breakfasts lightly; hurries off with his bread-and-butter yet undigested to his labour. He toils his eight, ten, nay twelve hours; comes home; eats his crust; and with hardly strength remaining to take off his stockings, slinks wearied to bed. In a brief time—how very brief!—the cock crows, and the industrious man has serious thoughts of shaving: again he is up—again has he bolted his morning meal,—and again is he out to go over the drudgery of how many thousand yesterdays! The year's wound up; and for all this toil, this anxiety, this daily crucifixion of spirit, the industrious man counts one—two—shall we say three hundred golden pieces? For all this tedious misery—three hundred pounds!

My son, turn your eyes to the gamester. He rises when he likes—dallies, at "his own sweet will," with his breakfast. He then lounges away the hours, pleasantly meditating on the coming night. He enters the arena. With what a graceful assurance doth he take the box in his hand. One—two—three; he throws sixes, and pockets five hundred pounds! What a miserable, felon, outcast sneak-up does your industrious man appear after this! What a poor sweating slave! Whilst on the other hand, what an air of power is about the gamester! What a glory—what a magic! He inherits in one minute, by the potent shake of his elbow, all that poor, sordid labour wears its back into a hoop for—its eyes into blindness! Will you, after this, ever dream of becoming that miserable negative—an industrious man? Depend upon it, the true jewels of life—rightly worn—are the four aces. Hope has been vulgarly pictured with an anchor. Let your hope carry a dice-box!

As for luck, you may nearly always ensure that, if you properly educate your perceptions, and your fingers. Cultivate your thumb-nails, my dear boy; the smallest sacrifice to the personal graces is not lost upon the gamester.

But I will take the worst side of the picture. You are doomed to be unlucky—you are fated always to lose. You have no genius—like the genius of Socrates, that always popped into its master's hand the very trump required—to aid and abet you. The world turns its back on you; and neither by cards nor dice can you fob your brother mortal out of a single guinea. Debts come in like the waves about you: you have no home—no abiding place! This is the moment, my son, for you to exercise the most heroic of virtues. There is cord—there is steel—there are silver rivers. If you cannot live, you can die; and dying you will have this consolation: if you have steadily and inexorably vindicated the character of a gamester, your death will inflict no pang upon a single creature left behind you; and you will have the pleasing consolation to reflect that you never did the world a greater service than when you quitted it.


## LETTER XXI.

### THE PHILOSOPHY OF GLORY: THE SWORD AND THE GOSLINGS.

MY DEAR BOY,—I hoped that, long ere this, your hankering passion after what is called glory, had died a natural death; and that you had begun to consider glory at the best but as a dull mountebank—a thing of strut, and frippery, and emptiness. When St. Austin was a little boy, he and his mother went on a day's pleasure with a certain Roman prætor, to pay their respects to the tomb of Cæsar. St. Austin has handed down to us the following lively portrait of the imperial corpse. "It looked of a blue mould; the bone of the nose laid bare; the flesh of the nether lip quite fallen off; his mouth full of worms; and in his eye-pit a hungry toad, feasting upon the remnant portion of flesh and moisture; and so," moralises the saint, "he dwelt in his house of darkness." He did no such thing; he had vacated his dwelling. Death had written on the corpse, "This house to let," and the worms and the toad became the tenants.

Well, and what had they to do with Cæsar? What had the "blue mouldy flesh" and the "nose laid bare" to do with Cæsar dead, more than the paring of Cæsar's nails with Cæsar living? Is the evil fame that may be flung upon a house, to attach to a previous occupant? Our maiden queen Elizabeth made sundry progresses; honoured sundry mansions with her night-cap. What, if in lapse of time, one of these houses should have so fallen in reputation, that its after iniquity has been published by candle and paper lanthorn? Does the evil fame of the house taint or soil the ermine fame of our spotless Elizabeth?

One Jeremy Taylor, who can occasionally twine death's-heads with rose-buds, and strew a coffin with spices, tells us a story[51] of a fair young German gentleman who, though much importuned by many young ladies to sit for his portrait, would never consent. (So far he was right; for if there be a plague upon earth, it is the plague of sitting under a continual struggle to call into your face and keep there your very prettiest and most amiable look, until duly fastened by pigments, upon wainscot or canvas.) The fair young Herr, however, made at last a compromise. He, in the handsomest manner, consented to sit for his portrait after a few days' burial, upon the honourable understanding that the painter, visiting the vault, should limn the corpse just as it appeared; giving no cheek "a little red," putting no complimentary dimple in the chin, but painting death to the life. The painter was sent upon his mission, and found his sitter with "his face half eaten, and his midriff and backbone full of serpents; and so he stands pictured among his armed ancestors." And a very foolish figure he must cut among such goodly company.

Fear not, my son; I am not about to clap in with shallow moralists who would show the nothingness of glory, by showing that which is, indeed, no part of it; who would put the living Cæsar's nose out of joint by displaying his nose "laid bare" in his coffin; who would prove that it was a vanity of vanities, to paint a fair young German whilst *in* the flesh, because, when he took his departure from it, and was no longer in any way answerable for any disgrace it might fall into—serpents might gender there. Let us follow out this philosophy.

The Germans, as you know, are a nation of cabbage-eaters. They sophisticate good wholesome worts with vinegar, and Beelzebub alone, who supplies some nations with cooks, knows what beside. This vegetable wickedness they call *sauer kraut*. Now, let us imagine the immediate descendant of the fair-haired young German, with his napkin tucked under his chin, about to plunge his fist into the dish. He pauses—looks

[51] *The Rule and Exercises of Holy Dying*, Chap. I, sec. 2.

serious—a tear steals into the corner of his eye: solemnly removing the napkin from his button-hole, he rises, and remembering that the church-yard wherein his ancestor was decently deposited, has been converted into a vegetable garden, he points to the *sauer kraut,* and exclaims,— "Behold the vanity of all earthly things; the particles of our beloved ancestors have undergone a very peculiar arrangement; what *was* our dear friend Karl, is now a—Cabbage!"

Now do we not gather as fine philosophy from the savoy as from the serpent? What is either cabbage or snake to Karl, who, crowned with amaranth, looks down from his starry home upon his would-be-wise descendant, and thinks him a prodigious noodle for pausing in his dinner?

I have, I know, in a former letter, indicated the shallowness of this reasoning, as exposed by my very intimate friend the Hermetic Philosopher; but your last letter, my son, in which you would fain draw a picture of military glory, has tempted me to this iteration. I have pondered upon your picture; now, look at mine.

Many years ago I solaced myself with a brief residence in France. Purchasing a blouse, and donning a cap, I avoided the intrusive honours that might otherwise have been paid to the reputation of Punch and to the vulgar I—

—appeared some harmless villager.[52]

On a certain Sunday, I had taken my customary stroll towards the fields. I well recollect it was Sunday, from a sudden jarring of my moral sense— a shock to my feelings. I was overtaken by a cart rattling on at a good pace: it contained half-a-dozen men and women, laughing as if there were no world to come, and looking as joyous and as happy as though the devil himself were a mere abstraction. The worst remains to be told; the cart, in addition to the merry-makers, contained a fiddle and a bass-viol; and it was but too evident, from the affectionate way in which the instruments of sin were hugged by two of the men in the cart, that the unhallowed catgut was to be fingered that very day to the tripping toes and heels of the wicked. I, who had for years been disciplined by the moral regularity of an English Sunday—I, who had spiritually paid reverence even to Sabbath-keeping housemaids, as, with noses flattened against parlour and kitchen panes, they solemnly pondered on sin and death, and the vacant street before them, wondering when the milkman would come, and especially wondering if John Roberts would keep his hour; I, thus naturalised to the proprieties, felt my blood bubble to my

52 "I shall appear some harmless villager." (Milton, *Comus,* l. 166.)

cheek as I beheld the fiddle and the viol, and was rushing forward to
check the horse, and I remonstrate with the wicked holiday-keepers,
when happily, I observed that the driver was furnished with a long and
unusually substantial whip. I stopped, said a short prayer for their souls,
and struck into the fields.

Sunk, many fathoms deep in my feelings, I was wandering over a field
of vetches, when I was startled by the loud and significant utterance of
miscellaneous oaths, while a half-quacking, half-whistling noise rose as
a sort of under accompaniment to the execration. Lifting up my eyes, I
beheld a *garde-champêtre*, in cocked hat, with a drawn-sword. Now, a
*garde-champêtre*, my son, is a sort of field-constable, who takes charge of
the crows in his district, with the sloe and blackberry-bushes; who sees
that the moles are not disturbed in their subterranean operations, and
who benevolently assists the hogs out of the mud, should they chance to
stick in it; albeit the provision of nature was never more beautifully displayed than in the anatomy of French hogs; for nature, knowing what
dreadful miry roads they have to walk upon, has benevolently put them
upon stilts. To return to the *garde-champêtre*.

I looked and beheld this field-officer, as I have said, in cocked hat and
with drawn sword: and there he was swearing and shouting, at what—
think you? Why, a drove of goslings! They had—bold birds!—intruded
beyond their own proprietary; and there was the *garde-champêtre* with
his drawn sword—methinks I see the blade now, gleaming in a July
sun!—driving those bits of quacking, whistling, waddling flannel before
him,—now with his weapon patting a straggler into the ranks—now
urging one—now chiding another—until he got them all into very good
marching order—and then with a sweet serenity, he subsided from swearing into singing, and cocking his cocked hat, he struck up—

> En avant, marchons!
> Contre leur cannon;[53]

the goslings, with all their might, quacking and whistling in chorus.

I turned round, and pensively leaning my back against a tree, watched
the *garde-champêtre* as he marched along; and as he sang the goslings
responded to him—the hapless goslings, guided by the sword to have
their throats cut some day for the kitchen,—I said to myself—

"There goes glory!"

From that day, my son, I have never seen a regiment of horse or foot
without thinking of the goslings.

---

53 "Forward, we march! / Against their cannon."

# LETTER XXII.

### ON THE CHOICE AND TREATMENT OF A WIFE.

MY DEAR SON,—It was the remark of a no less distinguished mountebank than Cardinal de Retz[54]—(he and I were very intimate, albeit he never publicly acknowledged the acquaintanceship,)—that it mattered little what were the talents of a man, what was his good fortune in every other respect, if he were unlucky in a wife. By which the Cardinal meant—and if he did not, I do—that a wife to be justly called the better part of a man, must bring with her a sufficient quantity of the precious metal: otherwise, she is only flesh of his flesh, and bone of his bone; a burden of clay, and not an ornament of gold. Happily, my son, this truth is now so generally acknowledged in good society that, unless you were wilfully callous to its influence, you could not fail to be affected by it. A wife is the husband's chattels—the philosophy of law declares it: indeed, the spouse of your bosom is considered by the law to be goods in a more especial degree than any other property. A man robs you of your wife, and thereby—I put an extreme case—snaps your heart-strings: you lose your better half, and you sue the thief to make good the loss by the payment of so many pieces of metal. The same man, respecting your heart-strings, makes a snatch at your watch-chain, and takes to his heels with the booty. You shout "Stop thief," but the rogue escapes you. Well, the thief would quietly arrange the matter; would, for a fair consideration that should remunerate him for skill and loss of time, render back the abstracted chronometer. Hereupon the law cries—"What are you about? what! compromise a felony? Beware of the penalty!" No: you must put the thief into the dock, if he can be caught; you must punish him for the wrong he has done to society by stealing your repeater. If, on the other hand, he steal your wife, the matter—by the benevolent aid of judge and jury—may be settled between you, and your attorney empowered to give a fair receipt for the damages. Thus, above all other mundane possessions, a wife is property.

It is with this conviction of the true value of female excellence, that you must cast your eyes about you for a wife. You are to reflect upon the huge amount of evil brought upon man by woman, and are therefore in your own person to obtain as great a degree of reparation as is possible from the daughters of the first offender.

---

[54] Cardinal de Retz (1613–1679), French prelate and politician; one of the leaders of the Fronde, a political party attempting to limit the growing authority of the crown during the reign of Louis XIV.

You know the condition of a wife in the savage state. She is the drudge of her despotic lord; who does little but look at himself in a glass, if he have been lucky enough to change skins for one; sings, eats, plays, and meets in council. His wife, with a wooden mattock, or the shoulder-blade of a buffalo, digs the earth and sows the corn; she drives away the birds, and, in due season, gathers the harvest: she pounds corn and salts buffalo's meat; and hews wood and draws water, and prepares the feast; in journeys, she carries the poles of the wigwam, and when a station is pitched upon, it is she who sets the wigwam up, her sovereign lord, the Great Eagle, doing nothing. My dear boy, it is even so in the very best society: that is, if the woman herself do not labour in all these menial offices, she brings the money by which they are done, and the convenience and enjoyment of her husband equally well insured. In whatever rank of life you are doomed to move, you are to choose your wife as the Indian chooses his squaw—for her ability to minister to your idleness.

I am sorry to say it, in England women are held in even superstitious veneration; for the most part treated as creatures of superior sensibility of heart and refinement of spirit. (There are, certainly—as I have already indicated—many exceptions to the rule, proved by those successful husbands who are lodged, boarded, dressed, and allowed pocket-money by their helpmates.) The absurd deference paid by us to our women is finely rebuked by continental nations, where they have the prettiest words for the *beau sexe,* and nothing beyond. I know not a more dignified condition of man than that frequently exhibited at a French *café*; where, at ten in the morning, husbands and fathers are to be seen immersed in *écarté,* the wife—the mere squaw—keeping a fitful eye upon her shop from the recesses of her back-parlour. My son, I know you are fond of billiards. Obtain a wife who by the work of her fingers, or by the produce of acquired gain, enables you to grow grey making cannons,—and at the worst, you will know something of the true dignity of wedlock, its beauty and its excellence.

In your choice of a wife, never forget that age is to be honoured when associated with money. Nothing more reverent than silver hairs with gold in the pockets. Besides, by marrying a woman well-stricken in years, you will be insured against the tortures of jealousy, at least on your own part; and what is more, you will have continually by your side (that is, when you are at home,) a memento of the certain decay of mortality; which memento, if you rightly consider it, will be the surest inducement for you to enjoy life by every strictly legal means in your power. In all your pleasure, however, respect the laws of your country. Remember, that an act of Parliament is like a rock; it matters not how nearly you approach it, so you do not bump against it.

As for your days of courtship, you are to remember that as woman is the weaker animal, it behoves your magnanimity never to cross her fancy, even in its most ridiculous whimsies. Give her, as horsemen have it, her head as much as she likes, until you turn *from* the church: you may afterwards assert the supremacy of manhood, and revenge the wrongs of Adam.

There are various ways of attaching the sex: but the surest is not to attempt to shine and sparkle, and go off in crackers of jokes before them. Women, somehow, have the same fear of witty men as of fireworks; and thus, how often do pretty lively creatures link themselves to fools! The most certain plan of success (I have it from a woman, and I believe an excellent authority,) is any way to *interest* them. In my own case—(I thought your poor mother had a deal of money, but—well, never mind,)—I at last affected consumption. For a long time your mother refused to have me; when, however, I made her believe that I should not live six weeks, she married me directly. If an heiress refuse you, pretend to take to your bed with typhus fever, and ten to one she'll insist upon your getting up to go to church with her.

If, after long courtship, you find the lady has not the money you at first imagined, hesitate not a moment, but drop her. It may seem cruel, but depend upon it, 'tis all for her good. As for the nonsense of romantic writers about the wear and tear of the female heart, 'tis a lie in print, and nothing more. Wear and tear! Female hearts never tear: no, my son; they always stretch.

# LETTER XXIII.

### A FEW LAST WORDS. PUNCH REVIEWS HIS LABOURS.
### THE LOTTERY OF LIFE

WELL, MY SON, I now approach the end of my labours. Reflecting upon what I have written, I feel that I may in a double sense call myself your father. You are not merely the offspring of my loins; but I trust, I may say, I have begotten your mind.

Yes, I have thrice scratched my head, and feel that I have nothing more to say to you. I have now merely to contemplate—with that delicious self-complacency which plays the divinest music on a man's heart-strings—the beauty and excelling utility of the labour undertaken by my parental love. I have now only to lean back in my easy chair, and twirling my thumbs, see, with dreaming eyes, my beloved child playing a most prosperous part in this eventful world. Let others call it a vale of tears, you, my son, will walk through it with a continual chuckle. Let others groan over the uncertainty of daily bread; you, my son, will have "your teeth white with milk, and your eyes red with wine." Let others look with longing glance at pauper sixpences, you—for you have taken your father's counsel—will know where to lay your hand upon ingots.

Consider, my son, what gratitude you owe to destiny for making you what you are. You are the son of PUNCH. You might have been the child of a Lord Chancellor. From your cradle you inherited a wisdom denied to millions of others. Had you been born to finest cambric and Brussels lace, you had never been taught the beautiful truths of life, which it has been my paternal care to *tattoo* in your adolescent mind. The son of PUNCH! Consider, my child, the many, many million chances you had against your being this, and be grateful for your exceeding felicity.

Mr. William Wordsworth says—

> Our birth is but a sleep and a forgetting:
> The soul that rises with us, our life's star
> Hath had elsewhere its setting,
> And cometh from afar.[55]

Now, for a moment adopting this poetical conceit, imagine the millions of souls about to be despatched to this world, as a sort of penal settlement, an uncomfortable half-way house, on the road to immortal fields of asphodel. Have you seen whole clouds of swallows congregating on the sea-shore for their mysterious flight to—*where*, still remains a mystery? This multitudinous fluttering of wings can give you but the poorest idea of the gathering of human souls, bound to earth, and "trailing clouds of glory" from the home they are about to leave. Your finite apprehension cannot grasp the marvel in its entirety; yet it may do something. You see the myriads of winged souls—you hear their fluttering; you see that they are like one another, as swallow is like to swallow; their chirp is in the same key; no soul asserts a dignity over its fellow-voyager; each has the same length of wing, the same hue of feather. These are souls not yet provided with lodgings; they are souls, so to speak, in the abstract. Well, swoop they come down on earth, and like the swallows I have spoken of, take their residence in clay.

[55] Wordsworth, "Ode: Intimations of Immortality," ll. 59–62.

Alas and alas! poor souls! Some are doomed to coal-pits, some to arsenic mines, some dig in misery and darkness, some toil and toil, and hunger and hunger; and every day is but the wretched repetition of the past. And yet with all this certain evil grinding and crushing of thousands, how few among them would consent to draw their lot again, if Destiny were to hold forth her human lucky-bag, to give another chance! "No, no," says the Hottentot, with a proud downward look at his girdle of sheep's-gut—"no, no; I don't draw again; for who knows, I might come up a Dutch boor." "No lucky-bag for me," cries the Esquimaux; "I might lose my delicious whale blubber, and turning up an Englishman, be doomed to beef and porter." "Much obliged to you," says the poor idiot with a *goître* at his throat as big as a foot-ball,—"I hear there are such folks as Patagonians; straight-limbed fellows, seven feet high; no lucky-bag for me—I might be one of them."

If such, then, be the contentment of the great mass of the suffering world,—how prodigious should be your felicity to know that you are the son of PUNCH!—to feel that you hold a position, the proudest, the noblest,—the—

  *  *  *  *  *  *  *

If the reader be a father, surely he will sympathise with my feelings.

I had not heard from my son for a long time. I was thinking of him, when I was startled by the knock of the postman. I know not how it was; but the smitten iron sent a chill through my heart, and the goose-quill fell from my fingers.

Our landlady—we were then in lodgings—brought me up a letter. My wife was happily from home; called to assist at a neighbour's labour. I immediately recognized the handwriting of my son; and, with trembling fingers, broke the wafer. I give the contents.

           *Condemned Cell, Newgate.*

HONOURED PARENT,—I have to the best of my abilities followed the advice sent to me from time to time in your Letters. You will, therefore, as the Ordinary says, not be surprised to find I write from this place. It is a case of mutton, and I am to be hanged on Monday.

             Your Son,
          PUNCH, THE YOUNGER.

P.S. You will find that, in spite of my misfortunes, I have the credit of my family still at heart. I shall therefore be hanged as John Jones.

My heroic boy kept his word: and until this very hour, his mother is ignorant of his fate, believing him to be at this moment Ambassador at the Court of ——

# $S$elections from
# PUNCH'S COMPLETE LETTER WRITER*

## LETTER I.

#### FROM A LADY INQUIRING THE CHARACTER OF A SERVANT.

MADAM,—Bridget Duster having applied to me for a place of maid-of-all-work, I beg to learn of you, as her last mistress, her fitness for the serious responsibilities of that situation. Having suffered so much from the impertinence and wickedness of servants—(I have often thought they were only sent into this world to torment respectable people),—you will, I am sure, forgive me if I appear somewhat particular in my inquiries. Experience, madam, has made me circumspect. There was a time when I thought all the world as good and honest as myself; but house-keeping wipes the bloom from the human heart, and makes us lock our tea-caddies.

I have kept house for five-and-twenty years, in which time I have constantly endeavoured to find a servant who should be without a fault; yet, though I have given eight pounds a year with tea and sugar,—would you believe it?—I have never once succeeded. However, I must say it, I like the face of Bridget; I never saw a deeper small-pox. As for handsome servants, I never have 'em; they always think more of their faces than their fire-irons, and are puckering up their mouths at the looking-glass when they should be rubbing the door-plate. Curls, too, I never suffer to cross my threshold. I know more than one instance in which curls have destroyed the peace of a family. For my money, a servant can't be too plain: in a word, I think ugliness to be a sort of cheap livery intended by Nature for maids-of-all-work—it keeps 'em in their proper place, and pre-

*The Writings of Douglas Jerrold (8 vols.; London, 1851–1858), V, 92–110, 113–125, 139–161.

vents 'em thinking of foolishness. So far Bridget's looks are most satisfactory.

And now, ma'am, for the article of dress. Servants have never been servants since linsey-woolsey went out. It makes my very flesh creep to see 'em flaunting about, for all the world as if they were born to silk gowns and open-work in their stockings. I *have* seen a housemaid go out for the day with a parasol! I prophesied her end, and—poor wretch!—so it came about. What I have suffered, too, from such presumption! I once had a creature who copied every new cap I had, and so violated my best feelings under my own roof! Bridget looks a humble dresser, fit for a kitchen: I trust she is so.

I hope, however, she is sober. When servants are very plain, they sometimes, to revenge themselves on nature, fly to drink. This is shocking; for with such people, with all one's locking and bolting, the brandy is never safe.

In the next place, does Bridget break? Not but what I always make my servants pay for all they destroy; still, they can't pay for one's nerves. Again, there is this danger—they may break beyond their wages.

Is Bridget honest? Pray, madam, be particular on this point, for I have been much deceived. I once took a servant with the finest character for honesty; and, only a week afterwards, detected her giving three cold potatoes to a little hurdy-gurdy foreigner with white mice.

Is Bridget civil? Will she bear wholesome reproof? A servant who answers is my abomination. It is clearly flying in the face of the best interests of society. Surely, people who pay wages have a right to find what fault they please; it is the natural privilege that marks the mistress from the maid. I would have a severe law to punish a servant who answers—even if right.

Is Bridget an early riser, without any reference to the time she may be allowed to go to bed? A good maid-of-all-work should, so to speak, be like a needle, and always sleep with one eye open.

Has Bridget any followers? Such creatures I never allow. I conceive that a servant ought to be a sort of nun, and, from the moment she enters your house, should take leave of all the world beside. Has she not her kitchen for willing hands always to do something in? And then for company, doesn't she see the butcher, the baker, the dustman—to say nothing of the sweeps?

Is Bridget industrious—is she clean? I hope, for the poor creature's sake, that you may be able to answer these few questions to my satisfaction, when Bridget may immediately bring her boxes. With me her duties will be few, but they must be punctually performed. Indeed, I require a servant to consider herself a sort of human kitchen clock. She must have no temper, no sulks, no flesh-and-blood feelings, as I've heard impudent hussies call their airs and graces, but must go as regularly through her work as though she was made of steel springs and brass pulleys. For such a person, there is a happy home in the house of

Your obedient Servant,
PAMELA SQUAW.


## LETTER II.

FROM A SERVANT, INQUIRING THE CHARACTER OF A MISTRESS.

DEAR MOLLY—Finding that you're in place next door to Mrs. Squaw, and remembering what friends we used to be when both of us lived with the pastry-cook, I have thought fit to write to you to inquire about your neighbour. It's all very fine, Molly, for mistresses to haggle about the characters of their maids, but surely we poor servants have as much right to ask the characters of our mistresses. However, folks who pay wages will always have the upper hand in this world, whatever to our comfort may happen to 'em afterwards.

I thank my stars I don't judge of people by their looks, otherwise I wouldn't go into Mrs. Squaw's kitchen, if it was made of gold; she's dreadful ugly, to be sure, but I don't despise her for that, if her temper's sweet. I can't bear a mistress that's always nagging and nagging. A good noise once in a way I don't mind—it brisks up one's blood; but I have known mistresses always pushing their words at you and about you, as if they were sticking pins in a cushion with no flesh and blood.

How does she like her maids to dress? Mind, I don't insist on ringlets *in* the house, but when I go out, I'm my own mistress. I've given up two places for my bird-of-paradise feather—it looks quite alive in my white chip!—and would give up twenty. After slaving among pots and pans for a month, it is so sweet to be sometimes taken for a lady on one's Sunday out.

And now, dear Molly, tell me truly; does Mrs. Squaw drink? I have lived in one family where the mistress kept a bottle in a thing that looked for all the world like the covering of a book. No wages should make me do this again; and—perhaps I am wrong—but, looking at Mrs. Squaw, I thought I never saw a redder nose. When a mistress has such a habit, a poor girl's character is never safe.

I've agreed to pay for all I break, but that I don't mind, as I never break nothing—it's always the cat. But then I've known mistresses mean enough to put off a cracked basin on a poor servant. What is Mrs. Squaw's character for crockery?

Mrs. Squaw asked me if I had any followers, as she allowed of no such thing. I said—and truly, Molly—that I had nobody that followed *me*; but, Molly, there is a young man that *I* have followed these two years, and will, so long as I've eyes to stare and limbs to move. Such a sweet the Life Guards,[1] Molly; quite a building of a man. You can't think how tachio on his lip—such a delicate thing, just the colour of a leech! He's in the Life Guards,[1] Molly; quite a building of a man. You can't think how fond he is of me; for these last two years he's smoked my wages in cigars. I lost one place about him, and gloried in it! It was one quarter-day, and he came whistling about the area.[2] Mistress saw his red coat, and ringing the bell, asked me what I meant by harbouring a low soldier! My blood was up like ginger-beer. "It's all very well for you, ma'am," says I, "to say low soldier. But, ma'am," says I, "you don't know what it is to be courted by a Life Guardsman."

Oh, these mistresses, Molly! they think poor servants have no more flesh and blood than a porridge-skillet. They can have their comfortable courtings in their parlours and drawing-rooms; and then, with their very toes at the fire, they can abuse a poor servant for only whispering a bit of love, all among the snow, perhaps, in the area. This is the treatment that often makes poor girls desperate, and drives 'em to marriage long afore their time.

No followers, indeed! No: they think that the cat and the kettle, and the kitchen clock, are company enough for a poor servant. They never think of us in the long winter nights, when they are playing at cards, or chatting with folks who've dropped in—they never think of us, all alone as we are, without a soul to speak to! No; we must have no followers, though, perhaps, the parlour's ringing again with laughter; and our only chance of opening our lips is the chance of being sent out to get oysters for the company.

However, dear Molly, write me all you know about the character of Mrs. Squaw: if she's sober and gives civil words and regular wages to her servants, I don't mind having her for a mistress, until the sweet day arrives when I become a soldier's wedded lady. Till then,

1 Life Guards, a body of soldiers assigned to guard the British monarch.
2 area, areaway.

Believe me, your friend and old fellow-servant,

BRIDGET DUSTER.

## LETTER III.

### FROM A GENTLEMAN TO A FRIEND, SOLICITING HIS ACCEPTANCE AND BOND.

MY DEAR RICHARDS,—In this our fleeting life, how few are the opportunities afforded us of really testing the hearts of our friends! Sorry, indeed, should I be for my own nature, were I of the barren creed of those who, from the depths of their would-be wisdom, smile knowingly at friendship, as though, like the word phœnix, it spoke of something very fine, but very fabulous: a spicy monster, building in the clouds, and never known to descend upon our earth. No: I should be among the most insensible of my kind—a very savage of social life—did I fail to worship friendship in my innermost heart as a virtue illustrated by one of the noblest of created men. Forgive me if I do not name him; for true worth, like the rose, *will* blush at its own sweetness!

Truly, it is pleasant to hear men abuse the world, as though, forsooth, they themselves were the only shining exceptions from the general selfishness they condemn. When I hear a man cry out, "It is a bad world," I must of course lump him with the aggregate iniquity; for how can he have the enormous vanity to select himself as the one pure Adam from naughty millions? No, Richards; be it my faith to think the best of the world; be it my special felicity to know that I hold the heart—ay, as though it were in my hand—of the truest and the best of friends. But what, indeed, is friendship, if it be not active? What but a harp, or the divinest of Cremonas,[3] resting in silence—all the melodious, ravishing sounds that waft our spirits to the clouds, sleeping in their strings, a dumb sleep? So is it with the heart of a true friend until touched by the wants of his companion.

My dear Richards, I enclose you a bill for a hundred and fifty pounds. That bill, like the harp or fiddle I have spoken of, is now as a dead thing. But only write across it "Accepted, John Richards," and it will have a voice of gold—yes, it will ring with sovereigns. Oh, friendship! thou divinest alchemist, that man should ever profane thee! Send the bill back by post, as I *must* have the cash to-morrow.

---

[3] Cremona, a city in Lombardy, Italy, famed for the violins made by the Amati, the Guarneri, and the Stradivari.

I have many acquaintance, any of whom would have gone through the little form (for it is only a form) I ask of you. But no: I should have thought such an act on my part a treason to our friendship. You know, my dear boy, that I am apt to be imaginative; and thus, it is a sweet and peculiar pleasure to me to fancy both our names linked indissolubly together—the union legalised by a five-shilling stamp,—each adding value to the other by being paired. Thus, it almost seems to me, that we merge two souls into one—that in very truth, by the potent spell of friendship, we are no longer single, but bound together by a bond unknown to these pagans of the ancient time, Orestes and Pylades, Damon and Pythias!

Yes; with a slight flourish of the pen, we shall feel what I once thought impossible, a greater interest in one another. We shall know that our names, written upon accredited paper, pass in the world as symbols of gold; you will have turned ink-drops into ready money, and *I* shall have received it. The roses that wreathe around the stamp are, to my mind's eye, Richards, the very types of our kindred minds. Do not, however, fail to post the bill to-night.

There is—I believe he calls it—a bond on my account for three or four hundreds to which a troublesome attorney wants your name. Come and breakfast with me on Monday, my dear boy, and it shall be ready for you. Heaven bless you,

> Your friend, to the Place of Tombs,
> MONTAGUE ST. GEORGE.

P.S. I have a *pâté de foie gras,* which I don't think you ever tasted, from Paris, for Monday. It's made of geese's liver. They put the live goose before the fire and make it drink and drink. Rather cruel, but there's no mistake in the liver.

## LETTER IV.

THE FRIEND'S ANSWER, REFUSING BOTH ACCEPTANCE AND BOND.

MY DEAR MONTAGUE,—Your letter has given me great pleasure. You know how highly I have always thought of friendship: it is, as you say, a divine thing. Indeed to my mind so divine, that it should never, no never, be mixed up with money.

Nevertheless, however we may differ on this little point, it is impossible for me to speak as I feel on your letter. It is charmingly written. There is a beauty, a fervour in your sentiments about friendship that convinces me you have felt its treasures, and are therein, though poor in the world's esteem, rich as an emperor. My dear friend, cultivate this style of writing: I am certain money is to be made by it.

I agree with you as to your opinion of the world; it is a glorious world—and glorious, indeed, are some of the people in it. The friendship that has so long subsisted between us, must make me acknowledge this. Your simile of a friend and a fiddle is perfect and touching. What, indeed, are they both made for, if not to be played upon?

Your picture of the unison of souls, when both the souls' hands are to the same bill, is beautiful, affecting. I have read the passage over twenty times. It has neither one word too many or too few. The picture is perfect: a cabinet gem to be locked up in one's heart. The unison of souls is a charming phrase; but, unhappily, my friend, it is too fine, of too subtle an essence to be acknowledged and respected by the coarse men of the world. The sheriff, for instance, cares not for souls, only inasmuch as they are in bodies. Now, unhappily, so far as we know, disembodied souls do not draw or accept; otherwise, what felicity would it be to me to meet and mingle with your spirit on a five-shilling stamp!

I confess, too, that it is tempting to think that, by the alchemy of a few ink-drops, I could put a hundred and fifty gold pieces (bating the discount) in the purse of my friend. Alas! if the ceremony began and ended with ink, I would spend a Black Sea upon you. You should have my name ten thousand times multiplied, with a good wish in every stroke, hair and thick.

That you have eschewed so many acquaintances, all happy with clean-nibbed pens to accept for you, and in the fulness of your friendship selected me, is a compliment, nay more, it is an evidence of your affection which I—I hope to deserve.

You know that *I*, as well as yourself, am apt to be imaginative. Imaginations, however, fly not always together. You say, that by accepting the bill, our souls would be united. My dear friend, for three months, I should feel ourselves growing together, every day strengthening the process. I should feel as if I breathed for two; nay, I should hardly turn in my bed unincumbered. I should, in my fancy, become a double man with only single strength to bear about my added load. You know the story of Sinbad and the Old Man of the Mountain?[4] That is a fine alle-

---

[4] In the *Arabian Nights*, Sinbad on his fifth voyage lands upon a desert island where he meets the Old Man of the Sea, who climbs onto his shoulders and refuses to get off. He clings there for several days until Sinbad, exhausted, finally escapes by making the old man drunk.

gory, though not understood. The truth is, the Old Man drew a bill, and Sinbad—guileless tar!—accepted it.

You speak of the roses that wreathe about the stamp. They are, indeed, very pretty. But, somehow, my eye fell upon the thistles; which I doubt not, the benevolence of Her Majesty causes to be embossed there: thistles, clearly significant that the man who accepts a bill, save for his own debt, is an ass.

I am, on the contrary,
Your affectionate friend,
JOHN RICHARDS.

P.S. I can't come on Monday, and I don't like *pâté de foie gras*. Why, in the name of mercy, should geese be treated as you described? *They* never accept bills of other geese.


## LETTER V.

FROM A VERY YOUNG GENTLEMAN TO A FAVORITE ACTRESS
WHOM HE HAS ONLY SEEN IN PUBLIC.

DEAREST MADAM,—For these past six months I have pulled against my heart—I have resisted my transports—I have fought with my passion. Yes—I determined—I will die, and my consuming secret shall perish with me. Alas! silence is no longer possible. Your witcheries of to-night have driven me with whirlwind force to pen and ink. Your voice is still in my ears—your eyes still upon my cheek—I will, I must write!

Madam, I have long adored you. Love is my witness, that I never hoped to breathe as much; but after your devotion of this evening—after the heroic sacrifice that you have made for love—after the happy willingness you have shown to give up fortune, rank, and friends, and retire with your lover from the world, though that lover was but a woodman, with nothing but his axe to provide for you both,—after the development of such a feeling (believe it, adored one, there was not a dry eye in the pit), I should wrong the sweet susceptibility of your nature, I should wrong myself, to keep silence. No; the way in which you withered the unprincipled nobleman, the tempting seducer in the second act, convinced me with an electric shock that we were made for one another! I thought—ecstatic thought!—that catching your eye from the third row, you read my heart, and while the theatre rang with plaudits, that our souls mingled! Ah! was it not so?

But why alone speak of your virtues to-night? Does not every night show you more than something earthly? In whatever situation of life you are placed, are you not in all equally angelic? Have I not known you accused of theft, nay, of murder—and have I not—witness it, Heaven!—adored you all the more for the charge? Has accident or malice thrown a shadow over you, that you have not burst forth all the brighter for the passing gloom? And in all these sorrows I have been with you! I, from the third row of the pit, have trembled with you—have visited you in prison—have attended you to the scaffold's foot, and then, in that delirious moment when the spoons were found, or the child, thought dead, ran on in a white frock,—then have I, though still in the third row, caught you innocent to my arms, and wept in ecstacy!

As a daughter, have I not seen you all your father could wish? As a wife, have you not cast a lustre upon all your wedding rings—as a young and tender mother—pardon me, sweet one,—have you not been more devoted than the pelican, gentler than the dove?

How was it possible, then, for six months to behold you, moving in and adorning every sphere—now to see you the polished countess, now the simple country maid—now smiling at want, and now giving away an unconsidered number of banknotes,—how, in the name of Cupid, I ask it, was it possible even from the third row of the pit to behold all this, and not as I have done to worship you?

Shall I, ought I, to attempt to describe to you my feelings for one night? Will my love bear with me while I write? Why do I ask? Can I doubt it?

Exactly at half-past six—my heart, my best watch—I take the third seat of the pit. Often, for many minutes, I am there alone. I like it—I enjoy the solitude. I have often wished that not another soul would enter the theatre, that I might, a mental epicure, have all the feast to myself. I seem to grudge every man his seat, as slowly one by one drops in. I unwillingly suffer anybody to participate in your smiles and honied words. No: I would have you act all to myself. Even applause sometimes throws me into a dangerous paroxysm: I feel it as an intrusion on my privilege that any one should dare to applaud but me; my blood boils to my fingers' ends; but I suppress my feelings, and have as yet, though sorely tempted, knocked no man from his seat.

I have breathed the secret of my love to nobody; and yet my eyes must have betrayed me. Forgive me; I could not control my eyes. Methinks you ask me, who has discovered my love? Smile not, I will tell you; the fruit-women. Good creatures! there is not one who does not hurry to me with a play-bill, folded down at the glorious letters that compose your name, her finger—as though by accident—pointed at the soul-delighting word. I will not tell you how I treasure those bills; no, you shall never know that every such play-bill is folded beneath my pillow at night, and is resigned to a morocco portfolio in the morning; my sensations at the theatre first briefly marked in the margin. This you shall *never* know.

Let me, however, return to my third seat. The curtain is down—the orchestra yet empty. That curtain seems to shut me from Paradise, for I know you are behind it. The musicians come in, and my heart begins to throb at the overture. The play begins: perhaps you are discovered in Scene I., in the depths of misery—how deliciously my brain beats to know it! You speak; and all my veins are throbbing like the tongue of a Jew's-harp. Perhaps you sing; and then I feel a kind of sweet swooning sickness—a sort of death made easy—that I can't describe. At times you dance; and then do I seem lifted by some invisible power, and made to float about you. Then you leave the stage, and all who come after are no more to me than jointed dolls with moving eyes. How I loathe the miserable buffoon—the comedy-man, as he is called—who, while I am languishing for your next appearance, makes the empty audience laugh about me: such mirth seems an insult to my feelings—a desecration of my love. No! you from the stage, plot and players are lost to me; I sit, only thinking of your return—sometimes abstracted from the scene, mechanically counting the scattered hairs in the head of the first fiddle.

And thus, until the curtain is about to drop, and then—my heart with it—I throw a bouquet, that has nestled all the night in my button-hole, at your fairy feet. Then do I rush from the pit to the stage-door; and there—the more delighted if it rains—there do I stand, until sweetly cloaked and shawled, I watch you—see your Adelaide boots emerge into the street, and with a thought, vanish into cab or coach. Ha! the door is closed with a slam that seems to snap my heart-strings. The horse-shoes sound in the distance—I am alone. I wander to my lodgings, sometimes in despair, and sometimes in delirious spirits, feeling that I have your arm warm and pressing under mine, and still seeing your eyes look at me, as I thought they looked at the third row of the pit.

I arrive at my cold lodging. Yet, ere I sleep, I look at your dozen faces—for I have at least a dozen—plain and coloured, hung about my walls. Yes, my beloved one! there you are, and though only published from half-a-crown to five shillings, worlds should not buy you of me!

If you have played a new part, I touch no breakfast until I read the papers. How my heart goes down upon its knees to the sensible critic who tries—although vainly—to sing your full deserts; whilst for the wretch who finds fault, or—but enough on this disgusting theme. They are monsters in the human form who write so-called criticisms for newspapers.

And now, my dearest love, in the same spirit of frankness—with that boundless gush of affection—which you have so wonderfully developed to-night—with that fervour and truth which prove to me that we were born for one another,—and that I have too rightly read your heart to believe that my want of fortune will be any defect in your eyes—rather, indeed, I should say, from what I have seen to-night, a recommendation—

I remain,<br>
Your devoted Lover,<br>
CHARLES SPOONBILL.

P.S. Please, dearest, leave an answer at the stage-door. And, dearest, pray let me catch your eye in the third row to-morrow.

## LETTER VI.

### ANSWER FROM THE ACTRESS'S FATHER TO
### THE VERY YOUNG GENTLEMAN.

SIR,—You are either a madman or a fool. I have to inform you that I usually carry a stout stick. Any more letters to my daughter, and you may become acquainted with it. Should you, however, be beyond my power of chastisement, there *is* a certain gentleman, to whom, on the advice of my daughter, I have only to show your letter, and he will commission his footman to thrash you as your impertinence deserves.

Your obedient Servant,<br>
THESPIS BURNTCORK.

P. S. In future I shall keep *my* eye upon the third row of the pit.

## LETTER VII.

### FROM A GENTLEMAN TO HIS FRIEND, ON BEING
### CALLED TO THE BAR.

MY DEAR TOM,—I hope I am the first to congratulate you. What a career is open to you! There is such loftiness of purpose—such true nobility of aim in the profession to which with a lover's fondness you have bound yourself—that in a measure I feel myself glorified by the advancement of my friend!

You are now called to the bar! Yes, you are of the happy few chosen by the solemn election of the law as the privileged champions of humanity. To you the widow and the orphan may prefer their prayers; in you they are taught to look for an adviser and a benefactor. Injured lowliness may claim the bounty of your counsel, and innocence betrayed demand the lightning of your words.

With these thoughts, what strengthening comfort must support you through the paths of study still to be adventured! Feeling the dignity of your mission, your mind will instinctively reject whatever is mean and mercenary—will assimilate to itself all that is beautiful, and pure, and good. In your hours of study you will feel that you are arming yourself for the overthrow of craft, oppression, and all the numerous brood of ignorance and ill: you will be sustained by the thought, that you are dedicating the powers you have received from Heaven to the noblest vindication of its grandest truth,—justice to all men. With this belief, you will labour rejoicingly: you will dedicate your night to study, and the early lark will greet you at your book.

It is, I know, averred that the study of law is dry and harsh—a barren, thankless theme; that "the Books" have that within them to weary the most patient spirit. And so, indeed, it may be to those who as mere word-catchers would study them; who, incapable of considering them in a phil-osophic light as operative on the social mass, would seek their pages as Indians seek poison berries,—only for better means to slay their game with.—But you, my dear friend, have nobler aspirations; you contem-plate law as the discreet and virtuous daughter of Justice, and not as her Abigail.[5]

When you look around and consider the various occupations of men, how sweet must be your self-complacency! You cannot but observe how thousands are doomed to a plodding obscurity; how thousands pass from birth to death with no one action of their lives to signalise themselves among their fellows: how, like corn, they grow, ripen, and are cut down, leaving behind them no mark of their past existence. Again, how many pass their days in acts of violence, making life one scene of wrong and tumult: whilst others creep and wind through the world timorous and

---

[5] Abigail, a lady's waiting maid (after Abigail, serving woman in Beaumont and Fletcher's play *The Scornful Lady*).

cunning, with little of the majesty of man to glorify them. Forgetful of the greatness of their mission as human creatures, they dwell within the small circle of their selfishness, all things beyond mere things of fable.

How different is your lot! You are "called to the bar:" you are chosen to play a part before the eyes of the whole world. You are to uplift your voice in defense of all that dignifies our nature: you are to work the daily champion of the weak and the distressed. Is it possible that man can have a more glorious vocation? Is it within the ambition of a truly virtuous mind to achieve greater triumphs?

Again, how beautiful will be the study of human nature laid before you! Every day you will be called to read that wondrous volume, the human heart, in all its strange yet fascinating contradictions. And when, in the fulness of fame, distinguished by every attribute of moral goodness, you are summoned to the bench,—you will display to the world one of its noblest spectacles, a great and good man honoured for his worth. Your elevation, whilst it rewards the labours of your own clear spirit, will, star-like, shine upon the hopes of others, inciting them to act your worthiness again and again. Thus will your excellence be multiplied, and example beget example.

Believe me, my dear Tom,<br>
Your sincere friend,<br>
Justus Hartley.

## LETTER VIII.

### REPLY OF THE GENTLEMAN CALLED TO THE BAR TO HIS FRIEND.

My dear Hartley,—You are, I find, the same enthusiastic, unsophisticated creature that I left at Cambridge. May you never meet with aught to change the noble simplicity of your nature!

True it is, I am "called;" and most true I may, if I would wish to starve, dub myself knight of all distressed matrons, virgins, and orphans. Unfortunately, however, for your rhapsody, it will always lie in the breast of the mother of accidents, whether I champion the wronged or the wronger: whether I am to pour oil and honey into wounds, or to be the humble instrument that adds another bruise: whether, indeed, I fight on the side of Virtue, or lustily take arms against her. This, however, is the accident of my fate; and so that good retainers come in, I am content to bow to it. In your noble philanthropy, Justus, please to consider the condition of the world, if only what seemed virtuous and innocent were defended—if all who, by the force of circumstance, appeared knaves were left to scramble for themselves. Look at the wrong committed under this ignorant devotion to abstract right. Virtue making victims by her very bigotry!

As for the hours of study, they certainly bring their sweets; but verily not after the fashion you, in your blithe ignorance, imagine. Law, my dear fellow, is not a region of fairy to be searched for golden fruits and amaranthine flowers; no, it is a deep, gloomy mine, to be dug and dug, with the safety lamp of patience lighting us, through many a winding passage—a lamp which, do what we will, so frequently goes out, leaving us in darkness.

I grant you many of the high, ennobling privileges of the profession that your eloquence has dwelt upon; but there are others which, if you know not, permit me in the freedom of friendship to say, you know nothing of the pleasures of the bar. Consider, what invulnerable armour is a wig—a gown! When they are once donned, you are permitted, by the very defence you wear, to play with the characters and feelings of men even as little girls play with dolls; ripping their seams, blackening their faces, making sport with them in any way for the prosperity of your cause, and the benefit of your client. By virtue of your profession you are emphatically a gentleman; and the very mode in which you are permitted to exercise your calling proves you to be a slanderer for so much money. You are protected by the Court, and, taking full advantage of your position, you may say in the face of Justice that which a regard for your anatomy would not permit you to utter even in a tavern. You are protected, and may to your heart's full wish enjoy your abuse. You are pistol-proof, and may therefore throw what mud and call what names you please. You have the privilege of the bar, which in this case means—the privilege of cowardice; and to the last letter you avail yourself of its immunity.

You have likewise forgotten another privilege, that of cross-examination. Ha! my friend, you know my love of a joke, and truly I anticipate much enjoyment from the freedom of tongue allowed me when I shall have a witness to practise upon. How I will "torture him with my wit"— how turn him inside out for the benefit of my client! Indeed, the true heroism of the advocate is only shown by his contempt of all things in honour of his fee. Hence, if retained by homicide to wash white and, if possible, to sweeten the blood-dyed ruffian for the world, I shall not hesitate (though assured of my client's guilt) to blacken all the witnesses against him. In pursuit of this high duty, I shall think it onerous upon me to impugn even the chastity of female virtue, so that by casting shame upon innocence, I may open the prison door to murder.

Your affectionate friend,
THOMAS BRASSBY.

P.S. Congratulate me. I have just received my maiden brief; a case against a sempstress, for illegally pawning a shirt.

## LETTER IX.

### FROM AN ELECTOR TO A MEMBER OF PARLIAMENT, SOLICITING HIS INTEREST FOR A PLACE.

HONOURED SIR,—According to my promise, when I last had the pleasure of shaking your worthy and high-minded hand, I take up my pen to let you know how matters go on in our borough of Pottlepot. Oh, sir! the Blues are done for ever! They ought, if they had any sense of their littleness, to crawl upon all fours the rest of their natural lives: it's downright impudence of 'em to think of walking upright on two legs, like incorruptible, independent voters. But, sir, they are done for ever! As I said at the club on Saturday, where we always drink your honoured health standing with nine times nine, as I said, after we had toasted your patriotism and all your public and private virtues,—Sir Curtius Turnstile, says I, sits for Pottlepot for life; it's as good as his own freehold. And so it is, sir. Be sure of it, there isn't a Yellow that wouldn't die for you, with all their wives and families included. You have touched their hearts, Sir Curtius, in the proper way, and there isn't a man that wouldn't bleed for you in return. And then for the women; why, I'm a sinner, if last Sunday there weren't six babies every one of 'em christened Curtius. There they were, sir—bless the little cherubs!—with yellow ribands in the caps, and ribands hung all over them, and their mothers and fathers smiling on the colours with all a parent's fondness. Ha, sir! it would have done your noble heart good to hear how the same night we drank the healths of the young Curtiuses—the baby Yellows—the future free and independent voters of Pottlepot.

But how, sir, should it be otherwise? Who can forget your kindness when you came among us to canvass? What condescension—what liberality! There's poor Mrs. Spriggs, the good soul who sells cakes; she never speaks of you without tears in her eyes; and as for her husband—a rascally Blue!—whom the kind creature made so drunk, and then shut the shutters on the day of poll, that when he woke he thought it was still night, and so went to sleep again,—dear Mrs. Spriggs says she can't enough bless you. Though you bought her jackdaw for ten pounds, she's got another; and for all her husband—like a brutal Blue as he is!—beats her once a week for't, the public spirited, patriotic soul, *will* teach the bird to cry out "Turnstile for ever! Down with the Blues!"

You'll be glad to hear, Sir Curtius, that little Bobby Windfall, the bellows-mender's child, has got over the small-pox, and won't be very much marked. I'm sure you'll be glad of this, from the kind manner with which I saw you kiss the suffering babe when it was so very bad indeed.

The organ that you sent down to the chapel plays very beautifully— very. It quite melts the heart of every true Yellow to listen to it. But I am sorry to say—I blush for my species while I write it—that several stiff-necked Blues stay away from chapel because of that organ: whilst one of 'em, with a sneer that meant I know not what, said, "The organ was a most appropriate gift from you, as no sinner could listen to it without thinking of corruption." What he meant by this 'twould puzzle me to discover.

Your kind hospitality in inviting all of us to your mansion in town whenever we should come to London, will in a few days be rewarded. Chops the pork-butcher, with Brads the blacksmith, and Strong-i'-th'-arm the farrier, will be with you—they desire me to say—next week. But pray, Sir Curtius, don't give Chops too much champagne, as he is apt to be very unruly. And Mrs. Brads hopes you'll not let Brads stir in London without you're by his side; she says she depends upon you. As for the farrier's wife, she says you're welcome to keep her husband for a month; only when he comes back, she says she shall expect to see what sort of caps they wear in London.

We are all on the look-out for your first speech, as you promised us on the hustings that it should be a teazer.

I am, Sir Curtius,
Your obedient Servant,
And very humble Voter,
HAMPDEN BRICK.

P.S.—I had almost forgotten to say, that my son Brutus—the youth to whom you jokingly gave a five-pound note to light a cigar with—is now anxious to enter upon the world. Forgive the feelings of a father; but please to write by return of post whether his place will be in the Excise,

the Customs, or the Treasury. I suppose we mustn't expect more than
two hundred a year *to begin with*.


## LETTER X.

ANSWER OF SIR CURTIUS TURNSTILE, M.P., TO HIS CONSTITUENT,
HAMPDEN BRICK.

MY DEAR SIR,—It gives me the deepest pleasure to learn the happiness
and tranquillity of the favoured borough of Pottlepot. Bound up as my
future public life is with the sympathies of the noble-minded and incorruptible men by whose votes I hold my present exalted situation—my
present enviable prominence in the eye of the world—it must be to me a
vital delight to know of their felicity. As for the Blues—that desperate
faction—that band of little Neros preying on the vitals of their mother-
country—but I dismiss them from my thoughts. Contempt relieves me
from the excess of indignation.

It is to me a deep happiness to find that I am remembered at your
hebdomadal meetings at the Angel. Believe me that every Saturday
night I shall spiritually return thanks for the honour that you do me.

The thought that I have awakened a feeling of respect in the bosoms
of my fair well-wishers and active supporters of Pottlepot, awards to me
the proudest moment of my life. That, with a delicacy which peculiarly
distinguishes the disinterested excellence of their sex from the too frequent selfishness of ours, they should give my name to the pledges of
their hallowed love, produces feelings in my breast much more easily
conceived than described. Tell them from me, good Mr. Brick, that
whilst they have complimented me, they have imposed a task upon me—
yes, sir, a task; for, henceforth, it must be the peculiar study of my life
to do nothing that shall be in the least unworthy of my interesting name-
sakes. It would, I assure you, have given me great pleasure to be their
godfather, but—another time.

I am delighted to learn that the excellent Mrs. Spriggs is in good
health. Though decidedly not a woman of high education, she has that
instinctive patriotism which made the glory of the ancient matron. She
might, without a blush, call the mother of the Gracchi sister. I am more
than amused to hear of her jackdaw: and, for her sake, hope for better
things from her husband.

Believe me, you only do justice to my feelings when you say that I shall be happy to hear of the recovery of Master Robert Windfall. Though asleep, and in a sad condition when I saw him, I *do* think I never looked upon a more intelligent child. I trust he will become a blessing to his parents, and an honour to the ancient mystery of bellows-mending.

What you tell me respecting the organ, shocks me. That the spirit of party can, in such a subject, find matter for its bitterness, makes one almost despair of human nature. Alas! alas! that even the humble present of a church organ cannot escape the ribaldry of party malice. But nothing, sacred or profane, *does* escape it!

You speak of a projected visit to town by Chops, Brads, and Strong-i'-th'-arm, my worthy and indefatigable constituents. There are no men for whose honesty—whose singleness of purpose—whose primitive simplicity of character—I have a higher admiration; but was there ever anything so unfortunate? At present my mansion is undergoing a thorough repair; filled with carpenters, bricklayers, plasterers—in fact, turned inside out. Hence, to my inexpressible annoyance, I shall not have the pleasure of seeing them under my own roof; and what is worse, I fear—I say, I fear—that unavoidable business will, for a week at least, take me from London. However, pray let me know *what day* they intend to set out. I depend upon you not to fail in this. I have not yet spoken in the House. It is my policy never to throw away powder. But *when* I do make myself heard, depend upon it that Pottlepot will hear the report.

> Believe me, my dear Sir,
> Yours faithfully ever,
> CURTIUS TURNSTILE.

P.S.—As for your son, I think it would be a pity that he should bury his precocious talents—for I never saw so young a boy smoke with so much maturity—in either the Excise, the Customs, or the Treasury. Take a friend's advice, and bring him up to the bar.

## LETTER XIII.

FROM A YOUNG GENTLEMAN, DESIROUS OF ENTERING THE
ARMY, TO HIS GUARDIAN.

MY DEAR SIR,—In our last conversation, you more than hinted at the necessity of my making choice of a profession. I have again and again considered the important subject, and am at length resolved. Yes; I have made my election—I will become a soldier. I have looked about me, I trust dispassionately; I have weighed and counterweighed all other things with the sword, and found them as nothing to the glorifying steel. Do not believe, sir, that I am biased in my judgment by the outward show and ceremonious parade of military life; no, sir, although I can well believe that they have a false influence on the youthful mind, I nevertheless trust that I have too well benefited by your philosophy to confound the noble profession of arms with its holiday blazonry—its review-day splendour. The mere human clod may turn the plough, beckoned by the fluttering ribands of the recruiting-serjeant—the clown's heart may, to his astonishment, beat to the beating sheepskin, and so beguile him into the ranks—but, sir, I trust that education has taught me a truer valuation of things, enabling me to consider the profession of a soldier in its abstract glory, in its naked loveliness. I look only at the wreath of Cæsar, and care not for the outward splendour of his legions.

Oh, sir, when I read the career of conquerors, I have a strange belief that I was born to be a soldier! I feel such a sympathising throb of heart at the achievements of an Alexander, that all other pursuits, save that of arms, seem to me poor, frivolous, and unworthy of the highest dignity of human nature. To me, soldiers appear the true lords of the earth; and other men, however rich, but as mere greasy serfs—creatures with their souls dwelling darkly in money-bags. The game of war is a pastime for gods, and man is sublimated by its exercise. And then death—death in the bed of glory—with a whole country weeping over our ashes! Is not that a prospect, sir, to quicken the blood of youth, and intoxicate the brain with the sweetest, the noblest draughts of ambition? And then, sir, the laurel, flourishing in everlasting green, and circling our memory for ever!

Nevertheless, should you wish me to delay the purchase of a commission for a few months, I trust you will permit me to visit Germany this autumn to witness the reviews. It is said that the troops expected to assemble will be the flower of the world. I know not, too, how many thousands. What a sublime spectacle! In their different uniforms—with their banners, their artillery, and their leaders—many of them with the history of the last wars cut in scars upon their bodies! I do not think the world can show a nobler sight. So superhuman in its power—so awful in its beauty!

And now, sir, having freely communicated to you my desire to enter the army, permit me to assure you that I shall devote my entire soul to the study of my duties as a soldier. They have, I know, their severity: but have they not also their rewarding sweetness? Yes, sir, for how delicious must it be—the heat and fury of the battle over—to solace the wounded, to protect the helpless! In those moments the noblest emotions of our common nature must be awakened; they must repay the warrior for toil, privation, suffering unutterable. Yes, sir—to know that in such an hour we are lessening the anguish of a fellow-creature, must for a time elevate us beyond the common impulses of poor humanity.

Anxiously awaiting your reply—and with it, as I fondly believe, your consent—

I remain, your affectionate ward,
ARTHUR BAYTWIG.

P.S.—Do not think, my dear sir, that the opinions of a certain young lady, who has always declared she would marry no one but a soldier, have had the least influence upon my determination. No, sir; not the least, I assure you.

## LETTER XIV.

ANSWER OF THE GUARDIAN TO THE YOUNG GENTLEMAN.

MY DEAR ARTHUR,—I thought more highly of your discrimination. I believed that you knew me better than to make so foolish a proposition. My opinions on war and its instruments are, I know, not the opinions of the world; it would save the world—I am vain enough to think—much guilt, much misery, if they were so.

You, doubtless, believe your letter the result of an honest enthusiasm; and yet, to my fancy, it is nothing more than the folly of a boy, who, unconscious of his prompter, writes with a fiend dictating at his elbow. Yes, my boy, a fiend; he is too often busy among us—one of the vilest and most mischievous demons of all the brood of wickedness. To be sure, he visits men not in his own name—oh no! he comes to them in the finest clothes and under the prettiest alias. He is clothed in gay colours—has yards of gold trimming about him—a fine feather in his cap—silken flags fluttering over him—music at his heels—and his lying, swindling name is— Glory. Strip the thing so called, and how often will you find the abhorred nakedness of a demon? Be assured of it, fife and drum make the devil's choicest music. He blows and beats—for, being a devil, he can do this at the same time—and makes the destructive passions of men twist and wriggle in the hearts of even peaceful folk, and with the magic of his tattoo drives them on to mischief. You know, people say I have strange, violent thoughts. Well! I think every sheep whose skin is turned into drum-parchment, has been sacrificed not to the gods but devils.

You tell me that you are smitten with glory in the abstract—with its naked honour. Pooh! like a poor-souled footman, you are content to take the blows for the fineness of the livery.

You say, that when you read the history of conquerors, you yearn to become a soldier. Well, I dispute it not; there have been men made soldiers by tyranny and wrong, whose memories may, like the eternal stars, shine down upon us; these men may be envied. But I, too, have read the lives of conquerors; and, as I live, they no more tempted me to emulate them, than the reading of Newgate Calendar[6] would make me yearn to turn footpad or housebreaker.

At best, soldiers are the evils of the earth. The children of human wrong, and human weakness. Understand me, I would not have men ground arms, and, with quaker-like submission, cry "friend" to the invader. Nevertheless, do not let us prank up a dire necessity with all sorts of false ornament, and glorify wholesale homicide. You say war is the pastime of gods. Homer tells us as much. And pretty gods they were who played at the sport! In my time, I have known many men who, for very humbly imitating them in some of the amusements, have died on the gallows or withered on board the hulks. I trust the time will come when it will bring as great shame to men to mimic Mars, as it now deals upon the other sex to imitate Venus.

You talk glibly enough of the bed of glory. What is it? A battle-field, with thousands blaspheming in agony about you! Your last moments sweetened, it may be, with the thought that somewhere on the field lies a bleeding piece of your handiwork—a poor wretch in the death-grasp of torture! Truly, that is a bed of greater glory which is surrounded by loving hearts—by hands uplifted in deep, yet cheerful prayer. There are thoughts too—it is my belief—better, sweeter far than thoughts of recent slaying, to help the struggling soul from out its tenement.

You talk, too, of the nation's tears! In what museum does the nation keep her pocket-handkerchiefs? Depend upon it, nations that love to fight, are not the nations that love to weep. I grant it; many a fine, simple fellow, has died in the belief of being wept over by his country, who has nevertheless been shamefully defrauded of his dues. My dear boy, never sell your life for imaginary drops of water. And then you rave about laurel—an accursed plant of fire and blood. Count up all the crowns of

---

[6] Newgate Calendar, a chronicle of biographies of the most notorious criminals confined within London's Newgate Prison.

Cæsar, and for the honest, healthful service of man, are they worth one summer cabbage?

You would wish to see the German review—you think it is so noble a sight? Be assured, if you can teach your eyes to look through the spectacles of truth, there cannot be a sadder, a more rueful exhibition—one reflecting more upon the true dignity of human nature—one more accusatory of the wisdom and goodness of man—than thousands of men dressed and harnessed, and nicely schooled for the destruction of their fellow creatures. All their finery, all their trappings, are to me but the gim-crackery of the father of wickedness. In my time, I have seen thousands of soldiers drawn up, with a bright sky shining above them; and I have thought them a foul mass—a blot—a shame upon the beautiful earth—an affront to the beneficence of Heaven! But then, I have odd thoughts—strange opinions.

You say it will be sweet, the battle over, to solace the wounded. My dear boy, it will be sweeter far not to begin the battle at all. It may be very humane to apply the salve after you have dealt the gash,—but surely it would be better wisdom, truer humanity, to inflict no hurt. And, in time, men will learn this truth; they *are* learning it; and as I would not see you in a profession which I trust is speedily becoming bankrupt, you will never, with my consent, purchase into the army.

Your affectionate friend,
BENJAMIN ALLPEACE.

## LETTER XV.

FROM A MAIDEN AUNT TO A NIECE ON
THE IMPRUDENCE OF MARRIAGE.

MY DEAR CLARIBEL,—I should ill acquit myself of the duties of an aunt— should show myself wickedly ungrateful for the goodness that has hitherto preserved me from the cares and frivolities of the marriage-state— were I to see you, my sister's child, ready to throw yourself into a bottomless pit, and never so much as scream to save you. It was only yesterday that Doctor Prunes acquainted me with your headstrong passion for an unworthy creature of a man. Although I had grouse for dinner—and you know how I love it!—I never ate so little; and, in the evening, revoked twice in only three rubbers. What with the news of Doctor Prunes and the tooth-ache, I have scarcely slept all night, and at breakfast, instead of buttered toast, absolutely gave chicken to the parrot. May you, even at the twelfth hour, prove worthy of all I suffer for you.

You are only three-and-twenty, and yet, with a forwardness that makes me blush for the true dignity of womanhood, you already think of marriage! I had hoped that my lessons of morality would have taught you better things. I had flattered myself that, strengthened by my principles, you would have risen above the too common weakness that unites a woman to a creature in every way inferior to herself, whatever the said creatures, in the fulness of their impudence, may trumpet to the contrary. I do not dispute that men may be necessary in the world; but, at the best, they are only necessary evils. It is thus that every really sensible woman should consider them. In the vulgar attribute of brutes—mere muscular strength—they are certainly our superiors; but how immeasurably beneath us are they in all that constitutes true greatness—in delicacy, liberality, tenderness, friendship, fortitude, and taciturnity! And, in their hypocrisy, they confess as much; for they call us angels—(though I am proud to say, no man ever so insulted *my* understanding)—yes, angels, that they may make us slaves. How any woman can read the marriage ceremony without having her eyes opened to the real intentions of the creatures, is to me most wonderful. Love, honour, and obey! My blood burns to think of it! To the ears of a sensible woman every syllable rattles like a dog-chain.

I did think that my own Claribel—taught by my precept and example —would as soon have put her finger into a rat-trap as a wedding-ring. I did believe that you would consider all the fine things that men utter as nothing more than the false notes of a bird-catcher; mere sounds to bring our free minds "from the heaven of high thoughts," as some poet says, and shut 'em up in cages. How women can listen to a jargon of loves and doves, is melancholy to think of. A woman of really strong mind hates Cupids as she hates cockroaches.

Nevertheless, my dear, I can sympathise with human infirmity. Everybody is not born to keep a heart of virgin ice that, pressed as it may be, no pressing can melt. Still, there is nothing like a diversion of thought to cure a hurt. It is wonderful how a wound heals, if we never think of it. Therefore, return his letters to the man who would ensnare you; and, forgetful of the cares and littlenesses of marriage, give up all your thoughts to astronomy. It is a charming study, and presents a more ennobling field for the human mind, than the small limits of wedlock. How insignificant seems the wife, studious of the goings-out and comings-in of a mere husband, compared to the nobler woman who knows all about the Great and Little Bear! How petty the noblest house in the noblest square to the House of Jupiter or Mars—how perplexing the cares of children, to the lofty contemplation of the Via Lactea (known, as Doctor Prunes says, to the lower orders as the Milky Way);—how insulting to the true greatness of the female mind the smallness of the wedding-ring, when the ring of Saturn may be all her own, with no incumbrance of Saturn himself!

Or if, Claribel, you want enthusiasm for the stars, why, is there not geology? Properly considered, can there be a more delightful employment for the female mind than to settle the ages of things that vulgar souls care nothing about? Who would not turn from the cries of a nursery to the elevating sounds of felspar and quartz? What really great woman would study the mere heart of a mere man, when she might discover fossil shrimps and caterpillars in marble? No. Woman will never assert her true dignity till she can wisely choose between the two.

Then, after some ten or fifteen years—for it is a study too rashly submitted to the young—botany may disclose its lovely mysteries. How delightful, what true freedom for the human soul, to be exempt from cares of husband and family, and to know everything about the operations of pollen! But I am incautiously anticipating a subject reserved for your maturer years.

Break, then, the chains with which mere tyrant man would bind you, and—defying the slavery of conjugal life—live like Diana,

And your still affectionate Aunt,
LUCRETIA DRAGONMOUTH.

P.S.—Is it true that the wife of Doctor Beetlebrow is really dead? I wouldn't utter a word against the departed; I should hope not, but—is she really dead?

## LETTER XVI.

### THE NIECE'S ANSWER.

MY DEAR AUNT,—How can I ever express my gratitude to you, how repay the care with which you seek to gather me to that sisterhood of which Lucretia Dragonmouth is the crowning rose? Alas, madam! I feel my unworthiness! I should but bring a scandal on the community by the frivolity of my words and the earthliness of my desires. I have the greatest respect for Diana, but feel it impossible to become lady's-maid to her. Therefore, dear Aunt, you must even leave me to my headlong fate; and unbroken rest, heartier meals, and successful rubbers, be your continual reward.

It would ill become my inexperience to dispute the sentence you pass upon the other sex. Men are, doubtless, all you say of them: therefore, forewarned by your opinion, I shall endeavour to support the necessary evil that may fall to my lot with all the fortitude I may. As for the marriage ceremony, I have read it again and again, and such is the hopeless perversity of my taste—think it the loveliest composition! To my ears, it murmurs the very music of Paradise.

I feel the full force of what you say about astronomy. No doubt, its study might relieve a wounded heart, but then as I feel no wound that is not most delicious, why should I go to the stars to get rid of it? Yes, madam, I can forgive your talking about the stars. *You* have never seen my Alfred's eyes! No doubt the Great and Little Bear have their attractions; but you never saw my Alfred's moustache!

Geology, too, may be fascinating. It may be musical tô talk of felspar and quartz; to seek for fossil bees that made honey for the pre-Adamites; but you never heard my Alfred sing *Love in thine eyes*—you never felt the pressure of his throbbing hand!

As for botany, I really feel its influence in a manner I never felt before; for I am just now called to choose my bridal wreath of orange flowers, and must therefore abruptly conclude—

> Your affectionate Niece,
> CLARIBEL MAYDEW.

P.S.—It is not true that Mrs. Bettlebrow is dead; though once she was given over by her physicians. Ah, my dear Aunt! how foolish it was of you thirty years ago to quarrel with the dear doctor, and only—as I've heard—for treading on the toes of a nasty little pug!

## LETTER XVII.

### FROM A GENTLEMAN TO HIS FRIEND, ENTREATING HIM
### TO RENOUNCE THE BOTTLE.

MY DEAR PETER,—May I, by a friendship of thirty years' growth, be permitted to address you on your faults, or, rather, your fault? for it is so capacious that it swallows every other error; in the same way that boa constrictors gulp toads and other unsightly creatures of smaller dimensions. May I venture to remonstrate with you on—well, it must be said—your habitual drunkenness? Alas! my friend, to what a condition has this folly, this wickedness reduced you! This morning only, I saw a full-grown cucumber in a bottle: there is nothing in the object; it is a commonplace, to be seen in the windows of every pickle-merchant: and yet did that imprisoned cucumber touch my heart, and bring pathetic moisture into my eyes; for by the tyranny of association, it made me think of my forlorn friend. Yes; looking at that cucumber, trained to grow in its glass prison, did I behold in it the hopeless condition of Peter Rubygill! There he is—thought I—there is Peter, and who shall deliver him? And how, alas! does that plethoric gourd fully declare the story of my friend! How, like him, was it insinuated in its green youth—a very sucker—into the bottle's throat; and how, when there, was it made to grow and swell, until far too large to be withdrawn, it possessed the whole of the bottle, and was then cut off for ever from the vine that had cherished it! And is it not thus, Peter, with a doomed drunkard? Does he not enter the bottle in the greenness of his days, and though he may again and again escape from the thing that threatens to enclose him, at length is it not impossible for him to get away? Habit makes him swell, and there is no hope for him; cut off from the genial world, he has no other dwelling-place than a bottle. Verily, Peter Rubygill, Bacchus—like a pickle-merchant—has his bottled cucumbers, and you are of them!

And yet, Peter, I would fain hope for you. In the name of all that is great and beautiful in the world, why seal your eyes to its grandeur and loveliness, why walk with your drowsy brain in a fog, when, touched by the light of beauty, it might answer the touch with most delicious music? What, in truth, can you know of the bounty and magnificence showered about you? No more than a silly fly, that, finding itself in the palace of a king, sips and sips, and tumbles headlong into the first syrup it may light upon. Have I not seen you leaden-eyed—clay-pated—almost dumb with pain hammering at your temples—degraded by nausea tugging at your stomach—your hand shaking like a leaf—your mouth like the mouth of an oven—and your tongue, I am sure of it, like burnt shoe-leather? And for what, Peter Rubygill? For some six hours' madness the night before?

You were left a comfortable competence. Where is it now? Gone. The bottle is the devil's crucible, and melts all!

You were tolerably good-looking. And now is your countenance but as a tavern sign; where numberless little imps—liberated by drawn corks—continue to give a daily touch and touch of red, proud of their work, as portrait-painters to the devil himself.

There was a time when your word was true as gold. And now, upon whom can you pass it? From the mouth of a drunkard, the most solemn promise is no better than the best-made bad money: it may pass for a time, but is certain to be nailed to the world's counter at last.

You had friends. But there is a mortal fever in the reputation of a drunkard, and sober men wisely avoid it.

You have a wife. Has she a husband? No. She vowed to love a man, and you are a liquor-cask. Can you expect her affection? You might as reasonably expect her wedding-ring to hoop a wine-barrel.

You have children. Poor things! They see a satyr sprawl and reel before them; and, in their innocence, blush not as yet to call the creature father!

But, my dear Peter, there is yet hope. Learn to love home. Avoid the tavern. It is in the tavern-cellar that the devil draws up his army array against the brains and good resolves of men. It is there that he reviews his legions of bottles, and prepares them for the attack upon weak humanity. But, arm yourself, Peter; meet the assailants with cold water; and, in the fight, you shall have the earnest prayers of your old friend,

CORYDON RIVERS.

## LETTER XVIII.

### THE ANSWER.

MY DEAR CORYDON,—*You* talk of the beauty of the earth—*you* talk of the magnificence of the world! Why, then, let moles sing psalms to the moon, and that hermit in feathers, the screech-owl, tune a ditty to the noonday sun. The bottle is the true philosopher's microscope, and shows him worlds within worlds that such as you, poor naked-eyed wretches, never had the heart to dream of.

You say that you have seen me with my brain in a fog. Poor ignorance! After a night's—say three nights'—continual happiness, you little know the bliss I walk in. You little think of the genius within me, that turns your scoundrel streets of London into the abodes of the blessed. What see I there but love and truest brotherhood? The very knockers wink and laugh at me; and roses and honeysuckles grow about every lamp-post. There are, I know, weak, puling creatures, who talk of headaches; but these are milksop neophytes, not yet of the true priesthood of our order. What if now and then I have a twinge? Think you I accuse the bottle? I should be a villain to do so. No: it's the d——d east wind.

As for the fortune that was left me, it is true I have invested it in the bottle; and, oh! what compound interest have I had for my money! Whilst you would count every rascal guinea, and, after you had counted all, would break into a cold sweat to think there was no more, I—seated on my tavern-throne—have had wealth that would confound all arithmetic. All about me has been glorious riches! I have drunk out of hollowed diamonds, and spat in gold-dust.

It is my darling faith that every bottle contains in it a pair of beautiful wings, to lift poor man above the gutter-mud which this sober world is made of. A pair of wings! And I, like Mercury, can't do without three pair.

I have somewhere read it at school—ha! Rivers, sometimes, at the heel of the night I see you again in your green jacket, and I sit and enjoy myself, and let the sweetest of tears run down my nose—well, never mind that—I read it at old Canetwig's—that Jupiter fastened the earth to heaven with a gold chain. All a flam, my dear boy! It was no chain, but a splendid, a most magnificent line of linked bottles. The higher you climb, the further you are from this vagabond world. Pity, my dear fellow—pity it is, that the road is so devilish slippery!

You say I had friends. *Had!* I have millions. Ha! my good creature—for you are good, I believe, sober and stupid as you are,—you don't know the philanthropy that a corkscrew lets out upon me. I may have been ruffled; may I be pardoned for it, I may now and then have thought harshly of my poor erring fellow creatures, when—pop!—out comes the cork, and the wine, as it bubbles forth, speaks pacifyingly, soothingly. Again—again! The bottle coos like any dove; and I have not listened to it above two or three hours, when I feel myself turned into one large lump of human honey! And then these two hands of mine are multiplied ten million times, and I shake hands with every man, woman, and child upon this beautiful earth, my creditors included.

But all this, though much, is nothing to the wisdom—the knowledge —that drink so subtly lets in upon poor, darkened man. What is it? You have studied these things; but then you have studied them with a dry, dusty throat; and so, can know no more of the true operations of the intellect—glorious intellect—of majestic man, than a monkey knows of a steam-engine. Well, what is it? I say, what is it? Ha! my dear soul, if you had only two bottles of the stuff that is now shining before me—shining like a lion's eye—you'd know all about it. Then you'd know metaphysics —that is, metaphysics assisted by glorious wine—here's a bumper to you, old cock! God bless your little green jacket!—metaphysics is this, as you'd know. Every man has an angel within him. Lord love us! and yet, sometimes, we use one another as though we lodged nothing but devils. Well, as I said, every man has an angel within him; and this angel—poor thing!—you dull, sober, miserly fellows, board in the most rascally way; giving him nothing generous to drink, or just wetting his lips, and there an end. And what's the consequence? Why, he tells you nothing worth knowing—just casts up your accounts for you—gives you a nudge when stocks are going, or some chandler matter of the kind; but, with a noble resentment of your shabbiness, he does nothing more. What does he to me, who know how to treat him? I give him bumper after bumper,—and my brain feels him expanding his wings—(you, poor wretch! don't know that he has wings)—yes, bumper after bumper, until, at last, my angel takes up his golden fiddle, and plays me such a tune (I can feel him rosining his bow at this minute,)—such a tune, that as it sounds I catch all sorts of wisdom; thoughts like diamonds, bright and everlasting!

Ha! ha! he's playing now, and I drop the pen to listen, and feel myself an emperor.

*    *    *    *    *    *    *

—My dear Corydon,—Don't mind the stuff I've scrawled above—for I've been mad this month past. I am just arrested. You'll find me at ——, Chancery-lane. Come, come—for God's sake, bring fifty pounds, and you will everlastingly oblige

Your wretched friend,<br>PETER RUBYGILL.

## LETTER XXVII.

FROM A LADY IN WANT OF A GOVERNESS, TO AN ACQUAINTANCE.

DEAR MADAM,—We are again in tribulation; for Miss Sinclair, the young person whose harp-playing you were pleased to admire, has left us—left us, too, in the most shameful and ungrateful manner, before we could provide another teacher for the dear children. Oh, these governesses! I am told there is some clever gentleman who has invented an arithmetical machine that will calculate any sum to a fraction. What a blessing would that man bestow upon really good society who should invent an instrument for teaching! I am sure, in these days, the thing might be done, and

would pay admirably; for how much annoyance would be spared us—
how much impertinence that we are daily exposed to from a class of individuals who can have no standing in society, and are nevertheless continually at one's elbow! The cook, the housemaid, the lady's-maid, all
know their place, and behave themselves accordingly: but there is no
teaching a governess that she is nothing more than a servant; a person
hired for wages to polish the minds of your children, just in the same
manner as Molly polishes your rosewood and mahogany—and to be as
careful of their morals as if, like the housekeeper, she was entrusted with
so much precious china. Your maid dresses your hair with due humility,
and takes your little bits of ill-temper with proper resignation; she
knows these things are considered in her wages, and thus she may be an
ornament to the sphere to which it has pleased Heaven to call her. But
governesses! they are continually flying in the face of Providence. There
is, too, an impertinence in their very meekness: at times, an insult in
their silence. They move about you with the air of injured beings—an
air that says to your very face—"We, too, are ladies, though you can't believe it." Ladies! as if the person who takes a salary is not, to all intents
and purposes, a servant—at best, a better sort of menial servant.

To return to that person Sinclair. I never liked her from the first; but
as I heard that she had an old father to provide for—the man was, I believe, in gaol at the time—I suffered my charity to cover a multitude of
her faults, and received her, as she was afterwards pleased to call it, into
my family,—into one of my back bed-rooms would have been a more re-
spectful phrase. Well, she would always be reading, when she ought to
have talked to and amused the dear children. It was only yesterday that
she repeated the fault. She had been out three or four hours walking, and
I found her again reading a book, whilst the dear things were moped to
death for something to enliven them. My indignation was roused, and I
asked her if she thought she was acting honestly by her employer? She
looked up at me—her face turned blood-red—her lips quivered with
some impertinent reply, I am certain, by their motion—and then dropping the book, she burst into tears. Governesses, my dear Madam, *always*
*can*. But I have not told you all. What book, think you, was it? *A Christ-*
*mas Carol*. I have never read the thing; but knowing it to be aimed at
the best interests of good society, all the feelings of a mother rushed
upon me, and I believe I *did* read her a pretty lesson. You hav'n't heard
all. Whilst I was reproaching her for her ingratitude, her baseness in
bringing such books into my family, and saying something, I forget exactly what, about a viper I had warmed—she sprang from the chair like

a play-house queen, and in a voice as searching as an east wind—told me that she would leave my house that instant! Her impudence—for I knew she must go to starvation—fairly took away my breath. Well, it isn't all told. She multiplied her insults, for with her wet, streaming face, she caught little Emmeline about the neck, and kissing her violently, cried "God bless the children!" I trust I am not unforgiving; no: but there was an emphasis upon "the children" that nothing would ever make me pardon. It was a refinement of abuse that made me quiver again. However, I had my satisfaction of my lady; for I would not suffer a servant to stir—no, I made her call a hackney-coach herself to take her boxes; though after the sort of book I caught her with, I certainly ought to have well rummaged them before they left the house.

Can you recommend me another governess—for although I have been but a day unprovided, I feel worn to death by the children? What's worse—but then she's only a child—Emmeline has been crying all day about the creature, and moreover says she loves her. The principles she might have instilled into the dear babe's mind, I shudder to think of! However, we are happily rid of her. If you can recommend me a really

useful, well-behaved person—you know the kind of individual I want—
you will confer a favour on

Your's obliged,
HONORIA ASPHALT.

P.S.—I hav'n't told you all my troubles. We are about to lose our treasure of a cook. Sir John and he have had some words about the soup—
the man feels his reputation wounded, and has resigned. I have myself
tried to pacify him, but as yet without success. I have scolded Sir John
well for his indiscretion towards so valuable a *chef*. I am, however, going
out, and shall see if a nice diamond ring will restore peace; if so, fifty or
seventy pounds will be well bestowed.

## LETTER XXVIII.

### THE ANSWER.

DEAR MADAM,—Whilst I sympathise with you, I must also use the privilege of a friend, and admonish. The truth is—and, though truth, like
medicine, is generally unpleasant, it must nevertheless, like medicine, be
sometimes administered—the truth is, you spoil all your governesses. You
do, indeed. I, who have had a large experience of that sort of people,
know it. Only a week ago, I saw Sinclair in the Park, talking with another governess. As your friend, I took the liberty of asking her who she
was? She replied—I thought very boldly—an old schoolfellow. Upon
which I told her you would be very angry if you knew of the indiscretion.
That, as a governess, she had no longer anything to do with schoolfel-
lows, and should speak to nobody but to the young ladies. That it was
her duty, as a young woman of principle—and I dwelt, as you know I can
dwell, upon the word—upon principle, to cut herself off from the rest of
the world, and study nobody but you and the dear children. My idea of
a good governess, I observed, is, that she should be a sort of nun engaged
upon wages; a person vowed to humility, gentleness, and resignation, for
so much salary. That she should mix in the world as though she were no
part of it—self-removed from its pleasures and its sympathies; in fact, as
a sort of machine ordained by Providence to await the behests of those
ordained above her. Upon this, she dropt her eyelids, I thought, very insolently, and, with a smile not to be mistaken, turned away. Never, my
dear madam, let your governess talk with another governess. Depend
upon it, their conversation is always about their employers; and such is

the ungrateful spirit of the people, I fear me always to their detriment. Besides, I have known the scarlet fever brought into a house by such a practice.

You will also pardon me, when I tell you that you are not sufficiently discreet as to the age of your governesses. Morris, I remember, who preceded Sinclair, must at least have been seven-and-thirty; whilst Sinclair cannot have been more than one-and-twenty. Now, a governess should never be chosen younger than five-and-twenty, or older than five-and-thirty. The intermediate time may be called the prime of governess-life. If you get them younger, their heads are full of most preposterous notions about affections, and sympathies, and what they call yearnings for home. Like unweaned lambs, they are always bleating and unsatisfied. At five-and-twenty, the governess-mind knows better what is due to itself and employer, and with a strong hand plucks up such weaknesses as unprofitable weeds; at least, if it doesn't, it ought. After five-and-thirty, the governess gets slow and prosy, and her heaviness may dangerously infect the light-heartedness of the dear children—therefore, she is not to be thought of an hour longer. Immediately supply her place with a junior teacher, as you value the morals and accomplishments of your beloved family.

If, in the course of ten years, with a salary of, let us say, twenty pounds a-year, out of which she has only to buy clothes fit to keep company with the children, the governess has not saved a sufficiency for her declining age—it is but too painful to know that she must have been a very profuse, improvident person, And yet, I fear me, there are lamentable instances of such indiscretion. I myself, at this moment, know a spendthrift creature who, as I have heard, in her prime—that is, for the ten years—lived in one family. Two of her pupils are now countesses. Well, she had saved next to nothing, and when discharged, she sank lower and lower as a daily governess, and at length absolutely taught French, Italian, and the harp, to the daughters of small tradesmen, at eighteen-pence a lesson. In time, she of course got too old for this. She now lives somewhere at Camberwell,[7] and, though sand-blind, keeps a sixpenny school for little boys and girls of the lower orders. With this, and the profits on her cakes, she contrives to eke out a miserable existence—a sad example, if they would only be warned, to improvident governesses.

I am now called away, and am therefore unable to answer your letter to the full. However, you shall have another epistle on the subject to-morrow.

Your's always,<br>DOROTHEA FLINT.

[7] Camberwell, a London middle-class suburb.

# LETTER XXIX.

FROM THE HON. MRS. FLINT TO LADY HONORIA ASPHALT,
ON THE CHOICE OF A GOVERNESS.

DEAR MADAM,—I resume my pen to finish my subject; and as I have had considerably more experience than yourself in the article of governesses, I will briefly tell you how *I* have always dealt with these people. You will then be able to contrast my practice with your own. Like myself when a very young mother, you have been too considerate—too yielding. Firmness, dear madam, firmness is the first essential—young governesses are as difficult to break as young horses; but it is to be done.

I told you that I always had my suspicions of Sinclair's German—I am sure it was not the true Saxon. Now I have never engaged a governess unless she had acquired French, German, and Italian, in their separate countries. Nothing like studying a language on its proper soil, otherwise the accent of the children becomes irretrievably ruined. It was only last week that my dear friend, Lady Dinah Grosbeak, called me in to examine a candidate for the place of daily governess. The creature had certainly learned French in Paris, but she knew no more of Florence or Dresden than the city giants. She played the piano remarkably well, and brought excellent testimonials to her knowledge of thorough-bass. She sang too, very nicely—and if the water-colour paintings she produced were really her own—they were—for I always like to do justice to everybody—very pretty. However, with all her accomplishments, humility was not among them, for what do you think she asked of Lady Dinah to attend only her three children as daily governess? Positively, thirty pounds a year, and by way of climax—her dinner!

However, to proceed with my own experience. Knowing the artifice of governesses—feeling assured that it is necessary to be quite alive to their whims and caprices, I always made it a principle to deduct their salary for any week or even day of illness. Bless you, madam, without this precaution, there is no knowing what one might lose in sham fevers and surreptitious headaches. Let your governess be aware of your inflexibility on this point, and be assured she is never ill; or if she is, it is all the same, you never hear of it. Again: I never allowed a bell in the bedroom of a governess—otherwise, the poor servants would, I knew, be continually rung up and down. No; if the governess wanted anything, she could certainly somehow get it, without raising the house for it. On one occasion, too, when we left town—leaving some of the children at home—

I gave to the governess a proper dietary; a certain scale of food which it was my order was not to be departed from. As *I* had to pay for the meat, bread, butter, milk, &c., to be consumed, I was of course the only fitting judge of the quantity—that is, for a governess.

There are, however, occasions when appearances may justify a little extra outlay on a governess. For instance, when my dear father died—ah, madam! if ever there was a true Christian, he was one—I made my person a present of a dress and bonnet. In fact, I had three dresses, for my maid, the nurse, and governess, all alike. A little liberality of this sort towards our fellow-creatures is, after all, not lost in this world, and can do us no harm in the next.

Whenever it was necessary that my governess should join any of my little social parties, I, of course, never introduced her. No—it was perfectly well understood who she was, and she was never drawn out of her place—never for a moment confounded with any of the ladies present. It is convenient, too, now and then, to have these persons with you: they relieve a dull moment or so in an evening, when desired to take the stool and play. And even here, one must be very guarded, lest the governess forgets herself. I remember, on one occasion, a governess I had

—a pale, puling thing, with large blue eyes and flaxen hair, and, by the way, a cough that entirely made her singing a bad bargain—I remember that, whilst she played, she once suffered my nephew Adolphus to turn the music! But when we retired, didn't I school her! She had red eyes for a fortnight.

I had written thus far, when I received a letter that accompanies this. It is from a young woman who has never yet been from home. She has been splendidly brought up, but her father would speculate in hops or some such things, and they are all beggars. Having a sort of feeling for the family, and hearing that girl must go into the world, I wrote to her—with a view to your service—asking *her* notions of the duties and responsibilities of a governess—the treatment she expected, &c, &c. You will read her reply. It is exquisite. Quite a leaf from an old French romance. Poor thing! with such ideas, what will become of her? I will, however, look somewhere else for you; in the mean time,

Believe me, yours always,
DOROTHEA FLINT.


# LETTER XXX.

FROM A YOUNG LADY DESIROUS OF AN ENGAGEMENT
AS FAMILY GOVERNESS.

MADAM,—It is, indeed, true that the sudden and total wreck of my father's fortune renders it necessary for me to earn my own bread; and, unhappily, not mine alone. Your letter, kind madam, came like a sunbeam upon our darkened dwelling. Now, indeed, do I feel grateful—past expression—for the few attainments I possess, for they will enable me to bear with cheerfulness the change prepared for me. They will raise me above the indifference and contempt of the world; and whilst they supply me with the means of honourable existence—and what, indeed, so honourable, so truly lofty, as a life dedicated to the mind of childhood?—they may haply not be deemed wholly useless to others. I am now tranquil—decided. When the truth first came upon me that I must henceforth exist by my own exertions, I own it, old vanities—the follies born of of fortune—clung for a moment closer to me. But I have laid apart false pride like a masque-night garment. I am instantly prepared to begin my working life.

You ask my notion of the duties, the cares, the responsibilities of a governess. Alas, madam! it is a contemplation of their seriousness, nay, of their solemnity, that makes us pause—falter, in my hopes. I cannot but fear my own unworthiness for the task, it is so vital. For is not the mind of childhood the tenderest, holiest thing, this side heaven! Is it not to be approached with gentleness, with love,—yes, with a heart-worship of the great God from whom, in almost angel-innocence, it has proceeded? A creature undefiled by the taint of the world—unvexed by its injustice— unwearied by its hollow pleasures? A being fresh from the source of light, with something of its innocent lustre in it? If childhood be this— how holy the duty to see that, in its onward growth, it shall be no other! To stand, as a watcher at the temple, lest any unclean thing shall enter it. This, surely, is one of the loftiest duties that can elevate infirm humanity; and this duty is especially required of him or her who tends upon the growing mind of youth: it is a task that, however misunderstood by the many, ennobles the doer. I know that all the world thinks not thus. I know, alas! that there are mothers who place their mere jewellery under bankers' locks, who, nevertheless, trust the jewelled minds of their children to the keeping of a stranger, with scarcely a thought of the fidelity of the keeper.

You have, now, madam, my idea of the duties of a governess—of her hard, her earnest, yet rewardful labours. As to her treatment, she is—if conscientious in her vocation—a gentle-woman. She has within her trust the greatest treasures that human life—with all its pride—can know: the hearts, and, indeed, the future souls of children. As her mission is a noble one, respect and courtesy are hers by right. To look upon her as a better-dressed drudge is, in very truth, not poorest insolence alone, but darkest error. Her patient, quiet labours, are to insure the best triumphs of life; for they make, or should make, good daughters, good wives, good mothers. In these the truthfulness and happiness of the world have, surely, some stake, and are, indeed, her lasting debtors.

I have heard many stories of the contumely, the hard-dealing of the world towards the governess. It was not so in *my* home—and, if only for the sake of woman, I must hope such tales are over-charged. For if, indeed, the poor governess be this frequent sufferer, to whom does she owe the misery, but to sister-woman? Of whom has she to complain of coldness of looks, harshness of words, of all the petty, reckless injuries that sting her daily life,—of all the scorn of pride, and arrogance of apathetic wealth? Why, to woman; to her richer sister; to one of her own sex—made hard, exacting, by undeserved good fortune. This is a scandal, madam, that women should rise against and defy; or if not, they must, in truth, remain unconscionable debtors to the poets.

With many thanks, madam, for the interest you have taken in our broken fortunes,

> I remain, yours gratefully,
> MARY WILTON.

# LETTER XXXI.

FROM A BISHOP TO A YOUNG FRIEND ABOUT TO TAKE ORDERS.

DEAR BASIL,—I have learned, with exceeding gladness, of your excellent father, that it is your determination to enter the Church. From what I know of your nature, I feel assured that this resolve is not the impulse of a vagrant, unthinking disposition, but the goodly fruit of a mind disciplined, and chastened of those vanities which, at your age, too commonly beset mankind. Believing that your election is that of an ardent and purified spirit, I hail it rejoicingly.

My dear young friend, be grateful—yea, in your inmost soul, be grateful—that you have been directed to a choice which, whilst it will abound with life-long satisfaction to yourself, will make you a daily providential comfort to your fellow-creatures. There is a happiness in this belief, too deep, too awful for any words of mine—a happiness only to be felt in the heart of consecrates.

From the moment of your ordination, you are set apart from the gross, vain, foolish desires of men; you are made a teacher and a watcher of your kind—the counsel, the reproof of the pastor, directed and softened by the love and sympathy of a brother. There is no despair so wild that the music of your comforting may not tame to gentleness and hope; there is no heart so stony that, smitten by your word, may not be made to gush with a living stream. High privilege—glorious prerogative, that makes man the mediator with Heaven—that gives him strength to raise from the dust the faint, crushed, guilt-defiled heart, assuring it a home and resting-place among the stars!

From how many blighting evils, cancerous cares, will your high office preserve you! You will see men pursuing vain wealth and vainer honours, even as little boys hunt butterflies: with frantic glee they seize the thing pursued, and it is worthless in their grasp. Whilst you, rich in the spirit that is within you, upraised by the dignity of the awful future, will smile, though not in pride, but with abounding pity, with compassionating love. To you poverty itself will be a robe of highest state: and though most frugal be your board, yet, as with the patriarch, angels may feast with you, though men know them not.

In every stage of mortal life, you are the elected comforter, adviser of mankind. Your glorious and beautiful mission begins with the babe that shrinks and wails beneath the baptismal water, nor ends but with the blessing prayer that leaves the image of man to become again dust. From the font to the grave how many the calls—how many the necessities of your infirm and erring brother—for that hope, that consolation, of which you are the chosen phial! How beautiful your daily intercourse with those who feed and thrive upon your sayings! How sweet that gentle familiarity that mixes itself in the working-day life of the poor; that with soft greetings and kindly smiles claims kindred with the meanest of the earth as fellow-sojourners in future heaven!——And now, hark! it is black midnight, and the tempest howls and claws like a famished wolf at your door. The thunder rolls, crashing above your roof! The lightning opens up the sky in one wide vault of fire—and now it is dark, and the wind moans like a despairing soul. There is a loud and urgent knocking at your door—again—again! Alas, dear sir, there is a poor creature, a cotter, one of your flock, in his last agony. His soul must from his flesh this awful night, and he begs your comforting, your benediction on its solemn journey.

You spring from your bed. Your cloak is old—thin almost as a web; nathless, you hug it closely around you, and with stout heart and composed soul follow your guide through path and no path—bog and mire. The thunder splits above you—the lightning chases your steps: but like a good spirit sent on God's own errand, you pass scathless on. You enter the hut of the dying; you comfort and strengthen the quivering soul. It departs to the Great Source it came from. And then in peace and prayer you retrace your steps, and sleep the sleep of the good.

But your own heart, my dear young friend, will best find out your duties. You will feel that every moment of your life must be a living example to all men. You must feel that your daily actions are as a mirror by which your flock are to dress their souls: that your every gesture should be gentle—your every word soft and sweet even as a note of well-touched music. Your life must be the active comment on the text you are sworn to, or your life is naught.

What! is there a man vowed to that text, who, worse than a hireling player, acts his part yet never feels it? Does he dress himself for some brief hour or so, to ape a mission? Is his daily life coarse chaffering? Is he a swiller at taverns? Does he, with embossed face, tell Cyprian[8] tales, laugh-

8 Cyprian, licentious.

ing the loudest at his noisome jest? Can there be such a man, and can he on the seventh day, with unabashed forehead, tempt God's thunder? No —it is impossible. He who says there is, gently rebuke. Say, "some enemy hath done this."

My dear Basil, I have endeavoured to place before you your duties as the parish pastor of a flock. Providence may, however, raise you to the bench. Yes, Basil; you may become a bishop. Nevertheless, seek not the dignity; nay, pray that it may never fall upon you. In your mid-day walks —in your closet—in your bed, let your constant ejaculation be—*Nolo episcopari.* Sweet, most sweet, is the humblest curacy—dangerous and difficult the richest see. How far happier—how more truly primitive the pastor of a Welsh mountain, than the bishop of even golden Durham![9] And the bishop—be assured of it—thinks so.

Nevertheless, I will suppose it your hard destiny to become a bishop. Power and wealth are poured upon you. Gold trickles in upon your treasury from a hundred curious crevices—from chinks, that in sooth might sometimes astonish the fathers. You cannot bless even so much churchyard clay, but that the clay, like a Potosi mine, shall render you so much gold. You would be bewildered by your wealth—you would weep in anguish of spirit at your riches, but that you always have with you the ignorant to teach—the poor to succour. Hence, you may with sweetest conscience clutch all the money you can; for why? As a bishop, are you not the almoner of Providence? Do not the hungry cluster at your gate? Send you not away the naked clothed and rejoicing? Oh, what a weight —a weight dragging the soul to earth would this mammon be, but that it stays not in the bishop's purse—but that, as the soft-hearted housewife feeds the winter birds, he scatters abroad his substance to the wretched and the suffering. Hence, being bishop, you may take all you can. Of course, you hold it but in trust. Every quarter your conscience audits the accounts with Heaven,—and you are serene, are happy in the humble sense of your own righteousness.

Being bishop, you are also law-maker. Beautiful, soul-exalting mission! You sit in the House of Lords as a Superior Intelligence; superior by the charity for all men that resides within you! Hence, you defile not yourself with politics. The lawn of the bishop is never, like the coat of Joseph, parti-coloured. The bishop knows no one side of the human heart. No; he is for humanity in all its breadth, and in all its depth. Hence, when lords talk of war, and tiger-looks steal into the eyes of men,

9 Durham, a county in northern England, on the North Sea between the Tees and Tyne rivers; after the Norman Conquest the county was organized as a palatinate under the bishops of Durham and was governed as such until 1836.

the awful bishop rises from his seat, and with a voice of thunder denounces the abomination. And then with tearful eyes, and with a voice broken with the heart's spasms, he shows the blasphemy of murderous war—paints in their own diabolic hues thousands and thousands of drilled and hireling Cains butchering their brothers! And thus the bishop sometimes—only sometimes—melts the House of Lords!

And now, my dear young friend, I have—though most imperfectly—laid before you the many blessings which await you in the Church, which, rightly ministered, is the vestibule to an immortal life. That you may serve in it with glory to yourself, and with profit to all men, is the prayer of

Yours affectionately,

SAMUEL OF ———.

## LETTER XXXII.

### THE ANSWER.

MY DEAR SIR,—It is impossible that I can sufficiently thank you for your letter. I have been all along in a sad mistake. My family having, by marriage, a snug thing or two in the Church, I thought it a good investment of the little talent I may possess. I don't boast of much—but at a fox-hunt I was never yet out at the death, and at a steeple-chase never *craned*[10] at anything. I therefore thought I might manage to rub on very well in canonicals; but, really, you have thrown so many difficulties in my way, that I certainly must give the clergy the go-by.

With thanks, however, for your very long letter,

I remain, yours truly,

BASIL JOLLY.

P.S.—They tell me I've the gift of gab—I think I shall go to the bar.

## LETTER XXXIII.

### FROM A YOUNG MAN ENTERING BUSINESS TO A RETIRED TRADESMAN.

RESPECTED SIR,—When we last met, you were kind enough to say that the benefit of your long experience in business should be always at my serv-

10 *craned*, hesitated.

ice; and that as the friend of my poor late father, it would always be a pleasure to you to advise his son. At the same time you desired me to give you my notions of the duties of a tradesman to the world and to himself, that you might at the onset correct my errors, and strengthen my judgment. I therefore hasten to comply with your request.

Of course, sir, I consider the old schoolboy copy that "Honesty is the best policy"[11] to be the golden rule of life, and that the shortest way from one point to another is always in a straight line. Hence, it will ever be my pride to let my practice illustrate this beautiful sentiment. I do not see why a shop may not be made a temple of truth—and cannot understand why a falsehood "in the way of business" is not, after all, a falsehood in all its bearings. Lies are lies, and no outside skin-deep gilding will give to the base metal the value of the precious ore. I have, I am sorry to say, known tradesmen with great wrathfulness nail a proffered pocket-piece to their counter,—and still from their own mouths continue to issue counterfeit truths—in fact, do nothing but speak pocket-pieces. Yes, sir; I have known them to do this, and never blush or stammer when their eye has fallen on the copper countenance of the false half-crown, gleaming reproachfully upon them. But then, to pass bad money is a statuteable offence—whilst to pass lies for truths, if adroitly uttered from behind the counter, is nothing more than to do a clever stroke of business. The one practice has led men to the gallows—the other has taken them to the Bank of England.

"All in the way of trade" is, I know, a phrase that covers great hypocrisy, great practical deceit, great injustice between man and man. It is a convenient phrase, that from long custom has become an allowed apology for the trickeries of dealers. But a highwayman, who takes a purse, might as well believe that the black crape which hides his face from the knowledge of the despoiled, does also hide from his own soul a knowledge of his iniquity. How often is the "way of trade" no other than so much black crape worn behind the counter! A man may be as completely robbed by means of a false protestation, as though the lie were a loaded pistol.

There is, I know, a tenderness in the law towards the trippings of trade, that seems to show a positive sympathy between law and roguery. Men, it would almost seem, by general understanding, allow the necessity of wrong as a proper alloy to keep society together. Pure unmixed gold is too good for coin that is to suffer the wear and tear of passing

---

11 Cervantes, *Don Quixote*, pt. II, bk. III, ch. 33.

from hand to hand; and so, that it may endure the longer, it is mingled with a little wholesome copper. In the like way, law seems to think pure honesty as altogether too refined for the hard working-day purposes of trade, and therefore looks indulgently upon its little shifts—its winning "ways." Let me further explain myself.

My opposite neighbour is a chandler and green-grocer: he makes his gains out of the veriest poor. Rags and keenest hunger are his miserable customers. You should think, sir, that when a tradesman held the scales for such buyers, justice would be to him a high religion. Well, sir, it was only yesterday that this very man was found to use false weights. It was his third offence; and he was fined by the compassionating law—ten pounds!

This same man has at the present moment a boy in gaol, doomed for six months, for stealing from his shop, when very hungry, one red herring. Thus, the tradesman may rob by means of scales and measures, merely paying for a sort of license to cheat, when detected: the very gains of his iniquity, too, go to lessen the fine; he can, in fact, with tolerable luck, afford to rob. Now, does not law that makes such robbery only fineable, look most tenderly upon the evil-doing? Does it not give a marked preference to the thief behind the counter above the picker and stealer before it? Hence—use light weights, and pay money for the theft; filch with your five fingers, and do hard-labour in gaol. Besides, the tradesman is sweetened—purified by the fine; the stain upon his reputation is blotted up by bank-paper: now the vulgar thief always bears about him the foul odour of a prison. The keen nostrils of the police continually smell in him his first iniquity.

Now, sir, it will be my endeavour, as a tradesman, to acknowledge no "ways of trade"—to consider truth as truth in the smallest as in the greatest affairs of life. With this belief, I shall take my daily stand behind the counter, and cheerfully leave to Providence the rest. Tell me, dear sir, if I am not right,

And believe me, yours sincerely,
JOHN BALANCE.

## LETTER XXXIV.

### ANSWER TO THE ABOVE.

MR. JOHN BALANCE,—I have known you from a boy—yes, from a very babe—and I did not think you capable of insulting the friend of your excellent father. Worthy soul! it is a good thing that he is out of the world: he is, it is my belief, saved that worst of all sorrows—a headlong, disobedient child. Your letter is enough to make him shiver in his coffin.

I can well understand your insinuation about the false weights. It is base and cruel. To me, with honourable grey hairs upon my head! To me, almost old enough to be your grandfather! It is true, that, in my time, I was fined, I think three times; but then, I always proved that the false weights had been substituted by a malicious servant. The fines were certainly never returned to me; but there was not one well-disposed person of the Sunday congregation—and twice a-day, Mr. John Balance, did I appear in my pew, reserving my evening of rest to look over my books—not one of them who did not believe in my innocence. But then, I always studied respectability.

Your notions of business are the notions of a noodle. Truth is very beautiful no doubt, but if stark-naked truth was always to stand behind a counter, I should like to know who'd go into the shop. I know the value of truth as well as any man. And throughout my long and useful life I always used it as the dear late partner of my joys used her silver teapot—upon holiday occasions. I had too much respect for the real value of truth to be always bringing it out upon working-days.

You have no knowledge of the real talent required by a tradesman, and therefore I should advise you to go to sea, or list for a soldier. There is nothing so worthy of the attention of man—of his immortal spirit, as the Reverend Mr. Doublechin used to call it—as business. It employs all the strength of the soul—for the end and aim of all business is for man to look upon the rest of the world as only so many people to make so much money of. He is to consider them—that is, in a business way—as made especially for his own profit as a tradesman. And so, if he has only common sense, he is to use it as he best can for his own advantage. As for what you stupidly call lies, I always looked upon them as necessary tools for business—things without which it would be impossible to keep open shop. Lies are a sort of wooden pegs that keep the world together as if it was a box; nice little things, so let into the work as never to be seen. Take out the pegs, and how would the box tumble to pieces!

When you are really come to years of discretion, you will know that the private man and the tradesman are not at all one. Certainly not. I, Isaac Smirk, behind the counter, was not the Isaac Smirk dressed for church on Sundays. How could I be? How was I to bring up a large family—as yet you don't know the expense of clothing and schooling six children—in respectability, if I'd played the antics you talk of? No; trade is one thing, and what we call morals are another. Six days for business, and the seventh for religious duties. That, Mr. John Balance, has always been my motto; and following it, I never yet had a bill protested, but became in time what I now am—a respectable, happy man, who can lay his hand upon his heart and say he has thirty thousand pounds: a man who has married his daughters to fortunes, and, moreover, subscribes to—it isn't for me to say how many charities.

Looking at your letter as the madness of a green boy, I have condescended to answer it at this length. I trust that years and experience may make you see the error of your ways. That they may do so, is the hope of

Your still well-wisher,
Isaac Smirk.

## LETTER XXXV.

### FROM A MATRON TO A NEWLY-MARRIED YOUNG LADY ON THE TREATMENT OF A HUSBAND.

My dear Claribel,—Your honeymoon being over, I feel it my duty—as, indeed, it will be my pleasure—to instruct you in the serious purposes of marriage. I have had my trials, my dear, in what is called the blessed state, and could if I chose write this letter in the tears of widowhood. Three times have I been bereft of the tenderest of husbands—for every one of the dear men was really so—and now am I left like the lonely dove to murmur alone. I have, however, this satisfaction, to know that I managed them all to my heart's content, whilst they—dear, simple lambs!—believed they managed me.

Men in their extreme ignorance call us the weaker sex. The weaker sex! When—and they know it—we can pull and play with their hearts'-strings as little children play with toy harlequins. However, never disabuse them of the fond conceit. Our weakness, as they are pleased to call it, is our best strength. Continue to make your husband think you the most delicate of creatures, and he will treasure you accordingly. We all of us seem pretty well to know and follow out this truth in days of courtship, but forget it almost as soon as the clerk has said Amen. This, my dear girl, is the great error of our sex: it is this that makes wife the slave and husband the master. Now it has ever been my plan to perpetuate the privilege that courtship gives us, throughout every day of wedlock. And very properly. What! is your lap-dog that obediently fetches and carries

—is he suddenly to refuse to obey you, and only because you have put a collar round his neck, and hold him by the ring of a chain at your third finger? Therefore, my dear, let your nerves be always delicate: hence, your husband will treasure you like a precious piece of china. Be foolish enough to appear robust, and, on the contrary, you will have no more care bestowed upon you than a red clay pipkin.

There are, I know, brutes in the human form, not to be deceived; but your husband is, I trust, not of them. As a girl, I remember a monster of the sort. My own dear mother—from whom, let me confess it, I learned many precious lessons—she made as much as any woman of her nerves. Well, one day, my father poking the fire, down came—as you know, sometimes, they will come, with such a clatter—the shovel and tongs. My mother screamed, declared my father wanted to get rid of her, and immediately retired to her chamber. Though a party was to dine with us, my mother—true to her principles—resolutely went to bed. My father was all self-reproach and sorrow. He related the unfortunate event to the monster I speak of, saying something about "the wear and tear of the female constitution." Whereupon, I shall never forget it, the wretch replied—"Pooh—pooh! Female constitution! It never wears, it never tears: at the worst it only stretches." And this—their conduct proves it—is the brutal faith of thousands. My dear father, however, was of the contrary belief; so well too did my dear mother manage, that after this fall of the shovel and tongs, he never after poked the fire as if the poker was really his own. And this is as it should be.

Hence, my dear girl, cultivate your nerves: you can't pet 'em too much. Something will always be happening in the house,—and unless your husband be worse than a stone,—every new fright will be as good as a new gown or a new trinket to you. There are some domestic wounds only to be healed by the jeweller.

I don't advise you not to love your husband, very much—but never show the abundance of it. How men impose upon what I call a superfluity of affection, it is dreadful to think of! No; there is a decent sort of tenderness—a sort of tepid love—that is the safest. It never permits a wife to commit herself; it never shows to the man that he is supreme in her affections, and so enables him to sport with them. However, do not let him think himself indifferent to you: certainly not; at least, let the poor man have the benefit of the doubt.

In the slightest case of sisterly frailty, be all indignation. It is the very easiest and cheapest way of airing your own excessive goodness. Now and then, too, you can—with great pain to yourself, of course—hazard suspicions of some of your acquaintance. Suspicion, skilfully used, is an excellent thing. Like a little dust of rouge, if very tenderly laid on, it throws out in fine relief the natural beauty of the wearer. Rouge is a darling little fib, that lies, as somebody says, like truth—and so, too, I take it, if properly applied, is a slight suspicion. They may both colour false modesty.

There is, too, a sort of side-wind way that will enable you at once to please and tease your husband. Jealousy—that is, a happy affectation of the passion—is a wonderful weapon in a skilful hand. Therefore, when walking with the poor man declare that he looks at every woman he meets, and sulk accordingly. Sometimes, however, vary the accusation, and declare that every woman he meets looks at him. From this assumed fact, you can make any deductions, and endeavour in a torrent of words to declare how very, very miserable you ought to be. The man, of course, must think himself dear to you, or wherefore such fantastic jealousy? He must feel, though with a feeling of wretchedness, that you love him; or wherefore show the love with so much misery to him? Does not puss love the live yet wounded mouse she bites and scratches?

Again, as to temper, never let it be certain. Husbands—I know them—presume upon evenness of temper. No, let your husband feel that he is never safe. He will accordingly be gentle, watchful, in his manner. Hence, be at times in the most exuberant spirits; and then, with a thought—at some unconscious look of your husband, some playful word —have a mute tongue, and brows of threatening thunder. In your very gayest moments, let your helpmate feel as if he is called upon to admire some curious gun—very beautiful, but to be most carefully handled, lest it go off, and destroy him.

If your husband wishes for music, declare you have a sudden head-ache, and add this, he ought to have seen as much, and not have asked you. If, on the contrary, he has a book, or would doze by the fire, immediately play the *"Battle of Prague,"*[12] with all the cannon accompaniments.

If he wish you to go out with him, say he always asks you when he knows you can't go; and then, on the contrary, desire that he shall take you to the opera or play, when you are well aware that he has some previous engagement.

On this point, too, be particularly obdurate. When your husband goes out with a likelihood of returning home late, insist upon sitting up for

12 *"Battle of Prague,"* a well-known piano piece during the nineteenth century; by the Bohemian composer, Franz Kotzwara (1730–1791).

him. He may urge, that he can take the key; that, in fact, it will annoy him to keep anybody from their bed. Meet all this with a cold, decisive assurance, that you *will* sit up for him. If he come home late, what a delicious triumph for you! There you are, my love—*I* always was—in your nightcap and wrapped in three shawls, making up yourself for the picture of a very much wronged woman. The culprit at length returns; you catch his eye, and lead it to dwell upon the reproachful candle guttering in the socket—that candle, which in very weariness of heart and for nothing else, you have every five minutes mangled with the snuffers, as though unconsciously to make the case all the stronger against your offending mate. Sometimes, on such occasions, say nothing, but cold as a statue walk up-stairs. Sometimes, too, it will add considerably to the pain of the criminal, if you carefully draw a sigh, and "wish you were in your grave."

As for your husband's friends, give them always a chilling welcome. If now and then they insist upon staying, as you think, late,—declare that they have had wine enough, and they ought to know it.

My dear mother had an admirable way. Two or three times—for my father never tempted her oftener—she sat up guarding the fire-place. No coal did she suffer to approach it. The fire went out: it was piercing winter; and then in a triumph only known to such a wife, did she retire to her room, comforting herself that "They'd soon be starved out, and must go."

I have herein, my love, thrown down only a few hints; but I can add a great many more to them, if I find you worthy of my teaching.

In the mean time, I remain your affectionate friend,
TABITHA TALONS.

## LETTER XXXVI.

### THE YOUNG LADY'S ANSWER.

MADAM,—At present, I have no wish that my husband should leave me; when I have, I shall lose no time in availing myself of your instructions, feeling quite convinced that they could not but very soon lead to such a conclusion.

I remain, yours, &c.,
CLARIBEL SMITH.

# LETTER XXXVII.

FROM A YOUNG GENTLEMAN, SOLICITING HIS FATHER
TO PAY HIS DEBTS.

My dear Father,—How often have you told me that I should see my folly! Indeed, sir, you are a true prophet. I never thought it possible that I could look upon the world as now, in very truth, I find it—a deceitful, hollow, seductive place, in which there is nothing worthy of the mind of man, save those inestimable comforts which, had I but followed your wise and excellent counsel, I should by this time have been in the enjoyment of. Ah, sir! there are many young men who, in their worst misfortunes—and can there be worse than debt?—are nevertheless spared the remorse which at this moment preys upon your wretched son. They—poor fellows!—may have been launched upon the sea of life—as you have often pertinently called this vale of tears—without rudder or compass; with nothing, sir, to direct or counsel them. It is no wonder when such men suffer shipwreck, or are stripped by pirates. But, sir, I vainly seek a single comforting excuse. I have had the best of men and kindest of fathers, who has bestowed upon me advice of greater value than pearls—more precious than gold. And yet how headstrong, wild, and vicious—yes, sir, I blush to write it—vicious I have been, reckless of those inestimable precepts which of themselves ought to have enriched me with a treasure more lasting than wealth. But, sir, at length I am convinced. Yes, sir, my eyes are opened, and I now behold the precipice on which I stand. Another step or two and I had been lost for ever. But there is yet time to draw back—yes, sir, aided by your parental hand—there is, I fondly hope, yet time for me to regain all that I have lost: except, indeed, the precious hours that, as you once beautifully expressed it, I have cast away like water in the sea.

I write, sir, as you will perceive, from a prison. Ha! my honoured father, it is—I humbly believe—impossible even for you to imagine the change that prison walls have worked in me. They have softened my heart—they have made me take an inside look into myself—they have shown me, written with a terrible hand, the long, long list of all my vices, all my follies: they have—but I cannot pursue the theme. The very recollection of the pain I have caused you almost makes me drop the pen abashed; nevertheless, I will struggle with my feelings, and, if only for penance, try to proceed.

With all my sufferings, I nevertheless try to feel grateful to my creditors who have placed me here. There are, I am sorry to write it, young men in this prison upon whom the moral of the place (as I call it) seems entirely lost. They give themselves up to the most reckless enjoyments; they drink—for, somehow, drink *is* smuggled—they game, they play at racket;—in fact, they sink from bad to worse, and when they return to the world, they will, I fear, visit it more like pests, than as reformed, rational creatures. Again and again have I been tempted by some of these brawlers to join in what they madly call their pleasures. But no, sir; I trust I am not wholly lost. Hitherto, I have lived as much as possible apart from all—I have read, sir, read the *one* Book, which it was your best advice to me always to read. There are lost young men in this place who say a father—"governor" is their slang expression—is a person made by Providence only to pay his son's bills: I hope, sir, that I have a truer, a nobler notion of the uses of a parent. I fervently trust that in entreating of you for this, the third and last time, to pay my debts, you will believe me when I assure you that I do this with the greatest reverence for your parental character—with (whether you grant or refuse my prayer) abounding gratitude for all that you have accomplished for a hitherto unworthy son.

I assure you, dear sir, this time my penitence is profound. From my present feelings, I know I can withstand all future temptations. "Ha, ha!" cried one of the spendthrifts here, "you'll soon get tired of this moping, miserable life; you'll soon be a jolly, roaring, drinking dog like one of us." But no, sir! although this prison should be my grave, it shall at least be the tomb of a penitent.

With many burning blushes I enclose you a list of all my debts—really all; pay them, my dearest father, and be assured of the gratitude and obedience of

> Your erring, but affectionate son,
> CHARLES BUTTER.

P.S.—I have been urged to liberate myself as a bankrupt; but I trust, sir, I can still feel like your son—can still respect the honour of the family. I'll die first.

## LETTER XXXVIII.

### THE FATHER'S ANSWER.

SIR,—You have seen your folly so often that, it is evident, by this time you are quite accustomed to it. All your long letter may be boiled down like spinach, into three words, "Pay my debts." All the rest is mere flourish—mere palaver. No, sir; you may break my heart, but you shall not break my fortune. I'll not pay a single sixpence.

I am, your affectionate Father,
JOHN BUTTER.

P.S.—You may become a bankrupt as soon as you please. Thank heaven! the honour of the family is too secure to be injured by such an unprincipled spendthrift. Not a sixpence, sir—not a single sixpence.


## LETTER XXXIX.

### FROM THE YOUNG GENTLEMAN'S MOTHER.

MY BELOVED BOY,—I hav'n't slept a wink since you've been in that horrid place. I hadn't yet dared to speak to your father, but I saved your letter, which, in a dreadful rage, he threw upon the fire. Ha! my dear boy, that letter made me almost happy. With the abilities you have to write such a letter, what might you not do in this world! If you would only be your own friend, what could stand in your way?

But I please myself in the belief that your repentance is sincere. I am heartily glad that you have nothing to do with the riotous and sinful set about you: most glad to find that you neither drink, nor game, nor do anything but read that *one* Book. Continue to do so, my dear boy, and depend upon it your father sha'n't have a minute's rest in his own house until you are again among us. God bless you!

Your affectionate Mother,
MARTHA BUTTER.

P.S.—I send you 10£. I hope this time that your list of debts is quite correct: that you have put all down: for you know how you deceived your poor father twice before.

RS. CAUDLE'S CURTAIN LECTURES*

## INTRODUCTION.

Poor Job Caudle was one of the few men whom Nature, in her casual
bounty to women, sends into the world as patient listeners. He was, perhaps, in more respects than one, all ears. And these ears, Mrs. Caudle—
his lawful, wedded wife, as she would ever and anon impress upon him,
for she was not a woman to wear chains without shaking them—took
whole and sole possession of. They were her entire property; as expressly made to convey to Caudle's brain the stream of wisdom that continually flowed from the lips of his wife, as was the tin funnel through
which Mrs. Caudle in vintage time bottled her elder wine. There was,
however, this difference between the wisdom and the wine. The wine
was always sugared: the wisdom, never. It was expressed crude from the
heart of Mrs. Caudle; who, doubtless, trusted to the sweetness of her husband's disposition to make it agree with him.

Philosophers have debated whether morning or night is most condu-
cive to the strongest and clearest moral impressions. The Grecian sage
confessed that his labours smelt of the lamp.[1] In like manner, did Mrs.
Caudle's wisdom smell of the rushlight. She knew that her husband was
too much distracted by his business as toy-man and doll-merchant to digest her lessons in the broad day. Besides, she could never make sure of
him: he was always liable to be summoned to the shop. Now from eleven
at night until seven in the morning, there was no retreat for him. He was
compelled to lie and listen. Perhaps there was little magnanimity in this

*The Writings of Douglas Jerrold (8 vols.; London, 1851–1858), III, ix–97.
    1 In Plutarch's Lives, Pytheas refers to the orations of Demosthenes as smelling of
the lamp, since the orator supposedly worked in an underground cave lighted only by
a lamp.

on the part of Mrs. Caudle; but in marriage, as in war, it is permitted to take every advantage of the enemy. Besides, Mrs. Caudle copied very ancient and classic authority. Minerva's bird, the very wisest thing in feathers, is silent all the day. So was Mrs. Caudle. Like the owl, she hooted only at night.

Mr. Caudle was blessed with an indomitable constitution. One fact will prove the truth of this. He lived thirty years with Mrs. Caudle, surviving her. Yes, it took thirty years for Mrs. Caudle to lecture and dilate upon the joys, griefs, duties, and vicissitudes comprised within that seemingly small circle—the wedding-ring. We say, seemingly small; for the thing, as viewed by the vulgar, naked eye, is a tiny hoop made for the third feminine finger. Alack! like the ring of Saturn, for good or evil it circles a whole world. Or to take a less gigantic figure, it compasses a vast region: it may be Arabia Felix, and it may be Arabia Petrea.

A lemon-hearted cynic might liken the wedding-ring to an ancient Circus, in which wild animals clawed one another for the sport of lookers-on. Perish the hyperbole! We would rather compare it to an elfin ring, in which dancing fairies made the sweetest music for infirm humanity.

Manifold are the uses of rings. Even swine are tamed by them. You will see a vagrant, hilarious, devastating porker—a full-blooded fellow that would bleed into many, many fathoms of black pudding—you will see him, escaped from his proper home, straying in a neighbour's garden. How he tramples upon the heart's-ease: how, with quivering snout, he roots up lilies—odoriferous bulbs! Here he gives a reckless snatch at thyme and marjoram—and here he munches violets and gillyflowers. At length the marauder is detected, seized by his owner, and driven, beaten home. To make the porker less dangerous, it is determined that he shall be *ringed*. The sentence is pronounced—execution ordered. Listen to his screams!

> Would you not think the knife was in his throat?
> And yet they're only boring through his nose!

Hence, for all future time, the porker behaves himself with a sort of forced propriety—for in either nostril he carries a ring. It is, for the greatness of humanity, a saddening thought, that sometimes men must be treated no better than pigs.

But Mr. Job Caudle was not of these men. Marriage to him was not made a necessity. No; for him call it if you will a happy chance—a golden accident. It is, however, enough for us to know that he was married;

and was therefore made the recipient of a wife's wisdom. Mrs. Caudle, like Mahomet's dove, continually pecked at the good man's ears; and it is a happiness to learn from what he left behind that he had hived all her sayings in his brain; and further, that he employed the mellow evening of his life to put such sayings down, that, in due season they might be enshrined in imperishable type.

When Mr. Job Caudle was left in this briary world without his daily guide and nocturnal monitress, he was in the ripe fulness of fifty-two. For three hours at least after he went to bed—such slaves are we to habit—he could not close an eye. His wife still talked at his side. True it was, she was dead and decently interred. His mind—it was a comfort to know it—could not wander on this point; this he knew. Nevertheless, his wife was with him. The Ghost of her Tongue still talked as in the life; and again and again did Job Caudle hear the monitions of by-gone years. At times, so loud, so lively, so real were the sounds, that Job, with a cold chill, doubted if he were really widowed. And then, with the movement of an arm, a foot, he would assure himself that he was alone in his holland. Nevertheless, the talk continued. It was terrible to be thus haunted by a voice: to have advice, commands, remonstrance, all sorts of saws and adages still poured upon him, and no visible wife. Now did the voice speak from the curtains; now from the tester; and now did it whisper to Job from the very pillow that he pressed. "It's a dreadful thing that her tongue should walk in this manner," said Job, and then he thought confusedly of exorcism, or at least of counsel from the parish priest.

Whether Job followed his own brain, or the wise direction of another, we know not. But he resolved every night to commit to paper one curtain lecture of his late wife. The employment would, possibly, lay the ghost that haunted him. It was her dear tongue that cried for justice, and when thus satisfied, it might possibly rest in quiet. And so it happened. Job faithfully chronicled all his late wife's lectures; the ghost of her tongue was thenceforth silent, and Job slept all his after nights in peace.

When Job died, a small packet of papers was found inscribed as follows:—

> *Curtain Lectures delivered in the course of Thirty Years by*
> *Mrs. Margaret Caudle, and suffered by Job, her Husband.*

That Mr. Caudle had his eye upon the future printer, is made pretty probable by the fact that in most places he had affixed the text—such text for the most part arising out of his own daily conduct—to the lecture of the night. He had also, with an instinctive knowledge of the dignity of literature, left a bank-note of very fair amount with the manuscript. Following our duty as editor, we trust we have done justice to both documents.

## LECTURE I.

### MR. CAUDLE HAS LENT FIVE POUNDS TO A FRIEND.

"You ought to be very rich, Mr. Caudle. I wonder who'd lend you five pounds? But so it is: a wife may work and may slave! Ha, dear! the many things that might have been done with five pounds. As if people picked up money in the street! But you always were a fool, Mr. Caudle! I've wanted a black satin gown these three years, and that five pounds would have entirely bought it. But it's no matter how I go,—not at all. Everybody says I don't dress as becomes your wife—and I don't; but what's that to you, Mr. Caudle? Nothing. Oh no! you can have fine feelings for everybody but those belonging to you. I wish people knew you, as I do—that's all. You like to be called liberal—and your poor family pays for it.

"All the girls want bonnets, and where they're to come from I can't tell. Half five pounds would have bought 'em—but now they must go without. Of course, *they* belong to you: and anybody but your own flesh and blood, Mr. Caudle!

"The man called for the water-rate to-day; but I should like to know how people are to pay taxes, who throw away five pounds to every fellow that asks them?

"Perhaps you don't know that Jack, this morning, knocked his shuttlecock through his bed-room window. I was going to send for the glazier to mend it; but after you lent that five pounds I was sure we couldn't afford it. Oh, no! the window must go as it is; and pretty weather for a dear child to sleep with a broken window. He's got a cold already on his lungs, and I shouldn't at all wonder if that broken window settled him. If the dear boy dies, his death will be upon his father's head; for I'm sure we can't now pay to mend windows. We might though, and do a good many more things, too, if people didn't throw away their five pounds.

"Next Tuesday the fire-insurance is due. I should like to know how it's to be paid? Why, it can't be paid at all! That five pounds would have more than done it—and now, insurance is out of the question. And there never were so many fires as there are now. I shall never close my eyes all night,—but what's that to you, so people can call you liberal, Mr. Caudle? Your wife and children may all be burnt alive in their beds—as all of us to a certainty shall be, for the insurance *must* drop. And after we've insured for so many years! But how, I should like to know, are people to insure who make ducks and drakes of their five pounds?

"I did think we might go to Margate this summer. There's poor little Caroline, I'm sure she wants the sea. But no, dear creature! she must stop at home—all of us must stop at home—she'll go into a consumption, there's no doubt of that; yes—sweet little angel!—I've made up my mind to lose her, *now*. The child might have been saved; but people can't save their children and throw away their five pounds too.

"I wonder where poor little Mopsy is? While you were lending that five pounds, the dog ran out of the shop. You know, I never let it go into the street, for fear it should be bit by some mad dog, and come home and bite all the children. It wouldn't now at all astonish me if the animal was to come back with the hydrophobia, and give it to all the family. However, what's your family to you, so you can play the liberal creature with five pounds?

"Do you hear that shutter, how it's banging to and fro? Yes,—I know what it wants as well as you; it wants a new fastening. I was going to send for the blacksmith to-day, but now it's out of the question: *now* it must bang of nights, since you've thrown away five pounds.

"Ha! there's the soot falling down the chimney. If I hate the smell of anything, it's the smell of soot. And you know it; but what are my feelings to you? *Sweep the chimney!* Yes, it's all very fine to say, sweep the chimney—but how are chimneys to be swept—how are they to be paid for by people who don't take care of their five pounds?

"Do you hear the mice running about the room? *I* hear them. If they were to drag only you out of bed, it would be no matter. *Set a trap for them!* Yes, it's easy enough to say—set a trap for 'em. But how are people to afford mouse-traps, when every day they lose five pounds?

"Hark, I'm sure there's a noise down stairs. It wouldn't at all surprise me if there were thieves in the house. Well, it *may* be the cat; but thieves are pretty sure to come in some night. There's a wretched fastening to the back-door; but these are not times to afford bolts and bars, when people won't take care of their five pounds.

"Mary Anne ought to have gone to the dentist's to-morrow. She wants three teeth taken out. Now, it can't be done. Three teeth that quite disfigure the child's mouth. But there they must stop, and spoil the sweetest face that was ever made. Otherwise, she'd been a wife for a lord. Now, when she grows up, who'll have her? Nobody. We shall die, and leave her alone and unprotected in the world. But what do you care for that? Nothing; so you can squander away five pounds."

"And thus," comments Caudle, "according to my wife, she—dear soul!—couldn't have a satin gown—the girls couldn't have new bonnets—the water-rate must stand over—Jack must get his death through a broken window—our fire-insurance couldn't be paid, so that we should all fall victims to the devouring element—we couldn't go to Margate, and Caroline would go to an early grave—the dog would come home and bite us all mad—the shutter would go banging for ever—the soot would always fall—the mice never let us have a wink of sleep—thieves be always breaking in the house—our dear Mary Anne be for ever left an unprotected maid,—and with other evils falling upon us, all, all because I would go on lending five pounds!"

# LECTURE II.

MR. CAUDLE HAS BEEN AT A TAVERN WITH A FRIEND, AND "IS
ENOUGH TO POISON A WOMAN" WITH TOBACCO-SMOKE.

"I'M SURE I don't know who'd be a poor woman! I don't know who'd tie themselves up to a man, if they knew only half they'd have to bear. A wife must stay at home, and be a drudge, whilst a man can go anywhere. It's enough for a wife to sit like Cinderella by the ashes, whilst her husband can go drinking and singing at a tavern. *You never sing?* How do I know you never sing? It's very well for you to say so; but if I could hear you, I dare say you're among the worst of 'em.

"And now, I suppose, it will be the tavern every night? If you think I'm going to sit up for you, Mr. Caudle, you're very much mistaken. No: and I'm not going to get out of my warm bed to let you in, either. No: nor Susan shan't sit up for you. No: nor you shan't have a latch-key. I'm not going to sleep with the door upon the latch, to be murdered before the morning.

"Faugh! Pah! Whewgh! That filthy tobacco-smoke! It's enough to kill any decent woman. You know I hate tobacco, and yet you will do it. *You don't smoke yourself?* What of that? If you go among people who *do* smoke, you're just as bad, or worse. You might as well smoke—indeed better. Better smoke yourself than come home with other people's smoke all in your hair and whiskers.

"I never knew any good come to a man who went to a tavern. Nice companions he picks up there! Yes; people who make it a boast to treat their wives like slaves, and ruin their families. There's that wretch, Harry Prettyman. See what he's come to. He doesn't now get home till two in the morning; and then in what a state! He begins quarreling with the door-mat, that his poor wife may be afraid to speak to him. A mean wretch! But don't think I'll be like Mrs. Prettyman. No: I wouldn't put up with it from the best man that ever trod. You'll not make me afraid to speak to you, however you may swear at the door-mat. No, Mr. Caudle, that you won't.

*"You don't intend to stay out till two in the morning?* How do you know what you'll do when you get among such people? Men can't answer for themselves when they get boozing one with another. They never think of their poor wives, who are grieving and wearing themselves out at home. A nice headache you'll have to-morrow morning—or rather *this* morning; for it must be past twelve. *You won't have a headache?* It's very well for you to say so, but I know you will; and then you may nurse yourself for me. Ha! that filthy tobacco again! No; I shall not go to sleep like a good soul. How's people to go to sleep when they're suffocated?

"Yes, Mr. Caudle, you'll be nice and ill in the morning! But don't you think I'm going to let you have your breakfast in bed, like Mrs. Prettyman. I'll not be such a fool. No; nor I won't have discredit brought upon the house by sending for soda-water early, for all the neighbourhood to say, 'Caudle was drunk last night.' No: I've some regard for the dear children, if you havn't. No: nor you shan't have broth for dinner. Not a neck of mutton crosses my threshold, I can tell you.

*"You won't want soda, and you won't want broth?* All the better. You wouldn't get 'em if you did, I can assure you.——Dear, dear, dear! That filthy tobacco! I'm sure it's enough to make me as bad as you are. Talking about getting divorced,—I'm sure tobacco ought to be good grounds. How little does a woman think, when she marries, that she gives herself up to be poisoned! You men contrive to have it all of your own side, you do. Now if I was to go and leave you and the children, a pretty noise there'd be! You, however, can go and smoke no end of pipes and——*You didn't smoke?* It's all the same, Mr. Caudle, if you go among smoking people. Folks are known by their company. You'd better smoke yourself, than bring home the pipes of all the world.

"Yes, I see how it will be. Now you've once gone to a tavern, you'll always be going. You'll be coming home tipsy every night; and tumbling down and breaking your leg, and putting out your shoulder; and bringing all sorts of disgrace and expense upon us. And then you'll be getting into a street fight—oh! I know your temper too well to doubt it, Mr. Caudle—and be knocking down some of the police. And then I know what will follow. It *must* follow. Yes, you'll be sent for a month or six weeks to the treadmill. Pretty thing that, for a respectable tradesman, Mr. Caudle, to be put upon the treadmill with all sorts of thieves and vagabonds, and—there, again, that horrible tobacco!—and riffraff of every kind. I should like to know how your children are to hold up their heads, after their father has been upon the treadmill?——No. I *won't* go to sleep. And I'm not talking of what's impossible. I know it will all happen—every bit of it. If it wasn't for the dear children, you might be ruined and I wouldn't so much as speak about it, but—oh, dear, dear! at least you might go where they smoke *good* tobacco—but I can't forget that I'm their mother. At least, they shall have *one* parent.

"Taverns! Never did a man go to a tavern who didn't die a beggar. And how your pot-companions will laugh at you when they see your name in the Gazette! For it *must* happen. Your business is sure to fall off; for what respectable people will buy toys for their children of a drunkard? You're not a drunkard! No: but you will be—it's all the same.

"You've begun by staying out till midnight. By-and-by 'twill be all night. But don't you think, Mr. Caudle, you shall ever have a key. I know you. Yes; you'd do exactly like that Prettyman, and what did he do, only last Wednesday? Why, he let himself in about four in the morning, and brought home with him his pot-companion, Puffy. His dear wife woke at six, and saw Prettyman's dirty boots at her bed-side. And where was the wretch, her husband? Why, he was drinking down stairs—swilling. Yes; worse than a midnight robber, he'd taken the keys out of his dear wife's pockets—ha! what that poor creature has to bear!—and had got at the brandy. A pretty thing for a wife to wake at six in the morning, and instead of her husband to see his dirty boots!

"But I'll not be made your victim, Mr. Caudle, not I. You shall never get at my keys, for they shall lie under my pillow—under my own head, Mr. Caudle.

"You'll be ruined, but if I can help it, you shall ruin nobody but yourself.

"Oh! that hor—hor—hor—i—ble tob—ac——co!"

To this lecture, Caudle affixes no comment. A certain proof, we think, that the man had nothing to say for himself.

# LECTURE III.

"WELL, IF A WOMAN hadn't better be in her grave than be married! That is, if she can't be married to a decent man. No; I don't care if you are tired, I *shan't* let you go to sleep. No, and I won't say what I have to say in the morning; I'll say it now. It's all very well for you to come home at what time you like—it's now half-past twelve—and expect I'm to hold my tongue, and let you go to sleep. What next, I wonder? A woman had better be sold for a slave at once.

"And so you've gone and joined a club? The Skylarks, indeed! A pretty skylark you'll make of yourself! But I won't stay and be ruined by you. No: I'm determined on that. I'll go and take the dear children, and you may get who you like to keep your house. That is, as long as you have a house to keep—and that won't be long, I know.

"How any decent man can go and spend his nights in a tavern!—oh, yes, Mr. Caudle; I dare say you *do* go for rational conversation. I should like to know how many of you would care for what you call rational conversation, if you had it without your filthy brandy-and-water; yes, and your more filthy tobacco-smoke. I'm sure the last time you came home, I had the headache for a week. But I know who it is who's taking you to destruction. It's that brute, Prettyman. He has broken his own poor wife's heart, and now he wants to—but don't you think it, Mr. Caudle; I'll not have my peace of mind destroyed by the best man that ever trod. Oh, yes! I know you don't care so long as you can appear well to all the world,—but the world little thinks how you behave to me. It shall know it, though—that I'm determined.

"How any man can leave his own happy fireside to go and sit, and smoke, and drink, and talk with people who wouldn't one of 'em lift a finger to save him from hanging—how any man can leave his wife—and a good wife, too, though I say it—for a parcel of pot-companions—oh, it's disgraceful, Mr. Caudle; it's unfeeling. No man who had the least love for his wife could do it.

"And I suppose this is to be the case every Saturday? But I know what I'll do. I know—it's no use, Mr. Caudle, your calling me a good creature: I'm not such a fool as to be coaxed in that way. No; if you want to go to sleep, you should come home in Christian time, not at half-past twelve. There was a time, when you were as regular at your fireside as the kettle. That was when you were a decent man, and didn't go amongst Heaven knows who, drinking and smoking, and making what you think your jokes. I never heard any good come to a man who cared about jokes. No respectable tradesman does. But I know what I'll do: I'll scare away your Skylarks. The house serves liquor after twelve of a Saturday; and if I don't write to the magistrates, and have the license taken away, I'm not lying in this bed this night. Yes, you may call me a foolish woman; but no, Mr. Caudle, no; it's you who are the foolish man; or worse than a foolish man; you're a wicked one. If you were to die to-morrow—and people who go to public-houses do all they can to shorten their lives—I should like to know who would write upon your tombstone, 'A tender husband and an affectionate father?' I——I'd have no such falsehoods told of you, I can assure you.

"Going and spending your money, and—nonsense! don't tell me—no, if you were ten times to swear it, I wouldn't believe that you only spent eighteen-pence on a Saturday. You can't be all those hours, and only spend eighteen-pence. I know better. I'm not quite a fool, Mr. Caudle. A great deal you could have for eighteen-pence! And all the Club married men and fathers of families. The more shame for 'em! Skylarks, indeed! They should call themselves Vultures; for they can only do as they do by eating up their innocent wives and children. Eighteen-pence a week! And if it was only that,—do you know what fifty-two eighteen-pences come to in a year? Do you ever think of that, and see the gowns I wear? I'm sure I can't, out of the house-money, buy myself a pincushion; though I've wanted one these six months. No—not so much as a ball of cotton. But what do you care so you can get your brandy-and-water? There's the girls, too—the things they want! They're never dressed like other people's children. But it's all the same to their father. Oh yes! So he can go with his Skylarks they may wear sackcloth for pinafores, and packthread for garters.

"You'd better not let that Mr. Prettyman come here, that's all; or, rather, you'd better bring him once. Yes, I should like to see him. He wouldn't forget it. A man who, I may say, lives and moves only in a spittoon. A man who has a pipe in his mouth as constant as his front teeth. A sort of tavern king, with a lot of fools, like you, to laugh at what he thinks his jokes, and give him consequence. No, Mr. Caudle, no; it's no use your telling me to go to sleep, for I won't. Go to sleep, indeed! I'm sure it's almost time to get up. I hardly know what's the use of coming to bed at all now.

"The Skylarks, indeed! I suppose you'll be buying a 'Little Warbler,'[2] and at your time of life, be trying to sing. The peacocks will sing next. A pretty name you'll get in the neighbourhood; and, in a very little time,

2 *The Little Warbler* is the title of a chapbook printed about 1820.

a nice face you'll have. Your nose is getting redder already: and you've just one of the noses that liquor always flies to. *You don't see it's red?* No —I dare say not—but *I* see it; I see a great many things you don't. And so you'll go on. In a little time, with your brandy-and-water—don't tell me that you only take two small glasses: I know what men's two small glasses are; in a little time you'll have a face all over as if it was made of red currant jam. And I should like to know who's to endure you then? I won't, and so don't think it. Don't come to me.

"Nice habits men learn at clubs! There's Joskins: he was a decent creature once, and now I'm told he has more than once boxed his wife's ears. He's a Skylark too. And I suppose, some day, you'll be trying to box *my* ears? Don't attempt it, Mr. Caudle; I say don't attempt it. Yes —it's all very well for you to say you don't mean it,—but I only say again, don't attempt it. You'd rue it till the day of your death, Mr. Caudle.

"Going and sitting for four hours at a tavern! What men, unless they had their wives with them, can find to talk about, I can't think. No good, of course.

"Eighteen-pence a week—and drinking brandy-and-water, enough to swim a boat! And smoking like the funnel of a steam-ship! And I can't afford myself so much as a piece of tape! It's brutal, Mr. Caudle. It's ve-ve-ve—ry bru——tal.''

"And here," says Caudle—"Here, thank Heaven! at last, she fell asleep."

## LECTURE IV.

MR. CAUDLE HAS BEEN CALLED FROM HIS BED TO BAIL
MR. PRETTYMAN FROM THE WATCH-HOUSE.

"Yes, Mr. Caudle, I knew it would come to this. I said it would, when you joined those precious Skylarks. People being called out of their beds at all hours of the night, to bail a set of fellows who are never so happy as when they're leading sober men to destruction. I should like to know what the neighbours will think of you, with people from the police knocking at the door at two in the morning? Don't tell me that the man has been ill-used: he's not the man to be ill-used. And you must go and bail him! I know the end of that: he'll run away, and you'll have to pay the money. I should like to know what's the use of my working and slaving to save a farthing, when you throw away pounds upon your precious Skylarks. A pretty cold you'll have to-morrow morning, being called out of your warm bed this weather; but don't you think I'll nurse you—not I; not a drop of gruel do you get from me.

"I'm sure you've plenty of ways of spending your money—not throwing it away upon a set of dissolute peace-breakers. It's all very well for you to say you haven't thrown away your money, but you will. He'll be certain to run off; it isn't likely he'll go upon his trial, and you'll be fixed with the bail. Don't tell me there's no trial in the matter, because I know there is; it's for something more than quarrelling with the policeman that he was locked up. People arn't locked up for that. No, it's for robbery, or something worse, perhaps.

"And as you've bailed him, people will think you are as bad as he is. Don't tell me you couldn't help bailing him; you should have shown yourself a respectable man, and have let him been sent to prison.

"Now people know you're the friend of drunken and disorderly persons, you'll never have a night's sleep in your bed. Not that it would matter what fell upon you, if it wasn't your poor wife who suffered. Of course all the business will be in the newspapers, and your name with it. I shouldn't wonder, too, if they give your picture as they do the other folks of the Old Bailey. A pretty thing that, to go down to your children. I'm sure it will be enough to make them change their name. No, I shall not go to sleep; it's all very well for you to say, go to sleep, after such a disturbance. But I shall not go to sleep, Mr. Caudle; certainly not."

"Her will, I have no doubt," says Caudle, "was strong; but nature was stronger, and she *did* sleep; this night inflicting upon me a remarkably short lecture."

## LECTURE V.

### MR. CAUDLE HAS REMAINED DOWN STAIRS TILL PAST ONE, WITH A FRIEND.

"PRETTY TIME OF NIGHT to come to bed, Mr. Caudle. Ugh! As cold, too, as any ice. Enough to give any woman her death, I'm sure. What! *I shouldn't have locked up the coals?* If I hadn't, I've no doubt the fellow would have stayed all night. It's all very well for you, Mr. Caudle, to bring people home,—but I wish you'd think first what's for supper.

That beautiful leg of pork would have served for our dinner to-morrow, —now it's gone. *I* can't keep the house upon the money, and I won't pretend to do it, if you bring a mob of people every night to clear out the cup-board.

"I wonder who'll be so ready to give you a supper when you want one: for want one you will, unless you change your plans. Don't tell me! I know I'm right. You'll first be eaten up, and then you'll be laughed at. I know the world. No, indeed, Mr. Caudle, I don't think ill of everybody; don't say that. But I can't see a leg of pork eaten up in that way, without asking myself what it's all to end in if such things go on? And then he must have pickles, too! Couldn't be content with my cabbage—no, Mr. Caudle, I won't let you go to sleep. It's very well for you to say let you go to sleep, after you've kept me awake till this time. *Why did I keep awake?* How do you suppose I could go to sleep, when I knew that man was below drinking up your substance in brandy-and-water? for he couldn't be content upon decent, wholesome gin. Upon my word, you ought to be a rich man, Mr. Caudle. You have such very fine friends. I wonder who gives you brandy when you go out!

"No, indeed, he couldn't be content with my pickled cabbage—and I should like to know who makes better—but he must have walnuts. And you, too, like a fool—now, don't you think to stop me, Mr. Caudle; a poor woman may be trampled to death, and never say a word—you, too, like a fool—I wonder who'd do it for you—to insist upon the girl going out for pickled walnuts. And in such a night too! With snow upon the ground. Yes; you're a man of fine feelings, you are, Mr. Caudle; but the world doesn't know you as I know you—fine feelings, indeed! to send the poor girl out, when I told you and told your friend, too—a pretty brute he is, I'm sure—that the poor girl had got a cold and I dare say chilblains on her toes. But I know what will be the end of that; she'll be laid up, and we shall have a nice doctor's bill. And you'll pay it, I can tell you—for *I* won't.

"*You wish you were out of the world?* Oh! yes, that's all very easy. I'm sure *I* might wish it. Don't swear in that dreadful way! Arn't you afraid that the bed will open and swallow you? And don't swing about in that way. *That* will do no good. *That* won't bring back the leg of pork, and the brandy you've poured down both of your throats. Oh, I know it. I'm sure of it. I only recollected it when I'd got into bed,—and if it hadn't been so cold, you'd have seen me down stairs again, I can tell you—I recollected it, and a pretty two hours I've passed—that I left the key in the cupboard,—and I know it—I could see by the manner of you, when you came into the room—I know you've got at the other bottle. However, there's one comfort: you told me to send for the best brandy—the very best—for your other friend, who called last Wednesday. Ha! ha! It was British—the cheapest British—and nice and ill I hope the pair of you will be to-morrow.

"There's only the bare bone of the leg of pork; but you'll get nothing else for dinner, I can tell you. It's a dreadful thing that the poor children should go without,—but, if they have such a father, they, poor things, must suffer for it.

"Nearly a whole leg of pork and a pint of brandy! A pint of brandy and a leg of pork."

## LECTURE VI.

### MR. CAUDLE HAS LENT AN ACQUAINTANCE THE FAMILY UMBRELLA.

"THAT's the third umbrella gone since Christmas. *What were you to do?* Why, let him go home in the rain, to be sure. I'm very certain there was nothing about *him* that could spoil. Take cold, indeed! He doesn't look like one of the sort to take cold. Besides, he'd have better taken cold than take our only umbrella. Do you hear the rain, Mr. Caudle? I say, do you hear the rain? And as I'm alive, if it isn't St. Swithin's day![3] Do you hear it against the windows? Nonsense; you don't impose upon me. You can't be asleep with such a shower as that! Do you hear it, I say? Oh, you *do* hear it! Well, that's a pretty flood, I think, to last for six weeks; and no stirring all the time out of the house. Pooh! don't think me a fool, Mr. Caudle. Don't insult me. *He* return the umbrella! Anybody would think you were born yesterday. As if anybody ever *did* return an umbrella! There—do you hear it? Worse and worse? Cats and dogs, and for six weeks—always six weeks. And no umbrella!

"I should like to know how the children are to go to school to-morrow? They shan't go through such weather, I'm determined. No: they shall stop at home and never learn anything—the blessed creatures!—sooner than go and get wet. And when they grow up, I wonder who they'll have to thank for knowing nothing—who, indeed, but their father? People who can't feel for their own children ought never to be fathers.

"But I know why you lent the umbrella. Oh, yes; I know very well. I

3 St. Swithin's day, July 15. According to legend, if it rains on his feast day, it will rain daily thereafter for forty days; if it is fair on St. Swithin's Day, it will be fair for forty days thereafter.

was going out to tea at dear mother's to-morrow—you knew that; and you did it on purpose. Don't tell me; you hate me to go there, and take every mean advantage to hinder me. But don't you think it, Mr. Caudle. No, sir; if it comes down in buckets-full, I'll go all the more. No: and I won't have a cab. Where do you think the money's to come from? You've got nice high notions at that club of yours. A cab, indeed! Cost me sixteen-pence at least—sixteen-pence! two-and-eightpence, for there's back again. Cabs, indeed! I should like to know who's to pay for 'em; *I* can't pay for 'em, and I'm sure you can't, if you go on as you do; throwing away your property, and beggaring your children—buying umbrellas!

"Do you hear the rain, Mr. Caudle? I say, do you hear it? But I don't care—I'll go to mother's to-morrow: I will; and what's more, I'll walk every step of the way,—and you know that will give me my death. Don't call me a foolish woman, it's you that's the foolish man. You know I can't wear clogs; and with no umbrella, the wet's sure to give me a cold—it always does. But what do you care for that? Nothing at all. I may be laid up for what you care, as I dare say I shall—and a pretty doctor's bill there'll be. I hope there will! It will teach you to lend your umbrella again. I shouldn't wonder if I caught my death; yes: and that's what you lent the umbrella for. Of course!

"Nice clothes, I shall get too, trapesing through weather like this. My gown and bonnet will be spoilt quite. *Needn't I wear 'em then?* Indeed, Mr. Caudle, I *shall* wear 'em. No, sir, I'm not going out a dowdy to please you or anybody. Gracious knows! it isn't often that I step over the threshold; indeed, I might as well be a slave at once,—better, I should say. But when I do go out, Mr. Caudle, I choose to go like a lady. Oh! that rain—if it isn't enough to break in the windows.

"Ugh! I do look forward with dread for to-morrow! How I am to go to mother's I'm sure I can't tell. But if I die, I'll do it. No, sir; I won't borrow an umbrella. No; and you shan't buy one. Now, Mr. Caudle, only listen to this: if you bring home another umbrella, I'll throw it in the street. I'll have my own umbrella, or none at all.

"Ha! and it was only last week I had a new nozzle put to that umbrella. I'm sure, if I'd have known as much at I do now, it might have gone without one for me. Paying for new nozzles, for other people to laugh at you. Oh, it's all very well for you—you can go to sleep. You've no thought of your poor patient wife, and your own dear children. You think of nothing but lending umbrellas!

"Men, indeed!—call themselves lords of the creation!—pretty lords, when they can't even take care of an umbrella!

"I know that walk to-morrow will be the death of me. But that's what you want—then you may go to your club, and do as you like—and then, nicely my poor dear children will be used—but then, sir, then, you'll be happy. Oh, don't tell me! I know you will. Else you'd never have lent the umbrella!

"You have to go on Thursday about that summons; and, of course, you can't go. No, indeed, you *don't* go without the umbrella. You may lose the debt for what I care—it won't be so much as spoiling your clothes— better lose it: people deserve to lose debts who lend umbrellas!

"And I should like to know how I'm to go to mother's without the umbrella? Oh, don't tell me that I said I *would* go—that's nothing to do with it; nothing at all. She'll think I'm neglecting her, and the little money we were to have, we shan't have at all—because we've no umbrella.

"The children, too! Dear things! They'll be sopping wet: for they shan't stop at home—they shan't lose their learning; it's all their father will leave 'em, I'm sure. But they *shall* go to school. Don't tell me I said they shouldn't: you are so aggravating, Caudle; you'd spoil the temper of an angel. They *shall* go to school; mark that. And if they get their deaths of cold, it's not my fault—I didn't lend the umbrella."

"At length," writes Caudle, "I fell asleep; and dreamt that the sky was turned into green calico, with whalebone ribs; that, in fact, the whole world turned round under a tremendous umbrella!"

## LECTURE VII.

MR. CAUDLE HAS VENTURED A REMONSTRANCE ON HIS DAY'S DINNER:
COLD MUTTON, AND NO PUDDING. MRS. CAUDLE DEFENDS
THE COLD SHOULDER.

"I'M SURE! Well! I wonder what it will be next? There's nothing proper, now—nothing at all. Better get somebody else to keep the house I think. I can't do it now, it seems; I'm only in the way here: I'd better take the children, and go.

"What am I grumbling about now? It's very well for you to ask that! I'm sure I'd better be out of the world than—there now, Mr. Caudle; there you are again! I *shall* speak, sir. It isn't often I open my mouth, Heaven knows! But you like to hear nobody talk but yourself. You ought to have married a negro slave, and not any respectable woman.

"You're to go about the house looking like thunder all the day, and I'm not to say a word. Where do you think pudding's to come from every day? You show a nice example to your children, you do; complaining, and turning your nose up at a sweet piece of cold mutton, because there's no pudding! You go a nice way to make 'em extravagant—teach 'em nice lessons to begin the world with. Do you know what puddings cost; or do you think they fly in at the window?

"You hate cold mutton. The more shame for you, Mr. Caudle. I'm sure you've the stomach of a lord, you have. No, sir; I didn't choose to hash the mutton. It's very easy for you to say hash it; but *I* know what a joint loses in hashing: it's a day's dinner the less, if it's a bit. Yes, I dare say; other people may have puddings with cold mutton. No doubt of it; and other people become bankrupts. But if ever you get into the Gazette, it shan't be *my* fault—no; I'll do my duty as a wife to you, Mr. Caudle: you shall never have it to say that it was *my* housekeeping that brought you to beggary. No; you may sulk at the cold meat—ha! I hope you'll never live to want such a piece of cold mutton as we had to-day! and you may threaten to go to a tavern to dine; but, with our present means, not a crumb of pudding do you get from me. You shall have nothing but the cold joint—nothing as I'm a Christian sinner.

"Yes; there you are, throwing those fowls in my face again! I know you once brought home a pair of fowls; I know it: and wer'n't you mean enough to want to stop 'em out of my week's money? Oh, the selfishness—the shabbiness of men! They can go out and throw away pounds upon pounds with a pack of people who laugh at 'em afterwards; but if it's anything wanted for their own homes, their poor wives may hunt for it. I wonder you don't blush to name those fowls again! I wouldn't be so little for the world, Mr. Caudle!

"What are you going to do? *Going to get up?* Don't make yourself ridiculous, Mr. Caudle; I can't say a word to you like any other wife, but you must threaten to get up. *Do* be ashamed of yourself.

"Puddings, indeed! Do you think I'm made of puddings? Didn't you have some boiled rice three weeks ago? Besides, is this the time of the year for puddings? It's all very well if I had money enough allowed me like any other wife to keep the house with: then, indeed, I might have preserves like any other woman; now, it's impossible; and it's cruel—yes, Mr. Caudle, cruel—of you to expect it.

"*Apples arn't so dear, are they?* I know what apples are, Mr. Caudle, without your telling me. But I suppose you want something more than apples for dumplings? I suppose sugar costs something, doesn't it? And that's how it is. That's how one expense brings on another, and that's how people go to ruin.

"*Pancakes?* What's the use of your lying muttering there about pancakes? Don't you always have 'em once a year—every Shrove Tuesday? And what would any moderate, decent man, want more?

"Pancakes, indeed! Pray, Mr. Caudle,—no, it's no use your saying fine words to me to let you go to sleep; I shan't!—pray do you know the price of eggs just now? There's not an egg you can trust to under seven and eight a shilling; well, you've only just to reckon up how many eggs— don't lie swearing there at the eggs, in that manner, Mr. Caudle; unless you expect the bed to let you fall through. You call yourself a respectable tradesman, I suppose? Ha! I only wish people knew you as well as I do! Swearing at eggs, indeed! But I'm tired of this usage, Mr. Caudle; quite tired of it; and I don't care how soon it's ended!

"I'm sure I do nothing but work and labour, and think how to make the most of everything: and this is how I'm rewarded. I should like to see anybody whose joints go further than mine. But if I was to throw away your money into the street, or lay it out in fine feathers on myself, I should be better thought of. The woman who studies her husband and her family is always made a drudge of. It's your fine fal-lal wives who've the best time of it.

"What's the use of your lying groaning there in that manner? That won't make me hold my tongue I can tell you. You think to have it all your own way—but you won't, Mr. Caudle! You can insult my dinner; look like a demon, I may say, at a wholesome piece of cold mutton—ha! the thousands of far better creatures than you are who'd been thankful for that mutton!—and I'm never to speak! But you're mistaken—I will! Your usage of me, Mr. Caudle, is infamous—unworthy of a man. I only wish people knew you for what you are; but I've told you again and again they shall some day.

"Puddings! And now I suppose I shall hear of nothing but puddings! Yes, and I know what it would end in. First, you'd have a pudding every day;—oh, I know your extravagance—then you'd go for fish—then I shouldn't wonder if you'd have soup; turtle, no doubt: then you'd go for a dessert; and—oh! I see it all as plain as the quilt before me—but no, not while I'm alive! What your second wife may do, I don't know; perhaps *she'll* be a fine lady; but you shan't be ruined by me, Mr. Caudle; that I'm determined. Puddings, indeed! Pu-dding-s! Pudd——"

"Exhausted nature," says Caudle, "could hold out no longer. She went to sleep."

# LECTURE VIII.

"Now, Mr. Caudle—Mr. Caudle, I say: oh! you can't be asleep already,
I know—now, what I mean to say is this; there's no use, none at all, in
our having any disturbance about the matter; but, at last my mind's
made up, Mr. Caudle; I shall leave you. Either I know all you've been
doing to-night, or to-morrow morning I quit the house. No, no; there's
an end of the marriage-state, I think—an end of all confidence between
man and wife—if a husband's to have secrets and keep 'em all to himself.
Pretty secrets they must be, when his own wife can't know 'em! Not fit
for any decent person to know, I'm sure, if that's the case. Now, Caudle,
don't let us quarrel; there's a good soul, tell me what's it all about? A
pack of nonsense, I dare say; still—not that I care much about it—still, I
*should* like to know. There's a dear. Eh? Oh, don't tell me there's nothing in it: I know better. I'm not a fool, Mr. Caudle; I know there's a
good deal in it. Now, Caudle; just tell me a little bit of it. I'm sure I'd
tell you anything. You know I would. Well?

"Caudle, you're enough to vex a saint! Now, don't you think you're
going to sleep; because you're not. Do you suppose I'd ever suffered you
to go and be made a mason, if I didn't suppose I was to know the secret,
too? Not that it's anything to know, I dare say; and that's why I'm determined to know it.

"But I know what it is; oh yes, there can be no doubt. The secret is,
to ill-use poor women; to tyrannise over 'em; to make 'em your slaves;
especially your wives. It must be something of the sort, or you wouldn't
be ashamed to have it known. What's right and proper never need be
done in secret. It's an insult to a woman for a man to be a free-mason,
and let his wife know nothing of it. But, poor soul! she's sure to know it
somehow—for nice husbands they all make. Yes, yes; a part of the secret
is to think better of all the world than their own wives and families. I'm
sure men have quite enough to care for—that is, if they act properly—to
care for them they have at home. They can't have much to spare for the
world besides.

"And I suppose they call you *Brother* Caudle? A pretty brother, indeed! Going and dressing yourself up in an apron like a turnpike man—
for that's what you look like. And I should like to know what the apron's
for? There must be something in it not very respectable, I'm sure. Well,

I only wish I was Queen for a day or two. I'd put an end to free-masonry, and all such trumpery, I know.

"Now, come, Caudle; don't let's quarrel. Eh! You're not in pain, dear? What's it all about? What are you lying laughing there at? But I'm a fool to trouble my head about you.

"And you're not going to let me know the secret, eh? You mean to say,—you're not? Now, Caudle, you know it's a hard matter to put me in a passion—not that I care about the secret itself: no, I wouldn't give a button to know it, for it's all nonsense I'm sure. It isn't the secret I care about: it's the slight, Mr. Caudle; it's the studied insult that a man pays to his wife, when he thinks of going through the world keeping something to himself which he won't let her know. Man and wife one, indeed! I should like to know how that can be when a man's a mason—when he keeps a secret that sets him and his wife apart? Ha, you men make the laws, and so you take good care to have all the best of 'em to yourselves: otherwise a woman ought to be allowed a divorce when a man becomes a mason: when he's got a sort of corner-cupboard in his heart—a secret place in his mind—that his poor wife isn't allowed to rummage!

"Caudle, you shan't close your eyes for a week—no, you shan't—unless you tell me some of it. Come, there's a good creature; there's a love. I'm sure, Caudle, I wouldn't refuse you anything—and you know it, or ought to know it by this time. I only wish I had a secret! To whom should I think of confiding it, but to my dear husband? I should be miserable to keep it to myself, and you know it. Now, Caudle?

"Was there ever such a man? A man, indeed! A brute!—yes, Mr. Caudle, an unfeeling, brutal creature, when you might oblige me, and you won't. I'm sure I don't object to your being a mason; not at all, Caudle; I dare say it's a very good thing; I dare say it is—it's only your making a secret of it that vexes me. But you'll tell me—you'll tell your own Margaret? You won't! You're a wretch, Mr. Caudle.

"But I know why: oh, yes, I can tell. The fact is, you're ashamed to let me know what a fool they've been making of you. That's it. You, at your time of life—the father of a family! I should be ashamed of myself, Caudle.

"And I suppose you'll be going to what you call your Lodge every night, now? Lodge, indeed! Pretty place it must be, where they don't admit women. Nice goings on, I dare say. Then you call one another brethren! Brethren! I'm sure you'd relations enough, you didn't want any more.

"But I know what all this masonry's about. It's only an excuse to get away from your wives and families, that you may feast and drink together, that's all. That's the secret. And to abuse women,—as if they were in-

Caudles in bed.

ferior animals, and not to be trusted. That's the secret; and nothing else.

"Now, Caudle, don't let us quarrel. Yes, I know you're in pain. Still Caudle, my love; Caudle! Dearest, I say! Caudle!"

"I recollect nothing more," says Caudle, "for I had eaten a hearty supper, and somehow became oblivious."

## LECTURE IX.

### MR. CAUDLE HAS BEEN TO GREENWICH FAIR.

"So, MR. CAUDLE: I hope you enjoyed yourself at Greenwich. *How do I know you've been at Greenwich?* I know it very well, sir: know all about it: know more than you think I know. I thought there was something in the wind. Yes, I was sure of it, when you went out of the house, to-day. I knew it by the looks of you, though I didn't say anything. Upon my word! And you call yourself a respectable man, and the father of a family! Going to a fair among all sorts of people,—at your time of life. Yes; and never think of taking your wife with you. Oh no! you can go and enjoy yourself out, with *I* don't know who: go out, and make yourself very pleasant, I dare say. Don't tell me; I hear what a nice companion Mr. Caudle is: what a good-tempered person. Ha! I only wish people could see you at home, that's all. But so it is with men. They can keep all their good temper for out-of-doors—their wives never see any of it. Oh dear! I'm sure I don't know who'd be a poor woman!

"Now, Caudle, I'm not in an ill temper; not at all. I know I used to be a fool when we were first married: I used to worry and fret myself to death when you went out; but I've got over that. I wouldn't put myself out of the way now for the best man that ever trod. For what thanks does a poor woman get? None at all. No: it's those who don't care for their families, who are the best thought of. I only wish I could bring myself not to care for mine.

"And why couldn't you say, like a man, you were going to Greenwich Fair when you went out? It's no use your saying that, Mr. Caudle: don't tell me that you didn't think of going; you'd made your mind up to it, and you know it. Pretty games you've had, no doubt? I should like to have been behind you, that's all. A man at your time of life!

"And I, of course, I never want to go out. Oh no! I may stay at home with the cat. You couldn't think of taking your wife and children, like any other decent man, to a fair. Oh no; you never care to be seen with us. I'm sure, many people don't know you're married at all: how can they? Your wife's never seen with you. Oh no; anybody but those belonging to you!

"Greenwich Fair, indeed! Yes,—and of course you went up and down the hill, running and racing with nobody knows who. Don't tell me; I know what you are when you're out. You don't suppose, Mr. Caudle, I've forgotten that pink bonnet, do you? No: I won't hold my tongue, and I'm not a foolish woman. It's no matter, sir, if the pink bonnet was fifty years ago—it's all the same for that. No: and if I live for fifty years to come, I never will leave off talking of it. You ought to be ashamed of yourself, Mr. Caudle. Ha! few wives would have been what I've been to you. I only wish my time was to come over again, that's all; I wouldn't be the fool I have been.

"Going to a fair! and I suppose you had your fortune told by the gipsies? You needn't have wasted your money. I'm sure I can tell your fortune if you go on as you do. Yes, the gaol will be your fortune, Mr. Caudle. And it would be no matter—none at all—if your wife and children didn't suffer with you.

"And then you must go riding upon donkeys.—*You didn't go riding upon donkeys?* Yes; it's very well for you to say so: but I dare say you did. I tell you, Caudle, I know what you are when you're out. I wouldn't trust any of you—you, especially, Caudle.

"Then you must go in the thick of the fair, and have the girls scratching your coat with rattles! *You couldn't help it, if they did scratch your coat?* Don't tell me; people don't scratch coats unless they're encouraged to do it. And you must go in a swing, too. *You didn't go in a swing?* Well, if you didn't, it was no fault of yours; you wished to go, I've no doubt.

"And then you must go into the shows? There,—you don't deny that. You did go into a show. *What of it, Mr. Caudle?*—A good deal of it, sir. Nice crowding and squeezing in those shows, I know. Pretty places! And you a married man and the father of a family. No, I won't hold my tongue. It's very well for you to threaten to get up. You're to go to Greenwich Fair, and race up and down the hill, and play at kiss in the ring.⁴ Pah! it's disgusting, Mr. Caudle. Oh, I dare say you *did* play at it; if you didn't, you'd have liked, and that's just as bad;—and you can go into swings, and shows, and roundabouts. If I was you, I should hide my head under the clothes, and be ashamed of myself.

"And what is most selfish—most mean of you, Caudle—you can go and enjoy yourself, and never so much as bring home for the poor children a gingerbread-nut. Don't tell me that your pocket was picked of a pound of nuts! Nice company you must have been in to have your pocket picked.

"But I dare say I shall hear all about it to-morrow. I've no doubt, sir, you were dancing at the Crown-and-Anchor.⁵ I should like to have seen you. No: I'm not making myself ridiculous. It's you that's making yourself ridiculous; and everybody that knows you says so. Everybody knows what I have to put up with from you.

"Going to a fair, indeed! At your time——"

"Here," says Caudle, "I dozed off, hearing confusedly the words—hill—gipsies—rattles—roundabouts—swings—pink bonnet—nuts."

---

4 kiss in the ring, an open-air game played by young people of both sexes, who stand in a ring with hands joined, except one who runs around outside the ring and touches one of the opposite sex, who thereupon leaves the ring and runs after the first, kissing him or her when caught.

5 Crown-and-Anchor, a tavern in the Strand, formerly frequented by Johnson and Boswell; in 1847 it became the Whittington Club, of which Jerrold was a member.

# LECTURE X.

"WELL, MR. CAUDLE, I hope you're in a little better temper than you were this morning? There—you needn't begin to whistle: people don't come to bed to whistle. But it's like you. I can't speak, that you don't try to insult me. Once, I used to say you were the best creature living: now, you get quite a fiend. *Do let you rest?* No, I won't let you rest. It's the only time I have to talk to you, and you *shall* hear me. I'm put upon all day long: it's very hard if I can't speak a word at night: besides it isn't often I open my mouth, goodness knows!

"Because *once* in your lifetime your shirt wanted a button, you must almost swear the roof off the house! *You didn't swear?* Ha, Mr. Caudle! you don't know what you do when you're in a passion. *You were not in a passion?* Wer'n't you? Well, then, I don't know what a passion is—and I think I ought by this time. I've lived long enough with you, Mr. Caudle, to know that.

"It's a pity you haven't something worse to complain of than a button off your shirt. If you'd *some* wives, you would, I know. I'm sure I'm never without a needle-and-thread in my hand. What with you and the children, I'm made a perfect slave of. And what's my thanks? Why, if once in your life a button's off your shirt—what do you cry '*oh*' at?—I say once, Mr. Caudle; or twice, or three times, at most. I'm sure, Caudle, no man's buttons in the world are better looked after than yours. I only wish I had kept the shirts you had when you were first married! I should like to know where were your buttons then?

"Yes, it *is* worth talking of! But that's how you always try to put me down. You fly into a rage, and then if I only try to speak you won't hear me. That's how you men always will have all the talk to yourselves: a poor woman isn't allowed to get a word in.

"A nice notion you have of a wife, to suppose she's nothing to think of but her husband's buttons. A pretty notion, indeed, you have of marriage. Ha! if poor women only knew what they had to go through! What with buttons, and one thing and another! They'd never tie themselves up,—no, not to the best man in the world, I'm sure. *What would they do, Mr. Caudle?* Why, do much better without you, I'm certain.

"And it's my belief, after all, that the button wasn't off the shirt; it's my belief that you pulled it off, that you might have something to talk about. Oh, you're aggravating enough, when you like, for anything! All I know is, it's very odd that the button should be off the shirt; for I'm sure no woman's a greater slave to her husband's buttons than I am. I only say, its very odd.

"However, there's one comfort; it can't last long. I'm worn to death with your temper, and shan't trouble you a great while. Ha, you may laugh! And I dare say you would laugh! I've no doubt of it! That's your love—that's your feeling! I know that I'm sinking every day, though I say nothing about it. And when I'm gone, we shall see how your second wife will look after your buttons. You'll find out the difference, then. Yes, Caudle, you'll think of me, then: for then, I hope, you'll never have a blessed button to your back.

"No, I'm not a vindictive woman, Mr. Caudle; nobody ever called me that, but you. What do you say? *Nobody ever knew so much of me?* That's nothing at all to do with it. Ha! I wouldn't have your aggravating temper, Caudle, for mines of gold. It's a good thing I'm not as worrying as you are—or a nice house there'd be between us. I only wish you'd had a wife that *would* have talked to you! Then you'd have known the difference. But you impose upon me, because, like a poor fool, I say nothing. I should be ashamed of myself, Caudle.

"And a pretty example you set as a father! You'll make your boys as bad as yourself. Talking as you did all breakfast-time about your buttons! And of a Sunday morning too! And you call yourself a Christian! I should like to know what your boys will say of you when they grow up? And all about a paltry button off one of your wristbands! A decent man wouldn't have mentioned it. *Why won't I hold my tongue?* Because I *won't* hold my tongue. I'm to have my peace of mind destroyed—I'm to be worried into my grave for a miserable shirt-button, and I'm to hold my tongue! Oh! but that's just like you men!

"But I know what I'll do for the future. Every button you have may drop off, and I won't so much as put a thread to 'em. And I should like to know what you'll do then? Oh, you must get somebody else to sew 'em, must you? That's a pretty threat for a husband to hold out to a wife! And to such a wife as I've been, too; such a negro-slave to your buttons, as I may say! Somebody else to sew 'em, eh? No, Caudle, no: not while I'm alive! When I'm dead—and with what I have to bear there's no knowing how soon that may be—when I'm dead, I say—oh! what a brute you must be to snore so!

"*You're not snoring?* Ha! that's what you always say; but that's nothing to do with it. You must get somebody else to sew 'em, must you? Ha! I shouldn't wonder. Oh no! I should be surprised at nothing, now! Nothing at all! It's what people have always told me it would come to,—and now, the buttons have opened my eyes! But the whole world shall know of your cruelty, Mr. Caudle. After the wife I've been to you. Somebody else, indeed, to sew your buttons! I'm no longer to be mistress in my own house! Ha, Caudle! I wouldn't have upon my conscience what you have, for the world! I wouldn't treat anybody as you treat—no, I'm not mad! It's you, Mr. Caudle, who are mad, or bad—and that's worse! I can't even so much as speak of a shirt-button, but that I'm threatened to be made nobody of in my own house! Caudle, you've a heart like a hearth-stone, you have! To threaten me, and only because a button—a button——"

"I was conscious of no more than this," says Caudle; "for here nature relieved me with a sweet, deep sleep."

## LECTURE XI.

### MRS. CAUDLE SUGGESTS THAT HER DEAR MOTHER SHOULD "COME AND LIVE WITH THEM."

"IS YOUR COLD better to-night, Caudle? Yes; I thought it was. 'Twill be quite well to-morrow, I dare say. There's a love! You don't take care enough of yourself, Caudle, you don't. And you ought, I'm sure; if only for my sake. For whatever I should do, if anything was to happen to you—but I won't think of it; no, I can't bear to think of *that*. Still, you ought to take care of yourself; for you know you're not strong, Caudle; you know you're not.

"Wasn't dear mother so happy with us, to-night? Now, you needn't go to sleep, so suddenly. I say, wasn't she so happy? *You don't know?* How can you say you don't know? You must have seen it. But she always is happier here than anywhere else. Ha! what a temper that dear soul has! I call it a temper of satin; it is so smooth, so easy, and so soft. Nothing puts her out of the way. And then, if you only knew how she takes your part, Caudle! I'm sure, if you had been her own son ten times over, she couldn't be fonder of you. Don't you think so, Caudle? Eh, love? Now, do answer. *How can you tell?* Nonsense, Caudle; you must have seen it. I'm sure, nothing delights the dear soul so much as when she's thinking how to please you.

"Don't you remember Thursday night, the stewed oysters when you came home? That was all dear mother's doings! 'Margaret,' says she to me, 'it's a cold night; and don't you think dear Mr. Caudle would like something nice before he goes to bed?' And that, Caudle, is how the oysters came about. Now, don't sleep, Caudle: do listen to me, for five minutes; 'tisn't often I speak, goodness knows.

"And then, what a fuss she makes when you're out, if your slippers arn't put to the fire for you. *She's very good?* Yes—I know she is, Caudle. And hasn't she been six months—though I promised her not to tell you— six months, working a watch-pocket for you! And with *her* eyes, dear soul—and at *her* time of life!

"And then what a cook she is! I'm sure, the dishes she'll make out of next to nothing! I try hard enough to follow her: but, I'm not ashamed to own it, Caudle, she quite beats me. Ha! the many nice little things she'd simmer up for you—and I can't do it; the children, you know it, Caudle, take so much of my time. I can't do it, love: and I often reproach myself that I can't. Now, you shan't go to sleep, Caudle; at least, not for five minutes. You must hear me.

"I've been thinking, dearest—ha! that nasty cough, love!—I've been thinking, darling, if we could only persuade dear mother to come and live with us. Now, Caudle, you can't be asleep; it's impossible—you were coughing only this minute—yes, to live with us. What a treasure we should have in her! Then, Caudle, you never need to go bed without something nice and hot. And you want it, Caudle. *You don't want it?* Nonsense, you do; for you're not strong, Caudle; you know you're not.

"I'm sure, the money she'd save us in housekeeping. Ha! what an eye she has for a joint! The butcher doesn't walk that could deceive dear mother. And then, again, for poultry! What a finger and thumb she has for a chicken! I never could market like her: it's a gift—quite a gift.

"And then you recollect her marrow-puddings? *You don't recollect 'em?* Oh, fie! Caudle, how often have you flung her marrow-puddings in my face, wanting to know why I couldn't make 'em? And I wouldn't pretend to do it after dear mother. I should think it presumption. Now, love, if she was only living with us—come, you're not asleep, Caudle—if she was only living with us, you could have marrow-puddings every day. Now, don't fling yourself about and begin to swear at marrow-puddings; you know you like 'em, dear.

"What a hand, too, dear mother has for a pie-crust? But it's born with some people. What do you say? *Why wasn't it born with me?* Now, Caudle, that's cruel—unfeeling of you; I wouldn't have uttered such a reproach to you for the whole world. Consider, dear; people can't be born as they like.

"How often, too, have you wanted to brew at home! And I never could learn anything about brewing. But, ha! what ale dear mother makes! *You never tasted it?* No, I know that. But I recollect the ale we used to have at home: and father never would drink wine after it. The best sherry was nothing like it. *You dare say not?* No; it wasn't indeed, Caudle. Then, if dear mother was only with us, what money we should save in beer! And then you might always have your own nice, pure, good, wholesome ale, Caudle: and what good it would do you! For you're not strong, Caudle.

"And then dear mother's jams and preserves, love! I own it, Caudle; it has often gone to my heart that with cold meat you hav'n't always had a pudding. Now, if mother was with us, in the matter of fruit puddings, she'd make it summer all the year round. But I never could preserve—now mother does it, and for next to no money whatever. What nice dogs-in-a-blanket[6] she'd make for the children! *What's dogs-in-a-blanket?* Oh, they're delicious—as dear mother makes 'em.

"Now, you *have* tasted her Irish stew, Caudle? You remember that? Come, you're not asleep—you remember that? And how fond you are of it! And I know I never have it made to please you! Well, what a relief to me it would be if dear mother was always at hand that you might have a stew when you liked. What a load it would be off my mind.

"Again, for pickles! Not at all like anybody else's pickles. Her red cabbage—why it's as crisp as biscuit! And then her walnuts—and her all-sorts! Eh, Caudle? You know how you love pickles; and how we sometimes tiff about 'em? Now if dear mother was here, a word would never pass between us. And I'm sure nothing would make me happier, for—you're not asleep, Caudle?—for I can't bear to quarrel, can I, love?

"The children, too, are so fond of her! And she'd be such a help to me with 'em! I'm sure, with dear mother in the house, I shouldn't care a fig for measles, or anything of the sort. As a nurse, she's such a treasure!

"And at her time of life, what a needlewoman! And the darning and mending for the children, it really gets quite beyond me now, Caudle. Now with mother at my hand, there wouldn't be a stitch wanted in the house.

"And then when you're out late, Caudle—for I know you must be out late, sometimes; I can't expect you, of course, to be always at home—why then dear mother could sit up for you, and nothing would delight the dear soul half so much.

"And so, Caudle, love, I think dear mother had better come, don't you? Eh, Caudle? Now, you're not asleep, darling; don't you think she'd better come? You say *No?* You say *No* again? *You won't have her,* you say; *You won't, that's flat?* Caudle—Cau-Cau-dle—Cau—dle——"

[6] dogs-in-a-blanket, a rolled currant dumpling or jam pudding.

"Here Mrs. Caudle," says her husband, "suddenly went into tears; and I went to sleep."

## LECTURE XII.

MR. CAUDLE, HAVING COME HOME A LITTLE LATE, DECLARES THAT
HENCEFORTH "HE WILL HAVE A KEY."

"UPON MY WORD, Mr. Caudle, I think it a waste of time to come to bed at all now! The cocks will be crowing in a minute. *Why did I sit up, then?* Because I choose to sit up—but that's my thanks. No, it's no use your talking, Caudle; I never *will* let the girl sit up for you, and there's an end. What do you say? *Why does she sit up with me, then?* That's quite a different matter: you don't suppose I'm going to sit up alone, do you? What do you say? *What's the use of two sitting up?* That's my business. No, Caudle, it's no such thing. I *don't* sit up because I may have the pleasure of talking about it; and you're an ungrateful, unfeeling creature, to say so. I sit up because I choose it; and if you don't come home all the night long—and 'twill soon come to that, I've no doubt— still, I'll never go to bed, so don't think it.

"Oh yes! the time runs away very pleasantly with you men at your clubs—selfish creatures! You can laugh and sing, and tell stories, and never think of the clock; never think there's such a person as a wife be- longing to you. It's nothing to you that a poor woman's sitting up, and telling the minutes, and seeing all sorts of things in the fire—and some- times thinking that something dreadful has happened to you—more fool she to care a straw about you!—This is all nothing. Oh no! when a wom- an's once married she's a slave—worse than a slave—and must bear it all!

"And what you men can find to talk about I can't think! Instead of a man sitting every night at home with his wife, and going to bed at a Christian hour,—going to a club, to meet a set of people who don't care a button for him—it's monstrous! What do you say? *You only go once a week?* That's nothing at all to do with it: you might as well go every night; and I dare say you will soon. But if you do, you may get in as you can: *I* won't sit up for you, I can tell you.

"My health's being destroyed night after night, and—oh, don't say it's only once a week; I tell you, that's nothing to do with it—if you had any eyes, you would see how ill I am; but you've no eyes for anybody belong- ing to you: oh no! your eyes are for people out of doors. It's very well for you to call me a foolish, aggravating woman! I should like to see the woman who'd sit up for you as I do. *You didn't want me to sit up?* Yes, yes; that's your thanks—that's your gratitude: I'm to ruin my health, and to be abused for it. Nice principles you've got at that club, Mr. Caudle!

"But there's one comfort—one great comfort; it can't last long: I'm sinking—I feel it, though I never say anything about it—but I know my own feelings, and I say it can't last long. And then I should like to know who will sit up for you! Then I should like to know how your second wife—what do you say? *You'll never be troubled with another?* Troubled, indeed! *I* never troubled you, Caudle. No; it's you who've troubled me; and you know it; though like a foolish woman I've borne it all, and never said a word about it. But it *can't* last—that's one blessing!

"Oh, if a woman could only know what she'd have to suffer, before she was married—Don't tell me you want to go to sleep! If you want to go to sleep, you should come home at proper hours! It's time to get up, for what I know, now. Shouldn't wonder if you hear the milk in five minutes—there's the sparrows up already; yes, I say the sparrows; and, Caudle, you ought to blush to hear 'em. *You don't hear 'em?* Ha! you won't hear 'em, you mean: *I* hear 'em. No, Mr. Caudle; it *isn't* the wind whistling in the key-hole; I'm not quite foolish, though you may think so. I hope I know wind from a sparrow!

"Ha! when I think what a man you were before we were married! But you're now another person—quite an altered creature. But I suppose you're all alike—I dare say, every poor woman's troubled and put upon, though I should hope not so much as I am. Indeed, I should hope not! Going and staying out, and—

"What! *You'll have a key?* Will you? Not while I'm alive, Mr. Caudle. I'm not going to bed with the door upon the latch for you or the best man breathing. *You won't have a latch—you'll have a Chubb's lock?*[7] Will you? I'll have no Chubb here, I can tell you. What do you say? *You'll have the lock put on to-morrow?* Well, try it; that's all I say, Caudle; try it. I won't let you put me in a passion; but all I say is,—try it.

"A respectable thing, that, for a married man to carry about with him,—a street-door key! That tells a tale, I think. A nice thing for the father of a family! A key! What, to let yourself in and out when you please! To come in, like a thief in the middle of the night, instead of knocking at the door like a decent person! Oh, don't tell me that you only want to prevent me sitting up,—if I choose to sit up, what's that

7 Chubb's lock, a patent lock with tumblers and, in addition, a lever called a detector, which fixes the bolt immovably when one of the tumblers is raised a little too high in an attempt to pick the lock.

to you? Some wives, indeed, would make a noise about sitting up, but *you've* no reason to complain,—goodness knows!

"Well, upon my word, I've lived to hear something. Carry the street-door key about with you! I've heard of such things with young good-for-nothing bachelors, with nobody to care what became of 'em; but for a married man to leave his wife and children in a house with the door upon the latch—don't talk to me about Chubb, it's all the same—a great deal you must care for us. Yes, it's very well for you to say, that you only want the key for peace and quietness—what's it to you, if I like to sit up? You've no business to complain; it can't distress you. Now, it's no use your talking; all I say is this, Caudle; if you send a man to put on any lock here, I'll call in a policeman; as I'm your married wife, I will!

"No, I think when a man comes to have the street-door key, the sooner he turns bachelor altogether the better. I'm sure, Caudle, I don't want to be any clog upon you. Now, it's no use your telling me to hold my tongue, for I—What? *I give you the head-ache, do I?* No, I don't, Caudle: it's your club that gives you the head-ache: it's your smoke, and your—well! if ever I knew such a man in all my life! there's no saying a word to you! You go out, and treat yourself like an emperor—and come home at twelve at night, or any hour, for what I know,—and then you threaten to have a key, and—and—and——"

"I *did* get to sleep at last," says Caudle, "amidst the falling sentences of 'take children into a lodging'—'separate maintenance'—'won't be made a slave of'—and so forth."

## LECTURE XIII.

MRS. CAUDLE HAS BEEN TO SEE HER DEAR MOTHER. CAUDLE, ON THE
"JOYFUL OCCASION," HAS GIVEN A PARTY, AND ISSUED
THE SUBJOINED CARD OF INVITATION.

"IT IS HARD, I think, Mr. Caudle, that I can't leave home for a day or two, but the house must be turned into a tavern: a tavern?—a pothouse! Yes, I thought you were very anxious that I should go; I thought you wanted to get rid of me for something, or you would not have insisted on my staying at dear mother's all night. You were afraid I should get cold coming home, were you? Oh, yes, you can be very tender, you can, Mr. Caudle, when it suits your own purpose. Yes! and the world thinks what

*Mr. Caudle's compliments to Mr. Prettyman, and expects to have the honour of his company on this joyful occasion, at half-past Eight o'Clock.*

a good husband you are! I only wish the world knew you as well as I do, that's all; but it shall, some day, I'm determined.

"I'm sure the house will not be sweet for a month. All the curtains are poisoned with smoke; and, what's more, with the filthiest smoke I ever knew. *Take 'em down, then?* Yes, it's all very well for you to say, take 'em down; but they were only cleaned and put up a month ago; but a careful wife's lost upon you, Mr. Caudle. You ought to have married somebody who'd have let your house go to wreck and ruin, as I will for the future. People who don't care for their families are better thought of that those who do; I've long found out *that*.

"And what a condition the carpet's in! They've taken five pounds out of it, if a farthing, with their filthy boots, and I don't know what besides. And then the smoke in the hearthrug, and a large cinder-hole burnt in it! I never saw such a house in *my* life! If you wanted to have a few friends, why couldn't you invite 'em when your wife's at home, like any other man? not have 'em sneaking in, like a set of housebreakers, directly a woman turns her back. They must be pretty gentlemen, they must; mean fellows, that are afraid to face a woman! Ha! and you all call yourselves the lords of the creation! I should only like to see what would become of the creation, if you were left to yourselves! A pretty pickle creation would be in very soon!

"You must all have been in a nice condition? What do you say? *You took nothing?* Took nothing, didn't you? I'm sure there's such a regiment of empty bottles, I havn't had the heart to count 'em. And punch, too! you must have punch! There's a hundred half-lemons in the kitchen, if there's one: for Susan, like a good girl, kept 'em to show 'em me. No, sir; Susan *shan't leave the house!* What do you say? *She has no right to tell tales, and you* WILL *be master of your own house?* Will you? If you don't alter, Mr. Caudle, you'll soon have no house to be master of. A whole loaf of sugar did I leave in the cupboard, and now there isn't as much as would fill a tea-cup. Do you suppose I'm to find sugar for punch for fifty men? What do you say? *There wasn't fifty?* That's no matter; the more shame for 'em, sir. I'm sure they drunk enough for fifty. Do you suppose out of my housekeeping money I'm to find sugar for punch for all the world? *You don't ask me?* Don't you ask me? You do; you know you do: for if I only want a shilling extra, the house is in a blaze. And yet a whole loaf of sugar can you throw away upon——No, I *won't* be still; and I *won't* let you go to sleep. If you'd got to bed at a proper hour last night, you wouldn't have been so sleepy now. You can sit up half the night with a pack of people who don't care for you, and your poor wife can't get in a word!

"And there's that China image that I had when I was married—I wouldn't have taken any sum of money for it, and you know it—and how do I find it? With its precious head knocked off! And what was more mean, more contemptible than all besides, it was put on again, as if nothing had happened. *You knew nothing about it?* Now, how can you lie there, in your Christian bed, Caudle, and say that? You know that that fellow, Prettyman, knocked off the head with the poker! You know that he did. And you hadn't the feeling,—yes, I will say it,—you hadn't the feeling to protect what you knew was precious to me. Oh no, if the truth was known, you were glad to see it broken for that very reason.

"Every way, I've been insulted. I should like to know who it was who corked whiskers on my dear aunt's picture? Oh! you're laughing, are you? *You're not laughing?* Don't tell me that. I should like to know what shakes the bed, then, if you're not laughing? Yes, corked whiskers on her dear face,—and she was a good soul to you, Caudle, and you ought to be ashamed of yourself to see her ill-used. Oh, you may laugh! It's very easy to laugh! I only wish you'd a little feeling, like other people, that's all.

"Then there's my china mug—the mug I had before I was married—when I was a happy creature. I should like to know who knocked the spout off that mug? Don't tell me it was cracked before—it's no such thing, Caudle; there wasn't a flaw in it—and now, I could have cried when I saw it. Don't tell me it wasn't worth twopence. How do you know? You never buy mugs. But that's like men; they think nothing in a house costs anything.

"There's four glasses broke, and nine cracked. At least, that's all I've found out at present; but I dare say I shall discover a dozen to-morrow.

"And I should like to know where the cotton umbrella's gone to—and I should like to know who broke the bell-pull—and perhaps you don't know there's a leg off a chair,—and perhaps—"

"I was resolved," says Caudle, "to know nothing, and so went to sleep in my ignorance."

## LECTURE XIV.

### MRS. CAUDLE THINKS IT "HIGH TIME" THAT THE CHILDREN SHOULD HAVE SUMMER CLOTHING.

"IF THERE'S ANYTHING in the world I hate—and you know it, Caudle—it is asking you for money. I am sure, for myself, I'd rather go without a thing a thousand times, and I do—the more shame of you to let me, but—there, now! there you fly out again! *What do I want now?* Why, you must know what's wanted, if you'd any eyes—or any pride for your children, like any other father. *What's the matter—and what am I driving at?* Oh, nonsense, Caudle! As if you didn't know! I'm sure if I'd any money of my own, I'd never ask you for a farthing; never; it's painful to me, goodness knows! What do you say? *If it's painful, why so often do it?* Ha! I suppose you call that a joke—one of your club jokes? I wish you'd think a little more of people's feelings, and less of your jokes. As I say, I only wish I'd any money of my own. If there is anything that humbles a poor woman, it is coming to a man's pocket for every farthing. It's dreadful!

"Now, Caudle, if ever you kept awake, you shall keep awake to-night —yes, you shall hear me, for it isn't often I speak, and then you may go to sleep as soon as you like. Pray do you know what month it is? And did you see how the children looked at church to-day—like nobody else's children? *What was the matter with them?* Oh, Caudle! How can you ask? Poor things! weren't they all in their thick merinos, and beaver bonnets? What do you say—*What of it?* What! you'll tell me that you didn't see how the Briggs's girls, in their new chips, turned their noses up at 'em? And you didn't see how the Browns looked at the Smiths, and then at our dear girls, as much as to say, 'Poor creatures! what figures for the month of May!' *You didn't see it?* The more shame for you—you would, if you'd had the feelings of a parent—but I'm sorry to say, Caudle, you haven't. I'm sure those Briggs's girls—the little minxes!—put me into such a pucker, I could have pulled their ears for 'em over the pew. What do you say? *I ought to be ashamed of myself to own it?* No, Mr. Caudle: the shame lies with you, that don't let your children appear at church like other people's children; that make 'em uncomfortable at their devotions, poor things; for how can it be otherwise, when they see themselves dressed like nobody else?

"Now, Caudle, it's no use talking; those children shall not cross the threshold next Sunday, if they haven't things for the summer. Now mind—they shan't; and there's an end of it. I won't have 'em exposed to the Briggses and the Browns again: no, they shall know they have a mother, if they've no father to feel for 'em. What do you say, Caudle? *A good deal I must think of church, if I think so much of what we go in?* I only wish you thought as much as I do, you'd be a better man than you are, Caudle, I can tell you; but that's nothing to do with it. I'm talking about decent clothes for the children for the summer, and you want to put me off with something about the church; but that's so like you, Caudle!

"*I'm always wanting money for clothes?* How can you lie in your bed and say that? I'm sure there's no children in the world that cost their father so little: but that's it; the less a poor woman does upon, the less she may. It's the wives who don't care where the money comes from who're best thought of. Oh, if my time was to come over again, would I mend and stitch, and make the things go so far as I have done? No—that I wouldn't. Yes, it's very well for you to lie there and laugh; it's easy to laugh, Caudle—very easy, to people who don't feel.

"Now, Caudle, dear! What a man you are! I know you'll give me the money, because, after all, I think you love your children, and like to see 'em well dressed. It's only natural that a father should. Eh, Caudle, eh! Now you shan't go to sleep till you've told me. *How much money do I want?* Why, let me see, love. There's Caroline, and Jane, and Susannah, and Mary Anne, and—What do you say? *I needn't count 'em, you know how many there are?* Ha! that's just as you take me up. Well, how much money will it take? Let me see; and don't go to sleep. I'll tell you in a minute. You always love to see the dear things like new pins, I know that, Caudle; and though I say it—bless their little hearts!—they do credit to you, Caudle. Any nobleman of the land might be proud of 'em. Now don't swear at noblemen of the land, and ask me what they've to do with your children; you know what I meant. But you *are* so hasty, Caudle.

*"How much?* Now, don't be in a hurry! Well, I think, with good pinching—and you know, Caudle, there's never a wife who can pinch closer than I can—I think, with pinching, I can do with twenty pounds. What did you say? *Twenty fiddlesticks?* What? *You won't give half the money?* Very well, Mr. Caudle; I don't care: let the children go in rags; let them stop from church, and grow up like heathens and cannibals, and then you'll save your money, and, I suppose, be satisfied. *You gave me twenty pounds five months ago!* What's five months ago to do with now? Besides, what I *have* had is nothing to do with it.

"What do you say? *Ten pounds are enough?* Yes: just like you men; you think things cost nothing for women: but you don't care how much you lay out upon yourselves. *They only want bonnets and frocks?* How do you know what they want? *How* should a man know anything at all about it? And you won't give more than ten pounds? Very well. Then you may go shopping with it yourself, and see what *you'll* make of it. I'll have none of your ten pounds, I can tell you. No, sir,—no; you have no cause to say that. *I don't want to dress the children up like countesses?* You often fling that in my teeth, you do; but you know it's false, Caudle; you know it. I only want to give 'em proper notions of themselves: and what, indeed, *can* the poor things think when they see the Briggses, and the Browns, and the Smiths—and their fathers don't make the money you do, Caudle—when they see them as fine as tulips? Why, they must think themselves nobody; and to think yourself nobody,—depend upon it, Caudle,—isn't the way to make the world think anything of you.

"What do you say? *Where did I pick up that?* Where do you think? I know a great deal more than you suppose—yes; though you don't give me credit for it. Husbands seldom do. However, the twenty pounds I *will* have, if I've any—or not a farthing.

"No, sir, no. *I don't want to dress up the children like peacocks and parrots!* I only want to make 'em respectable and—what do you say? *You'll give fifteen pounds?* No, Caudle, no—not a penny will I take under twenty; if I did, it would seem as if I wanted to waste your money: and I'm sure, when I come to  think of it, twenty pounds will hardly do. Still, if you'll give me twenty—no, it's no use your offering fifteen, and wanting to go to sleep. You shan't close an eye until you promise the twenty. Come, Caudle, love!—twenty, and then you may go to sleep. Twenty—twenty—twenty—"

"My impression is," writes Caudle, "that I fell asleep sticking firmly to the fifteen; but in the morning Mrs. Caudle assured me, as a woman of honour, that she wouldn't let me wink an eye, before I promised the twenty: and man is frail—and woman is strong—she had the money."

## LECTURE XV.

MR. CAUDLE HAS AGAIN STAYED OUT LATE. MRS. CAUDLE, AT
FIRST INJURED AND VIOLENT, MELTS.

"PERHAPS, Mr. Caudle, you'll tell we where this is to end? Though, goodness know, I needn't ask *that*. The end is plain enough. Out—out—out! Every night—every night! I'm sure, men who can't come home at reasonable hours have no business with wives: they have no right to destroy other people, if they choose to go to destruction themselves. Ha, lord! Oh, dear! I only hope none of my girls will ever marry—I hope they'll none of 'em ever be the slave their poor mother is: they shan't, if I can help it. What do you say? *Nothing?* Well, I don't wonder at that, Mr. Caudle; you ought to be ashamed to speak; I don't wonder that you can't open your mouth. I'm only astonished that at such hours you have the confidence to knock at your own door. Though I'm your wife, I must say it, I do sometimes wonder at your impudence. What do you say? *Nothing?* Ha! you are an aggravating creature, Caudle, lying there like the mummy of a man, and never as much as opening your lips to one. Just as if your own wife wasn't worth answering! It isn't so when you're out, I'm sure. Oh no! then you can talk fast enough; here, there's no getting a word from you. But you treat your wife as no other man does— and you know it.

"Out—out every night! What? *You haven't been out this week before?* That's nothing at all to do with it. You might just as well be out all the week as once—just! And I should like to know what could keep you out till these hours? *Business?* Oh, yes—I dare say! Pretty business a married man and the father of a family must have out of doors at one in the morning. What! *I shall drive you mad?* Oh, no; you haven't feelings enough to go mad—you'd be a better man, Caudle, if you had. *Will I listen to you?* What's the use? Of course you've some story to put me off with—you can all do that, and laugh at us afterwards.

"No, Caudle, don't say that. I'm not always trying to find fault—not I. I never speak but when there's occasion; and what in my time I've put up with, there isn't anybody in the world that knows. *Will I hear your story?* Oh, you may tell it if you please; go on: only mind, I shan't believe a word of it. I'm not such a fool as other women are, I can tell you. There, now—don't begin to swear—but go on———

"———And that's your story, is it? That's your excuse for the hours you keep! That's your apology for undermining my health and ruining your family! What do you think your children will say of you when they grow up—going and throwing away your money upon good-for-nothing, pot-house acquaintance? *He's not a pot-house acquaintance?* Who is he, then? Come, you haven't told me that; but I know—it's that Prettyman! Yes, to be sure it is! Upon my life! Well, if I've hardly patience to lie in the same bed! I've wanted a silver teapot these five years, and you must go and throw away as much money as—what! *You haven't thrown it away?* Haven't you! Then my name's not Margaret, that's all I know!

"A man gets arrested, and because he's taken from his wife and family, and locked up, you must go and trouble your head with it! And you must be mixing yourself up with nasty sheriff's officers—pah! I'm sure you're not fit to enter a decent house—and go running from lawyer to lawyer to get bail, and settle the business, as you call it! A pretty settlement you'll make of it—mark my words! Yes—and to mend the matter, to finish it quite, you must be one of the bail! That any man who isn't a born fool should do such a thing for another! Do you think anybody would do as much for you? *Yes?* You say yes? Well, I only wish—just to show that I'm right—I only wish you were in a condition to try 'em. I should only like to see you arrested. You'd find the difference—*that* you would.

"What's other people's affairs to you? If you were locked up, depend upon it, there's not a soul would come near you. No; it's all very fine now, when people think there isn't a chance of your being in trouble—but I should only like to see what they'd say to you if *you* were in a sponging-house. Yes—I should enjoy *that*, just to show you that I'm always right. What do you say? *You think better of the world?* Ha! that would be all very well if you could afford it; but you're not in means, I know, to think so well of people as all that. And of course they only laugh at you. 'Caudle's an easy fool,' they cry—I know it as well as if I heard 'em— 'Caudle's an easy fool, anybody may lead him.' Yes; anybody but his own wife;—and she—of course—is nobody.

"And now, everybody that's arrested will of course send to you. Yes, Mr. Caudle, you'll have your hands full now, no doubt of it. You'll soon know every sponging-house and every sheriff's officer in London. Your business will have to take care of itself; you'll have enough to do to run from lawyer to lawyer after the business of other people. Now, it's no use calling me a dear soul—not a bit! No; and I shan't put it off till to-morrow. It isn't often I speak, but I *will* speak now.

"I wish that Prettyman had been at the bottom of the sea before—what? *It isn't Prettyman?* Ha! it's very well for you to say so; but I know it is; it's just like him. He looks like a man that's always in debt—that's always in a sponging-house. Anybody might swear it. I knew it from the very first time you brought him here—from the very night he put his nasty wet boots on my bright steel fender. Any woman could see what the fellow was in a minute. Prettyman! A pretty gentleman, truly, to be robbing your wife and family!

"Why couldn't you let him stop in the sponging——Now don't call upon heaven in that way, and ask me to be quiet, for I won't. Why couldn't you let him stop there? He got himself in; he might have got himself out again. And you must keep me awake, ruin my sleep, my health, and, for what you care, my peace of mind. Ha! everybody but you can see how I'm breaking. You can do all this while you're talking with a set of low bailiffs! A great deal you must think of your children to go into a lawyer's office.

"And then you must be bail—you must be bound—for Mr. Prettyman! You may say, bound! Yes—you've your hands nicely tied, now. How he laughs at you—and serve you right! Why, in another week he'll be in the East Indies; of course, he will! And you'll have to pay his debts; yes, your children may go in rags, so that Mr. Prettyman—what do you say? *It isn't Prettyman?* I know better. Well, if it isn't Prettyman that's kept you out, —if it isn't Prettyman you're bail for,—who is it then? I ask, who is it then? What! *My brother? Brother Tom?* Oh, Caudle! dear Caudle—"

"It was too much for the poor soul," says Caudle; "she sobbed as if her heart would break, and I"—and here the MS. is blotted, as though Caudle himself had dropt tears as he wrote.

## LECTURE XVI.

BABY IS TO BE CHRISTENED; MRS. CAUDLE CANVASSES THE MERITS
OF PROBABLE GODFATHERS.

"COME, NOW, LOVE, about baby's name? The dear thing's three months old, and not a name to its back yet. There you go again! Talk of it to-morrow! No; we'll talk of it to-night. There's no having a word with you in the day-time—but here you can't leave me. Now don't say you wish you could, Caudle; that's unkind, and not treating a wife—especially the wife I am to you—as she deserves. It isn't often that I speak; but I *do* believe you'd like never to hear the sound of my voice. I might as well have been born dumb!

"I suppose the baby *must* have a godfather; and so, Caudle, who shall we have? Who do you think will be able to do the most for it? No, Caudle, no; I'm not a selfish woman—nothing of the sort—but I hope I've the feelings of a mother; and what's the use of a godfather, if he gives nothing else to the child but a name? A child might almost as well not be christened at all. And so who shall we have? What do you say? *Anybody?* Arn't you ashamed of yourself, Caudle? Don't you think something will happen to you, to talk in that way? I don't know where you pick up such principles. I'm thinking who there is among our acquaintance who can do the most for the blessed creature, and you say,—'*Anybody!*' Caudle, you're quite a heathen.

"There's Wagstaff. No chance of his ever marrying, and he's very fond of babies. He's plenty of money, Caudle; and I think he might be got. Babies, I know it—babies are his weak side. Wouldn't it be a blessed thing to find our dear child in his will? Why don't you speak? I declare, Caudle, you seem to care no more for the child than if it was a stranger's. People who can't love children more than you do, ought never to have 'em. *You don't like Wagstaff?* No more do I much; but what's that to do with it? People who've their families to provide for, mustn't think of their feelings. *I* don't like him; but then I'm a mother, and love my baby! *You won't have Wagstaff, and that's flat?* Ha, Caudle! you're like nobody else—not fit for this world, you're not.

"What do you think of Pugsby? I can't bear his wife; but that's nothing to do with it. *I* know my duty to my babe: I wish other people did. What do you say? *Pugsby's a wicked fellow?* Ha! that's like you—always giving people a bad name. We musn't always believe what the world says, Caudle; it doesn't become us as Christians to do it. I only know that he hasn't chick or child; and, besides that, he's very strong interest in the Blue-coats; and so, if Pugsby——Now, don't fly out at the man in that manner. Caudle, you ought to be ashamed of yourself! You can't speak well of anybody. Where *do* you think to go to?

"What do you say, then, to Sniggins? Now, don't bounce round in that way, letting the cold air into the bed! What's the matter with Sniggins? *You wouldn't ask him a favour for the world?* Well, it's a good thing the baby has somebody to care for it: *I* will. What do you say? *I shan't?* I will, I can tell you. Sniggins, besides being a warm man, has good interest in the Customs; and there's nice pickings there, if one only goes the right way to get 'em. It's no use, Caudle, your fidgetting about—not a bit. I'm not going to have baby lost—sacrificed, I may say, like its brothers and sisters. *What do I mean by sacrificed?* Oh, you know what I mean very well. What have any of 'em got by their godfathers beyond a half-pint mug, a knife and fork, and spoon—and a shabby coat, that I know was bought second-hand, for I could almost swear to the place? And then there was your fine friend Hartley's wife—what did she give to Caroline? Why, a trumpery lace cap it made me blush to look at. What? *It was the best she could afford?* Then she'd no right to stand for the child. People who can't do better than that have no business to take the responsibility of godmother. They ought to know their duties better.

"Well, Caudle, you can't object to Goldman? *Yes, you do!* Was there ever such a man! What for? *He's a usurer and a hunks?* Well, I'm sure, you've no business in this world, Caudle; you have such high-flown notions. Why, isn't the man as rich as the bank? And as for his being a usurer,—isn't it all the better for those who come after him? I'm sure it's well there's some people in the world who save money, seeing the stupid creatures who throw it away. But you are the strangest man! I really believe you think money a sin, instead of the greatest blessing; for I can't mention any of our acquaintance that's rich—and I'm sure we don't know too many such people—that you haven't something to say against 'em. It's only beggars that you like—people with not a shilling to bless themselves. Ha! though you're my husband, I must say it—you're a man of low notions, Caudle. I hope none of the dear boys will take after their father!

"And I should like to know what's the objection to Goldman? The only thing against him is his name; I must confess it, I don't like the name of Lazarus: it's low, and doesn't sound genteel—not at all respectable. But, after he's gone and done what's proper for the child, the boy could easily slip Lazarus into Laurence. I'm told the thing's done often. No, Caudle, don't say that—I'm not a mean woman; certainly not; quite the reverse. I've only a parent's love for my children; and I must say it—I wish everybody felt as I did.

"I suppose, if the truth was known, you'd like your tobacco-pipe friend, your pot-companion, Prettyman, to stand for the child? *You'd have no objection?* I thought not! Yes; I knew what it was coming to. He's a beggar, he is; and a person who stays out half the night; yes, he does; and it's no use your denying it—a beggar and a tippler, and that's the man you'd make godfather to your own flesh and blood! Upon my word, Caudle, it's enough to make a woman get up and dress herself to hear you talk.

"Well, I can hardly tell you, if you won't have Wagstaff, or Pugsby, or Sniggins, or Goldman, or somebody that's respectable, to do what's proper, the child shan't be christened at all. As for Prettyman, or any such raff—no, never! I'm sure there's a certain set of people that poverty's catching from, and that Prettyman's one of 'em. Now, Caudle, I won't have my dear child lost by any of your spittoon acquaintance, I can tell you.

"No; unless I can have *my* way, the child shan't be christened at all. What do you say? *It must have a name?* There's no 'must' at all in the case—none. No: it shall have no name; and then see what the world will say. I'll call it Number Six—yes, that will do as well as anything else, unless I've the godfather I like. Number Six Caudle! ha! ha! I think that must make you ashamed of yourself if anything can. Number Six Caudle —a much better name than Mr. Prettyman could give; yes, Number Six! What do you say? *Anything but Number Seven?* Oh, Caudle, if ever—"

"At this moment," writes Caudle, "little Number Six began to cry; and taking advantage of the happy accident, I somehow got to sleep."


## LECTURE XVII.

CAUDLE IN THE COURSE OF THE DAY HAS VENTURED TO QUESTION
THE ECONOMY OF "WASHING AT HOME."

"A PRETTY TEMPER you come to bed in, Mr. Caudle, I can see! Oh, don't deny it—I think I ought to know by this time. But it's always the way; whenever I get up a few things, the house can hardly hold you! Nobody cries out more about clean linen than you do—and nobody leads a poor woman so miserable a life when she tries to make her husband comfortable. Yes, Mr. Caudle—comfortable! You needn't keep chewing the word, as if you couldn't swallow it. *Was there ever such a woman?* No, Caudle; I hope not: I should hope no other wife was ever put upon as I am! It's all very well for you. I can't have a little wash at home like anybody else, but you must go about the house swearing to yourself, and looking at your wife as if she was your bitterest enemy. But I suppose you'd rather we didn't wash at all. Yes; then you'd be happy! To be sure

you would—you'd like to have all the children in their dirt, like potatoes: anything, so that it didn't disturb you. I wish you'd had a wife
who'd never washed—*she'd* have suited you, she would. Yes: a fine lady
who'd have let your children go that you might have scraped 'em. She'd
have been much better cared for than I am. I only wish I could let all of
you go without clean linen at all—yes, all of you. I wish I could! And if
I wasn't a slave to my family, unlike anybody else, I should.

"No, Mr. Caudle; the house isn't tossed about in water as if it was
Noah's Ark! And you ought to be ashamed of yourself to talk of Noah's
Ark in that loose manner. I'm sure I don't know what I've done to be
married to a man of such principles. No: and the whole house *doesn't*
taste of soap-suds either; and if it did, any other man but yourself would
be above naming it. I suppose I don't like washing day any more than
yourself. What do you say? *Yes I do?* Ha! you're wrong there, Mr. Caudle. No; I don't like it because it makes everybody else uncomfortable.
No; and I ought not to have been born a mermaid, that I might always
have been in water. A mermaid, indeed! What next will you call me?
But no man, Mr. Caudle, says such things to his wife as you. However,
as I've said before, it can't last long, that's one comfort. What do you
say? *You're glad of it?* You're a brute, Mr. Caudle! No, you *didn't* mean
washing: I know what you meant. A pretty speech to a woman who's
been the wife to you I have! You'll repent it when it's too late: yes, I
wouldn't have your feelings when I'm gone, Caudle; no, not for the
bank of England.

"And when we only wash once a fortnight! Ha! I only wish you had
some wives: they'd wash once a week! Besides, if once a fortnight's too
much for you, why don't you give me money that we may have things to
go a month? Is it *my* fault, if we're short? What do you say? My '*once a
fortnight' lasts three days?* No, it doesn't; never; well, very seldom, and
that's the same thing. Can I help it, if the blacks[8] will fly, and the things
must be rinsed again? Don't say that: I'm *not* made happy by the blacks,
and they *don't* prolong my enjoyment: and, more than that, you're an
unfeeling man to say so. You're enough to make a woman wish herself
in her grave—you are, Caudle.

"And a pretty example you set to your sons! Because we'd a little wash
to-day, and there wasn't a hot dinner—and who thinks of getting anything hot for washerwomen?—because you hadn't everything as you always have it, you must swear at the cold mutton—and you don't know
what that mutton cost a pound, I dare say—you must swear at a sweet,

8 blacks, soot.

wholesome joint like a lord. What! *You didn't swear?* Yes; it's very well for you to say so; but I know when you're swearing; and you swear when you little think it; and I say you must go on swearing as you did, and seize your hat like a savage, and rush out of the house, and go and take your dinner at a tavern! A pretty wife people must think you have, when they find you dining at a public-house. A nice home they must think you have, Mr. Caudle! What! *You'll do so every time I wash?* Very well, Mr. Caudle—very well. We'll soon see who's tired of that, first; for I'll wash a stocking a day if that's all, sooner than you should have everything as you like. Ha! that's so like you; you'd trample everybody under foot, if you could—you know you would, Caudle, so don't deny it.

"Now, if you begin to shout in that manner, I'll leave the bed. It's very hard that I can't say a single word to you, but you must almost raise the place. *You didn't shout?* I don't know what you call shouting, then! I'm sure the people must hear you in the next house. No—it won't do to call me soft names, now, Caudle: I'm not the fool that I was when I was first married—I know better now. You're to treat me in the manner you have, all day; and then at night, the only time and place when I can get a word in, you want to go to sleep. How can you be so mean, Caudle?

"What! *Why can't I put the washing out?* Now, you have asked that a thousand times, but it's no use, Caudle; so don't ask it again. I won't put it out. What do you say? *Mrs. Prettyman says it's quite as cheap?* Pray, what's Mrs. Prettyman to me? I should think, Mr. Caudle, that I know very well how to take care of my family, without Mrs. Prettyman's advice. Mrs. Prettyman, indeed! I only wish she'd come here, that I might tell her so! Mrs. Prettyman! But, perhaps she'd better come and take care of your house for you! Oh, yes! I've no doubt she'd do it much better than I do—*much.* No, Caudle! *I won't hold my tongue.* I think I ought to be mistress of my own washing by this time—and after the wife I've been to you, it's cruel of you to go on as you do.

"Don't tell me about putting the washing out. I say it isn't so cheap— I don't care whether you wash by the dozen or not—it isn't so cheap; I've reduced everything, and I save at least a shilling a week. What do you say? *A trumpery shilling?* Ha! I only hope to goodness you'll not come to want, talking of shillings in the way you do. Now, don't begin about your comfort: don't go on aggravating me, and asking me if your comfort's not worth a shilling a week? That's nothing at all to do with it— nothing: but that's your way—when I talk of one thing, you talk of another; that's so like you men, and you know it. Allow me to tell you, Mr. Caudle, that a shilling a week is two pound twelve a year, and take two pound twelve a year for, let us say, thirty years, and—well, you needn't groan, Mr. Caudle—I don't suppose it will be so long; oh, no! you'll have somebody else to look after your washing long before that—and if it wasn't for my dear children's sake I shouldn't care how soon. You know my mind—and so, good night, Mr. Caudle."

"Thankful for her silence," writes Caudle, "I was fast dropping to sleep; when, jogging my elbow, my wife observed—'Mind, there's the cold mutton to-morrow—nothing hot till that's gone. Remember, too, as it was a short wash to-day, we wash again on Wednesday.' "

## LECTURE XVIII.

CAUDLE, WHILST WALKING WITH HIS WIFE, HAS BEEN BOWED TO BY
A YOUNGER AND EVEN PRETTIER WOMAN THAN MRS. CAUDLE.

"IF I'M not to leave the house without being insulted, Mr. Caudle, I had better stay in-doors all my life.

"What! Don't tell me to let you have *one* night's rest! I wonder at your impudence! It's mighty fine, I never can go out with you, and—goodness knows!—it's seldom enough, without having my feelings torn to pieces by people of all sorts. A set of bold minxes! *What am I raving about?* Oh, you know very well—very well, indeed, Mr. Caudle. A pretty person she must be to nod to a man walking with his own wife! Don't tell me that it's Miss Prettyman—what's Miss Prettyman to me? Oh! *You've met her once or twice at her brother's house?* Yes, I dare say you have—no doubt of it. I always thought there was something very tempting about that house—and now I know it all. Now, it's no use, Mr. Caudle, your beginning to talk loud, and twist and toss your arms about as if you were as innocent as a born babe—I'm not to be deceived by such tricks now. No; there was a time when I was a fool and believed anything; but—I thank my stars!—I've got over that.

"A bold minx! You suppose I didn't see her laugh, too, when she nodded to you! Oh yes, I knew what she thought me; a poor miserable creature, of course. I could see that. No—don't say so, Caudle. I *don't* always see more than anybody else—but I can't and won't be blind, however agreeable it might be to you; I must have the use of my senses. I'm sure, if a woman wants attention and respect from a man, she'd better be anything than his wife. I've always thought so; and to-day's decided it.

"No; I'm not ashamed of myself to talk so—certainly not. *A good, amiable young creature, indeed!* Yes; I dare say; very amiable, no doubt. Of course, you think her so. You suppose I didn't see what sort of a bonnet she had on? Oh, a very good creature! And you think I didn't see the smudges of court plaster about her face? *You didn't see 'em?* Very likely; but I did. Very amiable, to be sure! What do you say? *I made her blush at my ill manners?* I should like to have seen her blush! 'Twould have been rather difficult, Mr. Caudle, for a blush to come through all that paint. No—I'm not a censorious woman, Mr. Caudle; quite the reverse. No; and you may threaten to get up, if you like—I will speak. I know what colour is, and I say it *was* paint. I believe, Mr. Caudle, *I* once had a complexion; though, of course, you've quite forgotten that: I think I once had a colour, before your conduct destroyed it. Before I knew you, people used to call me the Lily and Rose; but—what are you laughing at? I see nothing to laugh at. But as I say, anybody before your own wife.

"And I can't walk out with you but you're bowed to by every woman you meet! *What do I mean by every woman, when it's only Miss Prettyman?* That's nothing at all to do with it. How do I know who bows to you when I'm not by? Everybody of course. And if they don't look at you, why, you look at them. Oh! I'm sure you do. You do it even when I'm out with you, and of course you do it when I'm away. Now, don't tell me, Caudle—don't deny it. The fact is, it's become such a dreadful habit with you, that you don't know when you do it, and when you don't. But I do.

"Miss Prettyman, indeed! What do you say? *You won't lie still and hear me scandalise that excellent young woman?* Oh, of course, you'll take her part! Though, to be sure, she may not be so much to blame after all. For how is she to know you're married? You're never seen out of doors with your own wife—never. Wherever you go, you go alone. Of course people think you're a bachelor. What do you say? *You well know you're not?* That's nothing to do with it—I only ask what must people think, when I'm never seen with you? Other women go out with their husbands: but as I've often said, I'm not like any other woman. What are you sneering at, Mr. Caudle? *How do I know you're sneering?* Don't tell me: I know well enough, by the movement of the pillow.

"No; you never take me out—and you know it. No; and it's not my own fault. How can you lie there and say that? Oh, all a poor excuse! That's what you always say. You're tired of asking me, indeed, because I always start some objection? Of course I can't go out a figure. And when you ask me to go, you know very well that my bonnet isn't as it should be—or that my gown hasn't come home—or that I can't leave the

Caudles and Miss Prettyman.

children,—or that something keeps me in-doors. You know all this, well enough, before you ask me. And that's your art. And when I *do* go out with you, I'm sure to suffer for it. Yes; you needn't repeat my words. *Suffer for it.* But you suppose I have no feelings: oh no, nobody has feelings but yourself. Yes; I'd forgot: Miss Prettyman, perhaps—yes, she may have feelings, of course.

"And as I've said, I dare say a pretty dupe people think me. To be sure; a poor forlorn creature I must look in everybody's eyes. But I knew you couldn't be at Mr. Prettyman's house night after night till eleven o'clock—and a great deal you thought of me sitting up for you—I knew you couldn't be there without some cause. And now I've found it out! Oh, I don't mind your swearing, Mr. Caudle! It's I, if I wasn't a woman, who ought to swear. But it's like you men. Lords of the creation, as you call yourselves! Lords, indeed! And pretty slaves you make of the poor creatures who're tied to you. But I'll be separated, Caudle; I will; and then I'll take care and let all the world know how you've used me. What do you say? *I may say my worst?* Ha! don't you tempt any woman in that way—don't, Caudle; for I wouldn't answer for what I said.

"Miss Prettyman, indeed, and—oh, yes! now I see! Now the whole light breaks in upon me! Now, I know why you wished me to ask her with Mr. and Mrs. Prettyman to tea! And I, like a poor blind fool, was nearly doing it. But now, as I say, my eyes are open! And you'd have brought her under my own roof—now it's no use you're bouncing about in that fashion—you'd have brought her into the very house, where——"

"Here," says Caudle, "I could endure it no longer. So I jumped out of bed, and went and slept somehow with the children."

# LECTURE XIX.

### MRS. CAUDLE THINKS "IT WOULD LOOK WELL TO KEEP THEIR WEDDING-DAY."

"CAUDLE, love, do you know what next Sunday is? *No! you don't?* Well, was there ever such a strange man! Can't you guess, darling? Next Sunday, dear? Think, love, a minute—just think. *What! and you don't know now?* Ha! if I hadn't a better memory than you, I don't know how we should ever get on. Well, then, pet,—shall I tell you what next Sunday is? Why, then, it's our wedding day——What are you groaning at, Mr. Caudle? I don't see anything to groan at. If anybody should groan, I'm sure it isn't you. No: I rather think it's I who ought to groan!

"Oh, dear! That's fourteen years ago. You were a very different man, then, Mr. Caudle. What do you say?—*And I was a very different woman?* Not at all—just the same. Oh, you needn't roll your head about on the pillow in that way: I say, just the same. Well, then, if I'm altered, whose fault is it? Not mine, I'm sure—certainly not. Don't tell me that I couldn't talk at all then—I could talk just as well then as I can now; only then I hadn't the same cause. It's you who've made me talk. What do you say? *You're very sorry for it?* Caudle, you do nothing but insult me.

"Ha! you were a good-tempered, nice creature fourteen years ago, and would have done anything for me. Yes, yes, if a woman would be always cared for, she should never marry. There's quite an end of the charm when she goes to church! We're all angels while you're courting us; but once married, how soon you pull our wings off! No, Mr. Caudle, I'm not talking nonsense; but the truth is, you like to hear nobody talk but yourself. Nobody ever tells me that I talk nonsense but you. Now, it's no use your turning and turning about in that way, it's not a bit of—what do you say? *You'll get up?* No you won't, Mr. Caudle; you'll not serve me that trick again; for I've locked the door, and hid the key. There's no getting hold of you all the day-time,—but here you can't leave me. You needn't groan again, Mr. Caudle.

"Now, Caudle, dear, do let us talk comfortably. After all, love, there's a good many folks who, I dare say, don't get on half so well as we've done. We've both our little tempers, perhaps; but you *are* aggravating; you must own that, Caudle. Well, never mind; we won't talk of it; I won't scold you now. We'll talk of next Sunday, love. We never have kept our wedding-day, and I think it would be a nice day to have our friends. What do you say? *They'd think it hypocrisy?* No hypocrisy at all. I'm sure I try to be comfortable; and if ever man was happy, *you* ought to be. No, Caudle, no; it isn't nonsense to keep wedding-days; it isn't a deception on the world; and if it is, how many people do it? I'm sure, it's only a proper compliment that a man owes to his wife. Look at the Winkles—don't they give a dinner every year? Well, I know, and if they do fight a little in the course of the twelvemonth, that's nothing to do with it. They keep their wedding-day, and their acquaintance have nothing to do with anything else.

"As I say, Caudle, it's only a proper compliment that a man owes to his wife to keep his wedding-day. It's as much as to say to the whole world—'There! if I had to marry again, my blessed wife's the only woman I'd choose!' Well! I see nothing to groan at, Mr. Caudle—no, nor to sigh at either; but I know what you mean: I'm sure, what would have become of you, if you hadn't married as you have done—why, you'd have been a lost creature! I know it; I know your habits, Caudle; and—I don't like to say it—but you'd have been little better than a ragamuffin. Nice scrapes you'd have got into I know, if you hadn't had me for a wife. The trouble I've had to keep you respectable—and what's my thanks? Ha! I only wish you'd had some women!

"But we won't quarrel, Caudle. No; you don't mean anything, I know. We'll have this little dinner, eh? Just a few friends? Now don't say you don't care—that isn't the way to speak to a wife; and especially the wife I've been to you, Caudle. Well, you agree to the dinner, eh? Now, don't grunt, Mr. Caudle, but speak out. You'll keep your wedding day? What? *If I'll let you go to sleep?* Ha, that's unmanly, Caudle; can't you say, 'Yes' without anything else? I say—can't you say 'Yes?'—There, bless you! I knew you would.

"And now, Caudle, what shall we have for dinner? No—we won't talk of it to-morrow; we'll talk of it now, and then it will be off my mind. I should like something particular—something out of the way—just to show that we thought the day something. I should like—Mr. Caudle, you're not asleep? *What do I want?* Why, you know I want to settle about the dinner. *Have what I like?* No: as it's your fancy to keep the day, it's only right that I should try to please you. We never had one, Caudle; so what do you think of a haunch of venison? What do you say? *Mutton will do?* Ha! that shows what you think of your wife: I dare say if it was with any of your club friends—any of your pot-house companions—you'd have no objection to venison. I say if—what do you mutter? *Let it be venison?* Very well. And now about the fish? What do you think of a nice turbot? No, Mr. Caudle, brill won't do—it shall be turbot, or there shan't be any fish at all. Oh, what a mean man you are, Caudle! Shall it be turbot? *It shall?* Very well. And now about the soup—now, Caudle, don't swear at the soup in that manner; you know there must be soup. Well, once in a way, and just to show our friends how happy we've been, we'll have some real turtle. *No, you won't, you'll have nothing but mock?* Then, Mr. Caudle, you may sit at the table by yourself. Mock-turtle on a wedding day! Was there ever such an insult? What do you say? *Let it be real then, for once?* Ha, Caudle! as I say, you were a very different person fourteen years ago.

"And, Caudle, you'll look after the venison? There's a place I know, somewhere in the City, where you get it beautiful! You'll look to it? *You will?* Very well.

"And now who shall we invite? *Who I like?* Now, you know, Caudle, that's nonsense; because I only like whom you like. I suppose the Prettymans must come? But understand, Caudle, I don't have Miss Prettyman: I'm not going to have my peace of mind destroyed under my own roof: if she comes, I don't appear at the table. What do you say? *Very well?* Very well be it, then.

"And now, Caudle, you'll not forget the venison? In the City, my dear? You'll not forget the venison? A haunch, you know: a nice haunch. And you'll not forget the venison?——"

"Three times did I fall off to sleep," says Caudle, "and three times did my wife nudge me with her elbow, exclaiming—'You'll not forget the venison?' At last I got into a sound slumber, and dreamt I was a pot of currant-jelly."

## LECTURE XX.

"BROTHER" CAUDLE HAS BEEN TO A MASONIC CHARITABLE DINNER.
MRS. CAUDLE HAS HIDDEN THE "BROTHER'S" CHEQUE-BOOK.

"ALL I SAY is this: I only wish I'd been born a man. What do you say?

*You wish I had?* Mr. Caudle, I'll not lie quiet in my own bed to be insulted. Oh, yes, you *did* mean to insult me. I know what you mean. You mean, if I *had* been born a man, you'd never have married me. That's a pretty sentiment, I think? and after the wife I've been to you. And now I suppose you'll be going to public dinners every day! It's no use your telling me you've only been to one before; that's nothing to do with it—nothing at all. Of course you'll be out every night now. I knew what it would come to when you were made a mason: when you were once made a 'brother,' as you call yourself, I knew where the husband and father would be;—I'm sure, Caudle, and though I'm your own wife, I grieve to say it—I'm sure you haven't so much heart, that you have any to spare for people out of doors. Indeed, I should like to see the man who has! No, no, Caudle; I'm by no means a selfish woman—quite the contrary; I love my fellow-creatures as a wife and mother of a family, who has only to look to her own husband and children, ought to love 'em.

"A 'brother,' indeed! What would you say, if I was to go and be made a 'sister'? Why, I know very well—the house wouldn't hold you.

"*Where's your watch?* How should I know where your watch is? You ought to know. But to be sure, people who go to public dinners never know where anything is when they come home. You've lost it, no doubt; and 'twill serve you quite right if you have. If it should be gone—and nothing more likely—I wonder if any of your 'brothers' will give you another? Catch 'em doing it.

"*You must find your watch? And you'll get up for it?* Nonsense—don't be foolish—lie still. Your watch is on the mantelpiece. Ha! isn't it a good thing for you, you've somebody to take care of it?

"What do you say? *I'm a dear creature?* Very dear, indeed, you think me, I dare say. But the fact is, you don't know what you're talking about to-night. I'm a fool to open my lips to you—but I can't help it.

"*Where's your watch?* Haven't I told you—on the mantelpiece? *All right, indeed?* Pretty conduct you men call all right. There now, hold your tongue, Mr. Caudle, and go to sleep: I'm sure 'tis the best thing you can do to-night. You'll be able to listen to reason to-morrow morning; now, it's thrown away upon you.

"*Where's your cheque-book?* Never mind your cheque-book. I took care of that. *What business had I to take it out of your pocket?* Every business. No, no. If you choose to go to public dinners, why—as I'm only your wife—I can't help it. But I know what fools men are made of there; and if I know it, you never take your cheque-book again with you. What! Didn't I see your name down last year for ten pounds? 'Job Caudle, Esq.,

10£.' It looked very well in the newspapers, of course: and you thought
yourself a somebody, when they knocked the tavern tables; but I only
wish I'd been there—yes, I only wish I'd been in the gallery. If I wouldn't
have told a piece of my mind, I'm not alive. Ten pounds, indeed! and
the world thinks you a very fine person for it. I only wish I could bring
the world here, and show 'em what's wanted at home. I think the world
would alter their mind then; yes—a little.

"What do you say? *A wife has no right to pick her husband's pocket?*
A pretty husband you are, to talk in that way. Never mind: you can't
prosecute her for it—or I've no doubt you would; none at all. Some
men would do anything. What? *You've a bit of a head-ache?* I hope you
have—and a good bit, too. You've been to the right place for it. No—I
won't hold my tongue. It's all very well for you men to go to taverns—
and talk—and toast—and hurra—and—I wonder you're not all ashamed
of yourselves to drink the Queen's health with all the honours, I believe,
you call it—yes, pretty honours, you pay to the sex—I say, I wonder
you're not ashamed to drink that blessed creature's health, when you've
only to think how you use your own wives at home. But the hypocrites
that the men are—oh!

"*Where's your watch?* Haven't I told you? It's under your pillow—
there, you needn't be feeling for it. I tell you it's under your pillow. *It's
all right?* Yes; a great deal you know of what's right just now. Ha! was
there ever any poor soul used as I am! *I'm a dear creature?* Pah! Mr. Caudle! I've only to say, I'm tired of your conduct—quite tired, and don't
care how soon there's an end of it.

"*Why did I take your cheque-book?* I've told you—to save you from
ruin, Mr. Caudle. *You're not going to be ruined?* Ha! you don't know
anything when you're out! I know what they do at those public dinners—charities, they call 'em; pretty charities! True Charity, I believe,
always dines at home. I know what they do: the whole system's a trick.
No: *I'm not a stony-hearted creature:* and you ought to be ashamed to
say so of your wife and the mother of your children,—but, you'll not
make me cry to-night, I can tell you—I was going to say that—oh! you're
such an aggravating man I don't know what I was going to say!

"*Thank Heaven?* What for? I don't see that there's anything to thank
Heaven about! I was going to say, I know the trick of public dinners.
They get a lord, or a duke, if they can catch him—anything to make people say they've dined with nobility, that's it—yes, they get one of these
people, with a star perhaps in his coat, to take the chair—and to talk all
sorts of sugar-plum things about charity—and to make foolish men, with

wine in 'em, feel that they've no end of money; and then—shutting their eyes to their wives and families at home—all the while that their own faces are red and flushed like poppies, and they think to-morrow will never come—then they get 'em to put their hand to paper. Then they make 'em pull out their cheques. But I took your book, Mr. Caudle—you couldn't do it a second time. What are you laughing at? *Nothing?* It's no matter: I shall see it in the paper to-morrow; for if you gave anything, you were too proud to hide it. I know *your* charity.

"*Where's your watch?* Haven't I told you fifty times where it is? In the pocket—over your head—of course. Can't you hear it tick? No: you can hear nothing to-night.

"And now, Mr. Caudle, I should like to know whose hat it is you've brought home? You went out with a beaver worth three-and-twenty shillings—the second time you've worn it—and you bring home a thing that no Jew in his senses would give me fivepence for. I couldn't even get a pot of primroses—and you know I always turn your old hats into roots—not a pot of primroses for it. I'm certain of it now,—I've often thought it—but now I'm sure that some people dine out only to change their hats.

"*Where's your watch?* Caudle, you're bringing me to an early grave!"

We hope that Caudle was penitent for his conduct; indeed, there is, we think, evidence that he was so: for to this lecture he has appended no comment. The man had not the face to do it.


# LECTURE XXI.

### MR. CAUDLE HAS NOT ACTED "LIKE A HUSBAND"
### AT THE WEDDING DINNER.

"Ah me! It's no use wishing—none at all: but I do wish that yesterday fourteen years could come back again. Little did I think, Mr. Caudle, when you brought me home from church, your lawful wedded wife—little, I say, did I think that I should keep my wedding-dinner in the manner I have done to-day. Fourteen years ago! Yes, I see you now in your blue coat with bright buttons, and your white watered-satin waistcoat, and a moss rose-bud in your button-hole, which you said was like me. What? *You never talked such nonsense?* Ha! Mr. Caudle, you don't know what you talked that day—but I do. Yes; and you then sat at the table as if your face, as I may say, was buttered with happiness, and—

What? No. Mr. Caudle, don't say that; *I* have not wiped the butter off—not I. If you above all men are not happy, you ought to be, gracious knows!

"Yes, I *will* talk of fourteen years ago. Ha! you sat beside me then, and picked out all sorts of nice things for me. You'd have given me pearls and diamonds to eat if I could have swallowed 'em. Yes, I say, you sat beside me, and—What do you talk about? *You couldn't sit beside me to-day?* That's nothing at all to do with it. But it's so like you. I can't speak but you fly off to something else. Ha! and when the health of the young couple was drunk, what a speech you made then! It was delicious! How you made everybody cry, as if their hearts were breaking; and I recollect it as if it was yesterday, how the tears ran down dear father's nose, and how dear mother nearly went into a fit! Dear souls! They little thought, with all your fine talk, how you'd use me! *How have you used me?* Oh, Mr. Caudle, how can you ask that question? It's well for you I can't see you blush. *How* have you used me!

"Well, that the same tongue could make a speech like that, and then talk as it did to-day! *How did you talk?* Why, shamefully! What did you say about your wedded happiness? Why, nothing. What did you say about your wife? Worse than nothing: just as if she were a bargain you were sorry for, but were obliged to make the best of. What do you say? *And bad's the best?* If you say that again, Caudle, I'll rise from my bed. *You didn't say it?* What, then, did you say? Something very like it, I know. Yes, a pretty speech of thanks for a husband! And everybody could see that you didn't care a pin for me; and that's why you had 'em here: that's why you invited 'em, to insult me to their faces. What? *I made you invite 'em?* Oh, Caudle, what an aggravating man you are!

"I suppose you'll say next I made you invite Miss Prettyman? Oh yes; don't tell me that her brother brought her without your knowing it. What? *Didn't I hear him say so?* Of course I did; but do you suppose I'm quite a fool? Do you think I don't know that that was all settled between you? And she must be a nice person to come unasked to a woman's house? But I know why she came. Oh yes; she came to look about her. *What do I mean?* Oh, the meaning's plain enough. She came to see how she should like the rooms—how she should like my seat at the fire-place; how she—and if it isn't enough to break a mother's heart to be treated so!—how she should like my dear children.

"Now, it's no use your bouncing about at—but of course that's it; I can't mention Miss Prettyman, but you fling about as if you were in a fit. Of course that shows there's something in it. Otherwise, why should you disturb yourself? Do you think I didn't see her looking at the cyphers on the spoons as if she already saw mine scratched out and her's there? No, I shan't drive you mad, Mr. Caudle; and if I do it's your own fault. No other man would treat the wife of his bosom in—What do you say? *You might as well have married a hedgehog?* Well, now it's come to something! But it's always the case! Whenever you've seen that Miss Prettyman, I'm sure to be abused. A hedgehog! A pretty thing for a woman to be called by her husband! Now you don't think I'll lie quietly in bed, and be called a hedgehog—do you, Mr. Caudle?

"Well, I only hope Miss Prettyman had a good dinner, that's all. *I* had none! You know I had none—how was I to get any? You know that the only part of the turkey I care for is the merrythought.[9] And that, of course, went to Miss Prettyman. Oh, I saw you laugh when you put it on her plate! And you don't suppose, after such an insult as that, I'd taste another thing upon the table? No, I should hope I have more spirit than that. Yes; and you took wine with her four times. What do you say? *Only twice?* Oh, you were so lost—fascinated, Mr. Caudle; yes, fascinated—that you didn't know what you did. However, I do think while I'm alive I might be treated with respect at my own table. I say, while I'm alive; for I know I shan't last long, and then Miss Prettyman may come and take it all. I'm wasting daily, and no wonder. I never say anything about it, but every week my gowns are taken in.

"I've lived to learn something, to be sure! Miss Prettyman turned up her nose at my custards. It isn't sufficient that you're always finding fault yourself, but you must bring women home to sneer at me at my own table. What do you say? *She didn't turn up her nose?* I know she did; not but what it's needless—Providence has turned it up quite enough for her already. And she must give herself airs over my custards! Oh, I saw her mincing with the spoon as if she was chewing sand. What do you say? *She praised my plum-pudding?* Who asked her to praise it? Like her impudence, I think!

"Yes, a pretty day I've passed. I shall not forget this wedding-day, I think! And as I say, a pretty speech you made in the way of thanks. No, Caudle, if I was to live a hundred years—you needn't groan, Mr. Caudle, I shall not trouble you half that time—if I was to live a hundred years, I should never forget it. Never! You didn't even so much as bring one of your children into your speech. And—dear creatures!—what have *they* done to offend you? No; I shall not drive you mad. It's you, Mr. Caudle, who'll drive me mad. Everybody says so.

9 merrythought, wishbone.

"And you suppose I didn't see how it was managed, that you and *that* Miss Prettyman were always partners at whist? *How was it managed?* Why, plain enough. Of course you packed the cards, and could cut what you liked. You'd settled that, between you. Yes; and when she took a trick, instead of leading off a trump—*she* play whist, indeed!— what did you say to her, when she found it was wrong? Oh—It was impossible that *her* heart should mistake! And this, Mr. Caudle, before people—with your own wife in the room!

"And Miss Prettyman—I won't hold my tongue. I *will* talk of Miss Prettyman: who's she, indeed, that I shouldn't talk of her? I suppose she thinks she sings? What do you say? *She sings like a mermaid?* Yes, very— very like a mermaid: for she never sings but she exposes herself. She might, I think, have chosen another song. '*I love somebody,*' indeed; as if I didn't know who was meant by that 'somebody;' and all the room knew it, of course; and that was what it was done for, nothing else.

"However, Mr. Caudle, as my mind's made up, I shall say no more about the matter to-night, but try to go to sleep."

"And to my astonishment and gratitude," writes Caudle, "she kept her word."

## LECTURE XXII.

CAUDLE COMES HOME IN THE EVENING, AS MRS. CAUDLE HAS
"JUST STEPPED OUT, SHOPPING." ON HER RETURN,
AT TEN, CAUDLE REMONSTRATES.

"You ought to have had a slave—yes, a black slave, and not a wife. I'm sure, I'd better been born a negro at once—much better. *What's the matter, now?* Well, I like that. Upon my life, Mr. Caudle, that's very cool. I can't leave the house just to buy a yard of riband, but you storm enough to carry the roof off. *You didn't storm?—you only spoke?* Spoke, indeed! No, sir: I've not such superfine feelings; and I don't cry out before I'm hurt. But you ought to have married a woman of stone, for you feel for nobody: that is, for nobody in your own house. I only wish you'd show some of your humanity at home, if ever so little—that's all.

"What do you say? *Where's my feelings, to go a shopping at night?* When would you have me go? In the broiling sun, making my face like a gipsy's? I don't see anything to laugh at, Mr. Caudle; but you think of anybody's face before your wife's. Oh, that's plain enough; and all the world can see it. I dare say, now, if it was Miss Prettyman's face—now, now, Mr. Caudle! What are you throwing yourself about for? I suppose Miss Prettyman isn't so wonderful a person that she isn't to be named? I suppose she's flesh and blood. What? *You don't know?* Ha! I don't know that.

"What, Mr. Caudle? *You'll have a separate room?—you'll not be tormented in this manner?* No, you won't, sir—not while I'm alive. A separate room! And you call yourself a religious man, Mr. Caudle. I'd advise you to take down the Prayer Book, and read over the Marriage Service. A separate room, indeed! Caudle, you're getting quite a heathen. A separate room! Well, the servants would talk then! But no: no man—not the best that ever trod, Caudle—should ever make me look so contemptible.

"I *shan't* go to sleep; and you ought to know me better than to ask me to hold my tongue. Because you come home when I've just stepped out to do a little shopping, you're worse than a fury. I should like to know how many hours I sit up for you? What do you say? *Nobody wants me to sit up?* Ha! that's like the gratitude of men—just like 'em! But a poor woman can't leave the house, that—what? *Why can't I go at reasonable hours?* Reasonable! What do you call eight o'clock? If I went out at eleven and twelve, as you come home, then you might talk; but seven or eight o'clock—why, it's the cool of the evening; the nicest time to enjoy a walk; and, as I say, do a little bit of shopping. Oh yes, Mr. Caudle, I do think of the people that are kept in the shops just as much as you; but that's nothing at all to do with it. I know what you'd have. You'd have all those young men let away early from the counter to improve what you please to call their minds. Pretty notions you pick up among a set of free-thinkers, and I don't know what! When I was a girl, people never talked of minds—intellect, I believe you call it. Nonsense! a new-fangled thing, just come up; and the sooner it goes out, the better.

"Don't tell me! What are shops for, if they're not to be open late and early too? And what are shopmen, if they're not always to attend upon their customers? People pay for what they have, I suppose; and arn't to be told when they shall come and lay their money out, and when they shan't? Thank goodness! if one shop shuts, another keeps open; and I always think it a duty I owe to myself to go to the shop that's open last: it's the only way to punish the shopkeepers that are idle, and give themselves airs about early hours.

"Besides, there's some things I like to buy best at candlelight. Oh, don't talk to me about humanity! Humanity, indeed, for a pack of tall, strapping young fellows—some of 'em big enough to be shown for giants!

And what have they to do? Why, nothing, but to stand behind a counter, and talk civility. Yes, I know your notions; you say that everybody works too much: I know that. You'd have all the world do nothing half its time but twiddle its thumbs, or walk in the parks, or go to picture-galleries, and museums, and such nonsense. Very fine, indeed; but, thank goodness! the world isn't come to that pass yet.

"What do you say I am, Mr. Caudle? *A foolish woman, that can't look beyond my own fireside?* Oh yes, I can; quite as far as you, and a great deal farther. But I can't go out shopping a little with my dear friend, Mrs. Wittles—what do you laugh at? Oh, don't they? Don't women know what friendship is? Upon my life you've a nice opinion of us! Oh, yes, we *can*—we can look outside of our own fenders, Mr. Caudle. And if we can't, it's all the better for our families. A blessed thing it would be for their wives and children if men couldn't either. You wouldn't have lent that five pounds—and I dare say a good many other five pounds that I know nothing of—if you—a lord of the creation!—had half the sense women have. You seldom catch us, I believe, lending five pounds. I should think not.

"No: we won't talk of it to-morrow morning. You're not going to wound my feelings when I come home, and think I'm to say nothing about it. You have called me an inhuman person; you have said I have no thought, no feeling for the health and comfort of my fellow creatures; I don't know what you haven't called me; and only for buying a—but I shan't tell you what; no, I won't satisfy you there—but you've abused me in this manner, and only for shopping up to ten o'clock. You've a great deal of fine compassion, you have! I'm sure the young man that served me could have knocked down an ox; yes, strong enough to lift a house: but you can pity him—oh yes, you can be all kindness for him, and for the world, as you call it. Oh, Caudle, what a hypocrite you are! I only wish the world knew how you treated your poor wife!

"What do you say? *For the love of mercy let you sleep?* Mercy, indeed! I wish you could show a little of it to other people. O yes, I *do* know what mercy means; but that's no reason I should go shopping a bit earlier than I do—and I won't—No; you've preached this over to me again and again; you've made me go to meetings to hear all about it: but that's no reason women shouldn't shop just as late as they choose. It's all very fine, as I say, for you men to talk to us at meetings, where, of course we smile and all that—and sometimes shake our white pocket-handkerchiefs —and where you say we have the power of early hours in our own hands. To be sure we have; and we mean to keep it. That is, I do. You'll never catch me shopping till the very last thing; and—as a matter of principle—I'll always go to the shop that keeps open latest. It does the young men good to keep 'em close to business. Improve their minds, indeed! Let 'em out at seven, and they'd improve nothing but their billiards. Besides, if they want to improve themselves, can't they get up, this fine weather, at three? Where there's a will, there's a way, Mr. Caudle."

"I thought," writes Caudle, "that she had gone to sleep. In this hope, I was dozing off when she jogged me, and thus declared herself:—'Caudle, you want nightcaps; but see if I budge to buy 'em till nine at night!' "

## LECTURE XXIII.

MRS. CAUDLE "WISHES TO KNOW IF THEY'RE GOING TO THE SEA-SIDE,
OR NOT, THIS SUMMER—THAT'S ALL."

"Hот? Yes, it *is* hot. I'm sure one might as well be in an oven as in town this weather. You seem to forget it's July, Mr. Caudle. I've been waiting quietly—have never spoken; yet, not a word have you said of the seaside yet. Not that I care for it myself—oh, no; my health isn't of the slightest consequence. And, indeed, I was going to say—but I won't—that the sooner, perhaps, I'm out of this world, the better. Oh, yes: I dare say you think so—of course you do, else you wouldn't lie there saying nothing. You're enough to aggravate a saint, Caudle; but you shan't vex me. No; I've made up my mind, and never intend to let you vex me again. Why should I worry myself.

"But all I want to ask you is this: do you intend to go to the sea-side this summer? *Yes? you'll go to Gravesend?*[10] Then you'll go alone, that's all I know. Gravesend! You might as well empty a salt-cellar in the New River, and call that the sea-side. What? *It's handy for business?* There you are again! I can never speak of taking a little enjoyment, but you fling business in my teeth. I'm sure you never let business stand in the way of your own pleasure, Mr. Caudle—not you. It would be all the better for your family if you did.

"You know that Matilda wants sea-bathing; you know it, or ought to know it, by the looks of the child; and yet—I know you, Caudle—you'd

10 Gravesend, a seaport in NW Kent, on the Thames River.

have let the summer pass over, and never said a word about the matter. What do you say? *Margate's*[11] *so expensive?* Not at all. I'm sure it will be cheaper for us in the end; for if we don't go, we shall all be ill—every one of us—in the winter. Not that my health is of any consequence: I know that well enough. It never was yet. You know Margate's the only place I can eat a breakfast at, and yet you talk of Gravesend! But what's my eating to you? You wouldn't care if I never eat at all. You never watch my appetite like any other husband, otherwise you'd have seen what it's come to.

"What do you say? *How much will it cost?* There you are, Mr. Caudle, with your meanness again. When you want to go yourself to Blackwall or to Greenwich, you never ask, how much will it cost? What? *You never go to Blackwall?* Ha! I don't know that; and if you don't, that's nothing at all to do with it. Yes, you can give a guinea a plate for whitebait for yourself. No, sir; I'm not a foolish woman; and I know very well what I'm talking about—nobody better. A guinea for whitebait for yourself, when you grudge a pint of shrimps for your poor family. Eh? *You don't grudge 'em anything?* Yes, it's very well for you to lie there and say so. *What will it cost?* It's no matter what it will cost, for we won't go at all now. No; we'll stay at home. We shall all be ill in the winter—every one of us, all but you; and nothing ever makes you ill. I've no doubt we shall all be laid up, and there'll be a doctor's bill as long as a railroad; but never mind that. It's better—much better—to pay for nasty physic than for fresh air and wholesome salt water. Don't call me 'woman,' and ask 'what it will cost.' I tell you, if you were to lay the money down before me on that quilt, I wouldn't go now—certainly not. It's better we should all be sick; yes, then you'll be pleased.

"That's right, Mr. Caudle; go to sleep. It's like your unfeeling self! I'm talking of our all being laid up; and you, like any stone, turn round and begin to go to sleep. Well, I think that's a pretty insult! *How can you sleep with such a splinter in your flesh?* I suppose you mean to call me the splinter?—and after the wife I've been to you! But no, Mr. Caudle, you may call me what you please; you'll not make me cry now. No, no: I don't throw away my tears upon any such person now. What? *Don't?* Ha! that's your ingratitude! But none of you men deserve that any woman should love you. My poor heart!

"Everybody else can go out of town except us. Ha! if I'd only married Simmons—What! *Why didn't I?* Yes, that's all the thanks I get. *Who's Simmons?* Oh, you know very well who Simmons is. He'd have treated

11 Margate, a city in E. Kent, popular as a seaside resort.

Mr. and Mrs. Caudle at the Sea-side.

me a little better, I think. He *was* a gentleman. *You can't tell?* May be not; but I can. With such weather as this, to stay melting in London; and when the painters are coming in! *You won't have the painters in?* But you must; and if they once come in, I'm determined that none of us shall stir then. Painting in July, with a family in the house! We shall all be poisoned, of course; but what do you care for that?

"*Why can't I tell you what it will cost?* How can I or any woman tell exactly what it will cost? Of course lodgings—and at Margate, too—are a little dearer than living at your own house. *Pooh! You know that?* Well, if you did, Mr. Caudle, I suppose there's no treason in naming it. Still, if you take 'em for two months, they're cheaper than for one. No, Mr. Caudle, I shall not be quite tired of it in one month. No: and it isn't true that I no sooner get out than I want to get home again. To be sure, I was tired of Margate three years ago, when you used to leave me to walk about the beach by myself, to be stared at through all sorts of telescopes. But you don't do that again, Mr. Caudle, I can tell you.

"*What will I do at Margate?* Why, isn't there bathing, and picking up shells; and arn't there the packets, with the donkeys; and the last new novel—whatever it is, to read—for the only place where I really relish a book is at the sea-side. No, it isn't that I like salt with my reading, Mr. Caudle! I suppose you call that a joke? You might keep your jokes for the day-time, I think. But as I was saying—only you always will interrupt me—the ocean always seems to me to open the mind. I see nothing to laugh at; but you always laugh when I say anything. Sometimes at the sea-side—especially when the tide's down—I feel so happy: quite as if I could cry.

"When shall I get the things ready? For next Sunday? *What will it cost?* Oh, there—don't talk of it. No: we won't go. I shall send for the painters, to-morrow. What? *I can go and take the children, and you'll stay?* No, sir: you go with me, or I don't stir. I'm not going to be turned loose like a hen with her chickens, and nobody to protect me. So we'll go on Monday? Eh?

"*What will it cost?* What a man you are! Why, Caudle, I've been reckoning that, with buff slippers and all, we can't do it under seventy pounds. No: I won't take away the slippers, and say fifty: it's seventy pounds and no less. Of course, what's over will be so much saved. Caudle, what a man you are! Well, shall we go on Monday? What do you say—*You'll see?* There's a dear. Then, Monday."

"Anything for a chance of peace," writes Caudle. "I consented to the trip, for I thought I might sleep better in a change of bed."

## LECTURE XXIV.

MRS. CAUDLE DWELLS ON CAUDLE'S "CRUEL NEGLECT" OF HER ON
BOARD THE "RED ROVER." MRS. CAUDLE SO "ILL WITH THE SEA,"
THAT THEY PUT UP AT THE DOLPHIN, HERNE BAY.[12]

"CAUDLE, have you looked under the bed? *What for?* Bless the man! Why, for thieves to be sure. Do you suppose I'd sleep in a strange bed, without? Don't tell me it's nonsense! I shouldn't sleep a wink all night. Not that you'd care for that: not that you'd—hush! I'm sure I hear somebody. No; it's not a bit like a mouse. Yes; that's like you—laugh. It would

[12] Herne Bay, an urban district and seaside resort in Kent, twelve miles west of Margate.

be no laughing matter if—I'm sure there *is* somebody!—I'm sure there is!

"———Yes, Mr. Caudle; now I *am* satisfied. Any other man would have got up and looked himself; especially after my sufferings on board that nasty ship. But catch you stirring! Oh, no! You'd let me lie here and be robbed and killed, for what you'd care. Why, you're not going to sleep! What do you say! *It's the strange air—and you're always sleepy in a strange air?* That shows the feelings you have, after what I've gone through. And yawning, too, in that brutal manner! Caudle, you've no more heart than that wooden figure in a white petticoat at the front of the ship.

"No; I *couldn't* leave my temper at home. I dare say! Because for once in your life you've brought me out—yes, I say once, or two or three times, it isn't more; because, as I say, you once bring me out, I'm to be a slave and say nothing. Pleasure, indeed! A great deal of pleasure I'm to have, if I'm to hold my tongue. A nice way that of pleasing a woman.

"Dear me! if the bed doesn't spin round and dance about! I've got all that filthy ship in my head! No: I shan't be well in the morning. But nothing ever ails anybody but yourself. You needn't groan in that way, Mr. Caudle, disturbing the people, perhaps, in the next room. It's a mercy I'm alive, I'm sure. If once I wouldn't have given all the world for anybody to have thrown me overboard! What are you smacking your lips at, Mr. Caudle? But I know what you mean—of course, you'd never have stirred to stop 'em: not you. And then you might have known that the wind would have blown to-day; but that's why you came.

"Whatever I should have done if it hadn't been for that good soul— that blessed Captain Large! I'm sure all the women who go to Margate ought to pray for him; so attentive in seasickness, and so much of a gentleman! How I should have got down stairs without him when I first began to turn, I don't know. Don't tell me I never complained to you—you might have seen I was ill. And when everybody was looking like a bad wax-candle, you could walk about, and make what you call your jokes upon the little buoy that was never sick at the Nore,[13] and such unfeeling trash.

"Yes, Caudle; we've now been married many years, but if we were to live together for a thousand years to come—what are you clasping your hands at?—a thousand years to come I say, I shall never forget your conduct this day. You could go to the other end of the ship and smoke a cigar, when you knew I should be ill—oh, you knew it; for I always am. The brutal way, too, in which you took that cold brandy-and-water—you

[13] Nore, a sandbank in the Thames estuary and a famous anchorage.

thought I didn't see you; but ill as I was, hardly able to hold my head up, I was watching you all the time. Three glasses of cold brandy-and-water; and you sipped 'em, and drank the health of people you didn't care a pin about; whilst the health of your own lawful wife was nothing. Three glasses of brandy-and-water, and *I* left—as I may say—alone! You didn't hear 'em, but everybody was crying shame of you.

"What do you say? *A good deal my own fault? I took too much dinner?* Well, you are a man! If I took more than the breast and leg of that young goose—a thing, I may say, just out of the shell—with the slightest bit of stuffing, I'm a wicked woman. What do you say? *Lobster salad?* La!—how can you speak of it? A month old baby would have eaten more. What? *Gooseberry pie?* Well, if you'll name that, you'll name anything. Ate too much indeed! Do you think I was going to pay for a dinner, and eat nothing? No, Mr. Caudle; it's a good thing for you that I know a little more of the value of money than that.

"But, of course, you were better engaged than in attending to me. Mr. Prettyman came on board at Gravesend. A planned thing, of course. You think I didn't see him give you a letter. *It wasn't a letter; it was a newspaper?* I daresay; ill as I was, I had my eyes. It was the smallest newspaper I ever saw, that's all. But of course, a letter from Miss Prettyman—— Now, Caudle, if you begin to cry in that manner, I'll get up. Do you forget that you're not at your own house? making that noise! Disturbing everybody! Why, we shall have the landlord up! And you could smoke and drink 'forward' as you called it. What? *You couldn't smoke anywhere else?* That's nothing to do with it. Yes; forward. What a pity that Miss Prettyman wasn't with you. I'm sure nothing could be too forward for her. No, I won't hold my tongue; and I ought not to be ashamed of myself. It isn't treason, is it, to speak of Miss Prettyman? After all I've suffered to day, and I'm not to open my lips! Yes; I'm to be brought away from my own home, dragged down here to the sea-side, and made ill; and I'm not to speak. I should like to know what next.

"It's a mercy that some of the dear children were not drowned; not that their father would have cared, so long as he could have had his brandy and cigars. Peter was as near through one of the holes as—*It's no such thing?* It's very well for you to say so, but you know what an inquisitive boy he is, and how he likes to wander among steam-engines. No, I won't let you sleep. What a man you are! What? *I've said that before?* That's no matter; I'll say it again. Go to sleep, indeed! as if one could never have a little rational conversation. No, I shan't be too late for the Margate boat in the morning; I can wake up at what hour I like, and you ought to know that by this time.

"A miserable creature they must have thought me in the ladies' cabin, with nobody coming down to see how I was. *You came a dozen times?* No, Caudle, that won't do. I know better. You never came at all. Oh, no! cigars and brandy took all your attention. And when I was so ill, that I didn't know a single thing that was going on about me, and you never came. Every other woman's husband was there—ha! twenty times. And what must have been my feelings to hear 'em tapping at the door, and making all sorts of kind inquiries—something like husbands!—and I was left to be ill alone? Yes; and you want to get me into an argument. You want to know, if I was so ill that I knew nothing, how could I know that you didn't come to the cabin-door? That's just like your aggravating way; but I'm not to be caught in that manner, Caudle. No."

"It is very possible," writes Caudle, "that she talked two hours more: but, happily, the wind got suddenly up—the waves bellowed—and, soothed by the sweet lullaby (to say nothing of the Dolphin's brandy-and-water), I somehow sank to repose."

## LECTURE XXV.

### MRS. CAUDLE, WEARIED OF MARGATE, HAS
### "A GREAT DESIRE TO SEE FRANCE."

"ARN'T YOU TIRED, Caudle? *No?* Well, was there ever such a man! But nothing ever tires you. Of course, it's all very well for you: yes, you can read your newspapers and—What? *So can I?* And I wonder what would become of the children if I did! No; it's enough for their father to lose his precious time, talking about politics, and bishops, and lords, and a pack of people who wouldn't care a pin if we hadn't a roof to cover us— it's well enough for—no, Caudle, no: I'm not going to worry you; I never worried you yet, and it isn't likely I should begin now. But that's always the way with you—always. I'm sure we should be the happiest couple alive, only you do so like to have all the talk to yourself. We're out upon pleasure, and therefore let's be comfortable. Still, I must say it: when you like, you're an aggravating man, Caudle, and you know it.

"*What have you done now?* There, now; we won't talk of it. No; let's go to sleep: otherwise, we shall quarrel—I know we shall. What have you done, indeed! That I can't leave my home for a few days, but I must be insulted! Everybody upon the pier saw it. *Saw what?* How can you lie there in the bed and ask me? Saw what, indeed! Of course, it was a planned thing!—regularly settled before you left London. Oh yes; I like your innocence, Mr. Caudle; not knowing what I'm talking about. It's a heartbreaking thing for a woman to say of her own husband; but you've been a wicked man to me. Yes: and all your tossing and tumbling about in the bed won't make it any better.

"Oh, it's easy enough to call a woman 'a dear soul.' I must be very dear, indeed, to you, when you bring down Miss Prettyman to—there now; you needn't shout like a wild savage. Do you know that you're not in your own house—do you know that we're in lodgings? What do you suppose the people will think of us? You needn't call out in that manner, for they can hear every word that's said. What do you say? *Why don't I hold my tongue then?* To be sure; anything for an excuse with you. Anything to stop my mouth. Miss Prettyman's to follow you here, and I'm to say nothing. I know she *has* followed you; and if you were to go before a magistrate, and take a shilling oath to the contrary, I wouldn't believe you. No, Caudle; I wouldn't.

"*Very well then?* Ha! what a heart you must have, to say 'very well;' and after the wife I've been to you. I'm to be brought from my own home —dragged down here to the sea-side—to be laughed at before the world— don't tell me! Do you think I didn't see how she looked at you—how she puckered up her farthing mouth—and—what? *Why did I kiss her, then?* What's that to do with it? Appearances are one thing, Mr. Caudle; and feelings are another. As if women can't kiss one another without meaning anything by it! And you—I could see you—looked as cold and as formal at her as—well, Caudle! I wouldn't be the hypocrite you are for the world!

"There, now; I've heard all that story. I dare say she did come down to join her brother. How very lucky, though, that you should be here! Ha! ha! how very lucky that—ugh! ugh! ugh! and with the cough I've got upon me—oh, you've a heart like a sea-side flint! Yes, that's right. That's just like your humanity. I can't catch a cold, but it must be my own fault —it must be my thin shoes. I dare say you'd like to see me in ploughman's boots; 'twould be no matter to you how I disfigured myself. Miss Prettyman's foot, now, would be another thing—no doubt.

"I thought when you would make me leave home—I thought we were coming here on pleasure: but it's always the way you embitter my life. The sooner that I'm out of the world, the better. What do you say? *Nothing?* But I know what you mean, better than if you talked an hour. I only hope you'll get a better wife, that's all, Mr. Caudle. What? *You'd not try?*

Wouldn't you? I know you. In six months you'd fill up my place; yes, and dreadfully my dear children would suffer for it.

"Caudle, if you roar in that way, the people will give us warning to-morrow. *Can't I be quiet then?* Yes—that's like your artfulness: anything to make me hold my tongue. But we won't quarrel. I'm sure if it depend-ed upon me, we might be as happy as doves. I mean it—and you needn't groan when I say it. Good night, Caudle. What do you say? *Bless me!* Well, you are a dear soul, Caudle; and if it wasn't for that Miss Pretty-man—no, I'm not torturing you. I know very well what I'm doing, and I wouldn't torture you for the world; but you don't know what the feelings of a wife are, Caudle; you don't.

"Caudle—I say, Caudle. Just a word, dear. *Well?* Now, why should you snap me up in that way. *You want to go to sleep?* So do I; but that's no reason you should speak to me in that manner. You know, dear, you once promised to take me to France. *You don't recollect it?* Yes—that's like you; you don't recollect many things you've promised me; but I do. There's a boat goes on Wednesday to Boulogne, and comes back the day afterwards. *What of it?* Why, for that time we could leave the children with the girls, and go nicely. *Nonsense?* Of course; if I want anything it's always nonsense. Other men can take their wives half over the world; but you think it quite enough to bring me down here to this hole of a place, where I know every pebble on the beach like an old acquaintance—where there's nothing to be seen but the same machines[14]—the same jetty—the same donkeys—the same everything. But then, I'd forgot; Margate has an attraction for you—Miss Prettyman's here. No; I'm not censorious, and I wouldn't backbite an angel; but the way in which that young woman walks the sands at all hours—there! there!—I've done: I can't open my lips about that creature but you always storm.

"You know that I always wanted to go to France; and you bring me down here only on purpose that I should see the French cliffs—just to tantalise me, and for nothing else. If I'd remained at home—and it was against my will I ever came here—I should never have thought of France; but,—to have it staring in one's face all day, and not be allowed to go! it's worse than cruel, Mr. Caudle—it's brutal. Other people can take their wives to Paris; but you always keep me moped up at home. And what for? Why, that I may know nothing—yes; just on purpose to make me look little and for nothing else.

"*Heaven bless the woman?* Ha! you've good reason to say that, Mr.

---

[14] bathing machines, small bathhouses on wheels in which bathers dress and un-dress.

Caudle; for I'm sure she's little blessed by you. She's been kept a prisoner all her life—has never gone anywhere—oh yes! that's your old excuse,—
talking of the children. I want to go to France, and I should like to know
what the children have to with it? They're not babies *now*—are they? But
you've always thrown the children in my face. If Miss Prettyman—there
now; do you hear what you've done—shouting in that manner? The other
lodgers are knocking overhead: who do you think will have the face to
look at 'em to-morrow morning? *I* shan't—breaking people's rest in that
way!

"Well, Caudle—I declare it's getting daylight, and what an obstinate
man you are!—tell me, shall I go to France?"

"I forget," says Caudle, "my precise answer; but I think I gave her a
very wide permission to go somewhere, whereupon, though not without
remonstrance as to the place—she went to sleep."

## LECTURE XXVI.

MRS. CAUDLE'S FIRST NIGHT IN FRANCE.—"SHAMEFUL INDIFFERENCE"
OF CAUDLE AT THE BOULOGNE CUSTOM HOUSE.

"I suppose, Mr. Caudle, you call yourself a man? I'm sure, such men
should never have wives. If I could have thought it possible you'd have
behaved as you have done—and I might, if I hadn't been a forgiving
creature, for you've never been like anybody else—if I could only have
thought it, you'd never have dragged me to foreign parts. Never! Well, I
*did* say to myself, if he goes to France, perhaps he may catch a little politeness—but no: you began as Caudle, and as Caudle you'll end. I'm to
be neglected through life, now. Oh yes! I've quite given up all thoughts
of anything but wretchedness—I've made up my mind to misery, now.
*You're glad of it?* Well, you must have a heart to say that. I declare to
you, Caudle, as true as I'm an ill-used woman, if it wasn't for the dear
children far away in blessed England—if it wasn't for them, I'd never go
back with you. No: I'd leave you in this very place. Yes; I'd go into a con-
vent; for a lady on board told me there was plenty of 'em here. I'd go and
be a nun for the rest of my days, and—I see nothing to laugh at, Mr.
Caudle; that you should be shaking the bed-things up and down in that
way.—But you always laugh at people's feelings; I wish you'd only some
yourself. I'd be a nun, or a Sister of Charity. *Impossible?* Ha! Mr. Caudle,

you don't know even now what I can be when my blood's up. You've trod upon the worm long enough; some day won't you be sorry for it?

"Now none of your profane cryings out! You needn't talk about Heaven in that way: I'm sure you're the last person who ought. What I say is this. Your conduct at the Custom House was shameful—cruel! And in a foreign land too! But you brought me here that I might be insulted; you'd no other reason for dragging me from England. Ha! let me once get home, Mr. Caudle, and you may wear your tongue out before you get me into outlandish places again. *What have you done?* There now; that's where you're so aggravating. You behave worse than any Turk to me,—what? *You wish you were a Turk?* Well, I think that's a pretty wish before your lawful wife! Yes—a nice Turk you'd make, wouldn't you? Don't think it.

"*What have you done?* Well, it's a good thing I can't see you, for I'm sure you must blush. Done, indeed! Why, when the brutes searched my basket at the Custom House! *A regular thing, is it?* Then if you knew that, why did you bring me here? No man who respected his wife would. And you could stand by, and see that fellow with moustachios rummage my basket; and pull out my night-cap and rumple the borders, and— well! if you'd had the proper feelings of a husband, your blood would have boiled again. But no! There you stood looking as mild as butter at the man, and never said a word; not when he crumpled my night-cap— it went to my heart like a stab—crumpled it as if it was any duster. I dare say if it had been Miss Prettyman's night-cap—oh, I don't care about your groaning—if it had been her night-cap, her hair-brush, her curl-papers, you'd have said something then. Oh, anybody with the spirit of a man would have spoken out if the fellow had had a thousand swords at his side. Well, all I know is this: if I'd have married somebody I could name, he wouldn't have suffered me to be treated in that way, not he!

"Now, don't hope to go to sleep, Mr. Caudle, and think to silence me in that manner. I know your art, but it won't do. It wasn't enough that my basket was turned topsy-turvy, but before I knew it, they spun me in-to another room, and—*How could you help that?* You never tried to help it. No; although it was a foreign land, and I don't speak French—not but what I know a good deal more of it than some people who give them-selves airs about it—though I don't speak their nasty gibberish, still you let them take me away, and never cared how I was ever to find you again. In a strange country, too! But I've no doubt that that's what you wished: yes, you'd have been glad enough to have got rid of me in that cowardly manner. If I could only know your secret thoughts, Caudle, that's what you brought me here for, to lose me. And after the wife I've been to you!

"What are you crying out? *For mercy's sake?* Yes; a great deal you know about mercy! Else you'd never have suffered me to be twisted into that room. To be searched, indeed! As if I'd anything smuggled about me. Well, I will say it; after the way in which I've been used, if you'd the proper feelings of a man, you wouldn't sleep again for six months. Well, I know there was nobody but women there; but that's nothing to do with it. I'm sure, if I'd been taken up for picking pockets, they couldn't have used me worse. To be treated so—and 'specially by one's own sex!—it's *that* that aggravates me.

"And that's all you can say? *What could you do?* Why, break open the door; I'm sure you must have heard my voice: you shall never make me believe you couldn't hear that. Whenever I shall sew the strings on again, I can't tell. If they didn't turn me out like a ship in a storm, I'm a sinner! And you laughed! *You didn't laugh?* Don't tell me; you laugh when you don't know anything about it; but I do.

"And a pretty place you have brought me to. A most respectable place I must say! Where the women walk about without any bonnets to their heads, and the fish-girls with their bare legs—well, you don't catch me eating any fish while I'm here. *Why not?* Why not,—do you think I'd encourage people of that sort?

"What do you say? *Good night?* It's no use your saying that—I can't go to sleep so soon as you can. Especially with a door that has such a lock as that to it. How do we know who may come in? What? *All the locks are bad in France?* The more shame for you to bring me to such a place, then. It only shows how you value me.

"Well, I dare say you are tired. *I* am! But then, see what I've gone through. Well, we won't quarrel in a barbarous country. We won't do that. Caudle, dear,—what's the French for lace? I know it, only I forget it. The French for lace, love? What! *Dentelle?* Now, you're not deceiving me? *You never deceived me yet?* Oh! don't say that. There isn't a married man in this blessed world can put his hand upon his heart in bed, and say that. French for lace, dear? Say it again. *Dentelle?* Ha! Dentelle! Good night, dear. Dentelle! Den—telle."

"I afterwards," writes Caudle, "found out to my cost wherefore she enquired about lace. For she went out in the morning with the landlady to buy a veil, giving only four pounds for what she could have bought in England for forty shillings!"

# LECTURE XXVII.

"THERE, it isn't often that I ask you to do anything for me, Mr. Caudle, goodness knows! and when I do, I'm always refused—of course. Oh yes! anybody but your own lawful wife. Every other husband aboard the boat could behave like a husband—but I was left to shift for myself. To be sure, that's nothing new; I always am. Every other man, worthy to be called a man, could smuggle a few things for his wife—but I might as well be alone in the world. Not one poor half-dozen of silk stockings could you put in your hat for me; and everybody else was rolled in lace, and I don't know what. Eh? What, Mr. Caudle? *What do I want with silk stockings?* Well,—it's come to something now! There was a time, I believe, when I had a foot—yes, and an ankle, too: but when once a woman's married, she has nothing of the sort; of course. No: I'm *not* a cherub, Mr. Caudle; don't say that. I know very well what I am.

"I dare say now, you'd have been delighted to smuggle for Miss Prettyman? Silk stockings become her! *You wish Miss Prettyman was in the moon?* Not you, Mr. Caudle; that's only your art—your hypocrisy. A nice person too she'd be for the moon: it would be none the brighter for her being in it, I know. And when you saw the Custom House officers look at me, as though they were piercing me through, what was your conduct? Shameful. You twittered about, and fidgetted, and flushed up as if I really *was* a smuggler. *So I was?* What had that to do with it? It wasn't the part of a husband I think, to fidget in that way, and show it. *You couldn't help it?* Humph! And you call yourself a person of strong mind, I believe? One of the lords of the creation! Ha! ha! couldn't help it!

"But I may do all I can to save the money, and this is always my reward. Yes, Mr. Caudle, I shall save a great deal. *How much?* I sha'n't tell you: I know your meanness—you'd want to stop it out of the house allowance. No: it's nothing to you where I got the money from to buy so many things. The money was my own. Well, and if it was yours first, that's nothing to do with it. No; I hav'n't saved it out of the puddings. But it's always the woman who saves who's despised. It's only your fine-lady wives who're properly thought of. If I was to ruin you, Caudle, then you'd think something of me.

"I sha'n't go to sleep. It's very well for you who're no sooner in bed, than you're fast as a church; but I can't sleep in that way. It's my mind keeps me awake. And after all, I do feel so happy to-night, it's very hard I can't enjoy my thought. *No: I can't think in silence!* There's much enjoyment in that to be sure! I've no doubt now you could listen to Miss Prettyman—oh, I don't care, I will speak. It was a little more than odd, I think, that she should be on the jetty when the boat came in. Ha! she'd been looking for you all the morning with a telescope, I've no doubt—she's bold enough for anything. And then how she sneered and giggled when she saw me,—and said 'how fat I'd got': like her impudence, I think. What! *Well she might?* But I know what she wanted; yes—she'd have liked to have had me searched. She laughed on purpose.

"I only wish I'd taken two of the dear girls with me. What things I could have stitched about 'em! No—I'm not ashamed of myself to make my innocent children smugglers: the more innocent they looked, the better; but there you are with what you call your principles again; as if it wasn't given to everybody by nature to smuggle. I'm sure of it—it's born with us. And nicely I've cheated 'em this day. Lace, and velvet, and silk stockings, and other things,—to say nothing of the tumblers and decanters. No: I didn't look as if I wanted a direction, for fear somebody should break me.[15] That's another of what you call your jokes; but you should keep 'em for those who like 'em. *I* don't.

"*What have I made after all?* I've told you—you shall never never know. Yes, I know you'd been fined a hundred pounds if they'd searched me; but I never meant that they should. I dare say you wouldn't smuggle—oh no! you don't think it worth your while. You're quite a conjurer, you are, Caudle. Ha! ha! ha! *What am I laughing at?* Oh, you little know—such a clever creature! Ha! ha! Well, now, I'll tell you. I knew what an unaccommodating animal you were, so I made you smuggle whether or not. *How?* Why, when you were out at the *Café*, I got your great rough coat, and if I didn't stitch ten yards of best black velvet under the lining I'm a sinful woman! And to see how innocent you looked when the officers walked round and round you! It was a happy moment, Caudle, to see you.

"What do you call it? *A shameful trick—unworthy of a wife? I couldn't care much for you?* As if I didn't prove that, by trusting you with ten yards of velvet. But I don't care what you say: I've saved everything—all but that beautiful English novel, that I've forgot the name of. And if they didn't take it out of my hand, and chopped it to bits like so much dog's-meat. *Served me right?* And when I so seldom buy a book! No: I don't see how it served me right. If you can buy the same book in France

---

[15] In other words, should be stamped "fragile."

for four shillings that people here have the impudence to ask more than a guinea for—well, if they *do* steal it, that's their affair, not ours. As if there was anything in a book to steal!

"And now, Caudle, when are you going home! What? *Our time isn't up?* That's nothing to do with it. If we even lose a week's lodging—and we mayn't do that—we shall save it again in living. But you're such a man! Your home's the last place with you. I'm sure I don't get a wink of a night, thinking what may happen. Three fires last week; and any one might as well have been at our house as not. *No—they mightn't?* Well, you know what I mean—but you're such a man!

"I'm sure, too, we've had quite enough of this place. But there's no keeping you out of the libraries,[16] Caudle. You're getting quite a gambler. And I don't think it's a nice example to set to your children, raffling as you do for French clocks and I don't know what. But that's not the worst; you never win anything. Oh, I forgot. Yes; a needle-case, that under my nose you gave to Miss Prettyman. A nice thing for a married man to make presents: and to such a creature as that, too. A needle-case! I wonder whenever she has a needle in *her* hand!

"I know I shall feel ill with anxiety if I stop here. Nobody left in the house but that Mrs. Closepeg. And she is such a stupid woman. It was only last night that I dreamt I saw our cat quite a skeleton, and the canary stiff on its back at the bottom of the cage. You know, Caudle, I'm never happy when I'm away from home; and yet you will stay here. No, home's my comfort; I never want to stir over the threshold, and you know it. If thieves were to break in, what could that Mrs. Closepeg do against 'em? And so, Caudle, you'll go home on Saturday? Our dear— dear home! On Saturday, Caudle?"

"What I answered," says Caudle, "I forget; but I know that on the Saturday, we were once again shipped on board the *Red Rover.*"


## LECTURE XXVIII.

MRS. CAUDLE HAS RETURNED HOME.—THE HOUSE (OF COURSE)
"NOT FIT TO BE SEEN." MR. CAUDLE, IN SELF-DEFENCE,
TAKES A BOOK.

"After all, Caudle, it is something to get into one's own bed again. I

---

[16] libraries, that is, lotteries.

*shall* sleep to-night. What! *You're gald of it?* That's like your sneering; I know what you mean. Of course; I never can think of making myself comfortable, but you wound my feelings. If you cared for your own bed like any other man, you'd not have staid out till this hour. Don't say that I drove you out of the house as soon as we came in it. I only just spoke about the dirt and the dust,—but the fact is, you'd be happy in a pig-sty! I thought I could have trusted that Mrs. Closepeg with untold gold; and did you only see the hearth-rug? When we left home there was a tiger in it: I should like to know who could make out the tiger, now? Oh, it's very well for you to swear at the tiger, but swearing won't revive the rug again. Else you might swear.

"You could go out and make yourself comfortable at your club. You little know how many windows are broken. How many do you think? No: I sha'n't tell you to-morrow—you shall know now. I'm sure. Talking about getting health at Margate; all my health went away directly I went into the kitchen. There's dear mother's china bowl cracked in two places. I could have sat down and cried when I saw it: a bowl I can recollect when I was a child. Eh? *I should have locked it up then?* Yes; that's your feeling for anything of mine. I only wish it had been your punch-bowl; but, thank goodness! I think that's chipped.

"Well, you haven't answered about the windows—you can't guess how many? *You don't care?* Well, if nobody caught cold but you, it would be little matter. Six windows clean out, and three cracked! *You can't help it?* I should like to know where the money's to come from to mend 'em! They shan't be mended, that's all. Then you'll see how respectable the house will look. But I know very well what you think. Yes; you're glad of it. You think that this will keep me at home—but I'll never stir out again. Then you can go to the sea-side by yourself; then, perhaps, you can be happy with Miss Prettyman?—Now, Caudle, if you knock the pillow with your fist in that way, I'll get up. It's very odd that I can't mention that person's name, but you begin to fight the bolster, and do I don't know what. There must be something in it, or you wouldn't kick about so. A guilty conscience needs no—but you know what I mean.

"She wasn't coming to town for a week; and then, of a sudden, she'd had a letter. I dare say she had. And then, as she said, it would be company for her to come with us. No doubt. She thought I should be ill again, and down in the cabin: but with all her art, she does not know the depth of me—quite. Not but what I was ill; though, like a brute, you wouldn't see it.

"What do you say? *Good night, love?* Yes: you can be very tender, I

dare say—like all of your sex—to suit your own ends: but I can't go to
sleep with my head full of the house. The fender in the parlour will never come to itself again. I haven't counted the knives yet, but I've made
up my mind that half of 'em are lost. No: I don't always think the worst;
no, and I don't make myself unhappy before the time; but of course,
that's my thanks for caring about your property. If there arn't spiders in
the curtains as big as nutmegs, I'm a wicked creature. Not a broom has
the whole place seen since I've been away. But as soon as I get up, won't
I rummage the house out, that's all. I hadn't the heart to look at my
pickles; but for all I left the door locked, I'm sure the jars have been
moved. Yes, you can swear at pickles when you're in bed; but nobody
makes more noise about 'em when you want 'em.

"I only hope they've been to the wine-cellar: then you may know what
my feelings are. That poor cat, too—What? *You hate cats?* Yes, poor
thing! because she's my favourite—that's it. If that cat could only speak
—What? *It isn't necessary?* I don't know what you mean, Mr. Caudle: but
if that cat could only speak, she'd tell me how she's been cheated. Poor
thing! I know where the money's gone to that I left for her milk—I know.
Why, what have you got there, Mr. Caudle? A book? What! *If you arn't
allowed to sleep, you'll read?* Well, now it is come to something! If that
isn't insulting a wife to bring a book to bed, I don't know what wedlock
is. But you sha'n't read, Caudle, no, you sha'n't; not while I've strength
to get up and put out a candle.

"And that's like your feelings! You can think a great deal of trumpery
books; yes, you can't think too much of the stuff that's put into print;
but for what's real and true about you, why, you've the heart of a stone.
I should like to know what that book's about? What? *Milton's Paradise
Lost?* I thought some rubbish of the sort—something to insult me. A nice
book, I think, to read in bed; and a very respectable person he was who
wrote it. *What do I know of him?* Much more than you think. A very
pretty fellow, indeed, with his six wives. What? *He hadn't six—he'd only
three?* That's nothing to do with it; but of course you'll take his part.
'Poor women! A nice time they had with him, I dare say! And I've no
doubt, Mr. Caudle, you'd like to follow Mr. Milton's example: else you
wouldn't read the stuff he wrote. But you don't use me as he treated the
poor souls who married him. Poets, indeed! I'd make a law against any
of 'em having wives except upon paper; for goodness help the dear creatures tied to them! Like innocent moths lured by a candle! Talking of
candles, you don't know that the lamp in the passage is split to bits! I
say you don't—do you hear me, Mr. Caudle? Won't you answer? Do you

know where you are? What? *In the Garden of Eden?* Are you? Then
you've no business there at this time of night."

"And saying this," writes Caudle, "she scrambled from the bed, and
put out the light."


## LECTURE XXIX.

MRS. CAUDLE THINKS "THE TIME HAS COME TO HAVE A COTTAGE
OUT OF TOWN."

"CAUDLE, you ought to have had something nice to-night; for you're not
well, love—I know you're not. Ha! that's like you men,—so headstrong!
You will have it that nothing ails you; but I can tell, Caudle. The eye of
a wife—and such a wife as I've been to you—can at once see whether a
husband's well or not. You've been turning like tallow all the week; and
what's more you eat nothing, now. It makes me melancholy to see you at
a joint. I don't say anything at dinner before the children; but I don't
feel the less. No, no; you're not very well; and you're not as strong as a
horse. Don't deceive yourself—nothing of the sort. No, and you don't eat
as much as ever: and if you do, you don't eat with a relish, I'm sure of
that. You can't deceive me there.

"But I know what's killing you. It's the confinement; it's the bad air
you breathe; it's the smoke of London. Oh yes, I know your old excuse:
you never found the air bad before. Perhaps not. But as people grow
older, and get on in trade—and, after all, we've nothing to complain of,
Caudle—London air always disagrees with 'em. Delicate health comes
with money: I'm sure of it. What a colour you had once, when you'd
hardly a sixpence; and now, look at you!

" 'Twould add thirty years to your life—and think what a blessing that
would be to me; not that I shall live a tenth part of the time—thirty
years, if you'd take a nice little house somewhere at Brixton.[17] *You hate
Brixton?* I must say it, Caudle, that's so like you: any place that's really
genteel, you can't abide. Now Brixton and Baalam Hill[18] I think delightful. So select! There, nobody visits nobody, unless they're somebody. To say nothing of the delightful pews that make the churches so
respectable!

17 Brixton, a suburban district in Surrey.
18 Baalam Hill, located to the south side of Clapham Common.

"However, do as you like. If you won't go to Brixton, what do you say to Clapham Common?[19] Oh, that's a very fine story! Never tell me! No; you wouldn't be left alone, a Robinson Crusoe with wife and children, because you're in the retail way. What! *The retired wholesales never visit the retired retails at Clapham?* Ha! that's only your old sneering at the world, Mr. Caudle; but I don't believe it. And after all, people should keep to their station, or what was this life made for? Suppose a tallow-merchant does keep himself above a tallow-chandler,—I call it only a proper pride. What? *You call it the aristocracy of fat?* I don't know what you mean by aristocracy; but I suppose it's only another of your dictionary words, that's hardly worth the finding out.

"What do you say to Hornsey[20] or Muswell Hill?[21] Eh? *Too high?* What a man you are! Well then—Battersea?[22] *Too low?* You're an aggravating creature, Caudle, you must own that! Hampstead,[23] then? *Too cold?* Nonsense; it would brace you up like a drum, Caudle; and that's what you want. But you don't deserve anybody to think of your health or your comforts either. There's some pretty spots, I'm told, about Fulham.[24] Now, Caudle, I won't have you say a word against Fulham. That must be a sweet place: dry, and healthy, and every comfort of life about it—else is it likely that a bishop would live there? Now, Caudle, none of your heathen principles—I won't hear 'em. I think what satisfies a bishop ought to content you; but the politics you learn at the club are dreadful. To hear you talk of bishops—well, I only hope nothing will happen to you, for the sake of the dear children!

"A nice little house and a garden! I know it—I was born for a garden! There's something about it makes one feel so innocent. My heart somehow always opens and shuts at roses. And then what nice currant wine we could make! And again, get 'em as fresh as you will, there's no radishes like your own radishes! They're ten times as sweet! What? *And twenty times as dear?* Yes; there you go! Anything that I fancy, you always bring up the expense.

[19] Clapham Common, an open space of over two hundred acres on the west side of the main road to Stockwell and Kennington; the Common was surrounded by expensive residences of city bankers and merchants.

[20] Hornsey, a rural borough near London containing the suburbs of Crouch End and Muswell Hill.

[21] Muswell Hill, situated to the north of Crouch End, known for its fine residences and fashionable shops.

[22] Battersea, a parish and manor on the Surrey side of the Thames.

[23] Hampstead, a distinguished rural suburb, once a favorite spa and pleasure resort for people of fashion.

[24] Fulham, a parish known for its cultivated-garden markets, villas, and country seats.

"No, Mr. Caudle, I should not be tired of it in a month. I tell you I was made for the country. But here you've kept me—and much you've cared about my health—here, you've kept me in this filthy London, that I hardly know what grass is made of. Much you care for your wife and family to keep 'em here to be all smoked like bacon. I can see it—it's stopping the children's growth; they'll be dwarfs, and have their father to thank for it. If you'd the heart of a parent, you couldn't bear to look at their white faces. Dear little Dick! he makes no breakfast. What? *He ate six slices this morning?* A pretty father you must be to count 'em. But that's nothing to what the dear child could do, if, like other children, he'd a fair chance.

"Ha! and when we could be so comfortable! But it's always the case, you never will be comfortable with me. How nice and fresh you'd come up to business every morning; and what pleasure it would be for me to put a tulip or a pink in your button-hole, just, as I may say, to ticket you from the country.

"But then, Caudle, you never were like any other man! But I know why you won't leave London. Yes, I know. Then, you think, you couldn't go to your filthy club—that's it. Then you'd be obliged to be at home, like any other decent man. Whereas, you might, if you liked, enjoy yourself under your own apple-tree, and I'm sure I would never say anything about your tobacco out of doors. My only wish is to make you happy, Caudle, and you won't let me do it.

"You don't speak, love? Shall I look about a house to-morrow? It will be a broken day with me, for I'm going out to have little pet's ears bored —What? *You won't have her ears bored?* And why not, I should like to know? *It's a barbarous, savage custom?* Oh, Mr. Caudle! the sooner you go away from the world, and live in a cave, the better. You're getting not fit for Christian society. What next? My ears were bored and—what? *So are yours?* I know what you mean—but that's nothing to do with it. My ears, I say, were bored, and so were dear mother's, and grandmother's before her; and I suppose there were no more savages in our family than in yours, Mr. Caudle? Besides,—why should little pet's ears go naked any more than any of her sisters'? They wear ear-rings, you never objected before. What? *You've learned better now?* Yes, that's all with your filthy politics again. You'd shake all the world up in a dice-box, if you'd your way: not that you care a pin about the world, only you'd like to get a better throw for yourself,—that's all. But little pet *shall* be bored, and don't think to prevent it.

"I suppose she's to be married some day, as well as her sisters? And who'll look at a girl without ear-rings, I should like to know? If you knew any thing of the world, you'd know what a nice diamond ear-ring will sometimes do—when one can get it—before this. But I know why you can't abide ear-rings now; Miss Prettyman doesn't wear 'em; she would—I've no doubt—if she could only get 'em. Yes,—it's Miss Prettyman, who—

"There, Caudle, now be quiet, and I'll say no more about pet's ears at present. We'll talk when you're reasonable. I don't want to put you out of temper, goodness knows! And so, love, about the cottage? What? *'Twill be so far from business?* But it needn't be far, dearest. Quite a nice distance; so that on your late nights, you may always be at home, have your supper, get to bed, and all by eleven. Eh,—sweet one?"

"I don't know what I answered," says Caudle, "but I know this; in less than a fortnight I found myself in a sort of a green bird-cage of a house, which my wife—gentle satirist—insisted upon calling 'The Turtle-Dovery.' "

# LECTURE XXX.

MRS. CAUDLE COMPLAINS OF THE "TURTLE-DOVERY."—DISCOVERS
BLACK-BEETLES.—THINKS IT "NOTHING BUT RIGHT"
THAT CAUDLE SHOULD SET UP A CHAISE.

"You'd never have got me into this wilderness of a place, Mr. Caudle, if I'd only have thought what it was. Yes, that's right: throw it in my teeth that it was my choice—that's manly, isn't it? When I saw the place the sun was out, and it looked beautiful—now, it's quite another thing. No, Mr. Caudle; I don't expect you to command the sun,—and if you talk about Joshua in that infidel way, I'll leave the bed. No, sir; I don't expect the sun to be in your power, but that's nothing to do with it. I talk about one thing, and you always start another. But that's your art.

"I'm sure a woman might as well be buried alive as live here. In fact, I am buried alive; I feel it. I stood at the window three hours this blessed day, and saw nothing but the postman. No: it isn't a pity that I hadn't something better to do; I had plenty: but that's my business, Mr. Caudle. I suppose I'm to be mistress of my own house? If not, I'd better leave it.

"And the very first night we were here, you know it, the black-beetles came into the kitchen. If the place didn't seem spread all over with a black cloth, I'm a story teller. What are you coughing at, Mr. Caudle?

I see nothing to cough at. But that's just your way of sneering. Millions of black-beetles! And as the clock strikes eight, out they march. What? *They're very punctual?* I know that. I only wish other people were half as punctual: 'twould save other people's money and other people's peace of mind. You know I hate a black-beetle! No: I don't hate so many things. But I do hate black-beetles, as I hate ill-treatment, Mr. Caudle. And now I have enough of both, goodness knows!

"Last night they came into the parlour. Of course, in a night or two, they'll walk up into the bed-room. They'll be here—regiments of 'em— on the quilt. But what do you care? Nothing of the sort ever touches you: but you know how they come to me; and that's why you're so quiet. A pleasant thing to have black-beetles in one's bed? *Why don't I poison 'em?* A pretty matter, indeed, to have poison in the house? Much you must think of the dear children. A nice place too, to be called the Turtle-Dovery! *Didn't I christen it myself?* I know that,—but then I knew nothing of the black-beetles. Besides, names of houses are for the world outside; not that anybody passes to see ours. Didn't Mrs. Digby insist on calling their new house 'Love-in-Idleness,' though everybody knew that that wretch Digby was always beating her? Still, when folks read 'Rose Cottage' on the wall, they seldom think of the lots of thorns that are inside. In this world, Mr. Caudle, names are sometimes quite as good as things.

"That cough again! You've got a cold, and you'll always be getting one —for you'll always be missing the omnibus as you did on Tuesday,—and always be getting wet. No constitution can stand it, Caudle. You don't know what I felt when I heard it rain on Tuesday, and thought you might be in it. What? *I'm very good?* Yes, I trust so; I try to be so, Caudle. And so, dear, I've been thinking that we'd better keep a chaise. *You can't afford it, and you won't?* Don't tell me: I know you'd save money by it. I've been reckoning what you lay out in omnibusses; and if you'd a chaise of your own—besides the gentility of the thing—you'd be money in pocket. And then again, how often I could go with you to town,—and how, again, I could call for you when you liked to be a little late at the club, dear? Now, you're obliged to be hurried away, I know it, when, if you'd only a carriage of your own, you could stay and enjoy yourself. And after your work you want enjoyment. Of course, I can't expect you always to run home directly to me: and I don't, Caudle; and you know it.

"A nice, neat, elegant little chaise. What! *You'll think of it?* There's a love! You are a good creature, Caudle; and 'twill make me so happy to think you don't depend upon an omnibus. A sweet little carriage, with our arms beautifully painted on the panels. What? *Arms are rubbish; and you don't know that you have any?* Nonsense: to be sure you have—and if not, of course they're to be had for money. I wonder where Chalkpit's, the milkman's arms came from? I suppose you can buy 'em at the same place. He used to drive a green cart; and now he's got a close yellow carriage, with two large tortoise-shell cats, with their whiskers as if dipt in cream, standing on their hind legs upon each door, with a heap of Latin underneath. You may buy the carriage, if you please, Mr. Caudle; but unless your arms are there, you won't get me to enter it. Never! I'm not going to look less than Mrs. Chalkpit.

"Besides, if you hav'n't arms, I'm sure my family have, and a wife's arms are quite as good as a husband's. I'll write to-morrow to dear mother, to know what we took for our family arms. What do you say? What? *A mangle in a stone-kitchen proper?* Mr. Caudle, you're always insulting my family—always: but you shall not put me out of temper to-night. Still, if you don't like our arms, find your own. I dare say you could have found 'em fast enough, if you'd married Miss Prettyman. Well, I will be quiet; and I won't mention that lady's name. A nice lady she is! I wonder how much she spends in paint! Now, don't I tell you I won't say a word more, and yet you will kick about!

"Well, we'll have the carriage and the family arms? No, I don't want the family legs too. Don't be vulgar, Mr. Caudle. You might, perhaps, talk in that way before you'd money in the Bank; but it doesn't at all become you now. The carriage and the family arms! We've a country-house as well as the Chalkpits; and though they praise their place for a little Paradise, I dare say they've quite as many black-beetles as we have, and more too. The place quite looks it.

"Our carriage and our arms! And you know, love, it won't cost much —next to nothing—to put a gold band about Sam's hat on a Sunday. No: I don't want a full-blown livery. At least, not just yet. I'm told the Chalkpits dress their boy on a Sunday like a dragon-fly; and I don't see why we shouldn't do what we like with our own Sam. Nevertheless, I'll be content with a gold band, and a bit of pepper-and-salt. No: I shall not cry out for plush next; certainly not. But I will have a gold band, and— *You won't; and I know it?* Oh yes! that's another of your crotchets, Mr. Caudle; like nobody else—you don't love liveries. I suppose when people buy their sheets, or their table cloths, or any other linen, they've a right to mark what they like upon it, haven't they? Well, then? You buy a servant, and you mark what you like upon him, and where's the difference? None, that I can see."

"Finally," says Caudle, "I compromised for a gig: but Sam did not wear pepper-and-salt and a gold band."


# LECTURE XXXI.

### MRS. CAUDLE COMPLAINS VERY BITTERLY THAT MR. CAUDLE HAS "BROKEN HER CONFIDENCE."

"You'll not catch me, Mr. Caudle, telling you anything again. Now I don't want to have any noise: I don't wish you to put yourself in a passion. All I say is this; never again do I open my lips to you about anybody. No: if man and wife can't be one, why, there's an end of everything. Oh, you know very well what I mean, Mr. Caudle: you've broken my confidence in the most shameful, the most heartless way, and I repeat it—I can never be again to you as I have been. No: the little charm—it wasn't much—that remained about married life, is gone for ever. Yes; the bloom's quite wiped off the plum now.

"Don't be such a hypocrite, Caudle; don't ask me what I mean! Mrs. Badgerly has been here—more like a fiend, I'm sure, than a quiet woman. I haven't done trembling yet! You know the state of my nerves, too; you know—yes, sir, I *had* nerves when you married me; and I haven't just found 'em out. Well, you've something to answer for, I think. The Badgerlys are going to separate: she takes the girls, and he the boys, and all through you. How you can lay your head upon that pillow and think of going to sleep, I can't tell. *What have you done?* Well, you have a face to ask the question. Done? You've broken my confidence, Mr. Caudle: you've taken advantage of my tenderness, my trust in you as a wife—the more fool I for my pains!—and you've separated a happy couple for ever. No; I'm not talking in the clouds; I'm talking in your bed, the more my misfortune.

"Now, Caudle—yes, I shall sit up in the bed if I choose; I'm not going to sleep till I have this properly explained; for Mrs. Badgerly shan't lay her separation at my door. You won't deny that you were at the Club last night? No, bad as you are, Caudle—and though you're my husband, I can't think you a good man; I try to do, but I can't—bad as you are, you can't deny you were at the Club. What? *You don't deny it?* That's what I say—you can't. And now, answer me this question. What did you say—before the whole world—of Mr. Badgerly's whiskers? There's nothing to laugh at, Caudle; if you'd have seen that poor woman, to-day, you'd have a heart of stone to laugh. What did you say of his whiskers? Didn't you tell everybody he dyed 'em? Didn't you hold the candle up to 'em, as you said, to show the purple? *To be sure you did!* Ha! people who break jokes never care about breaking hearts. Badgerly went home like a demon; called his wife a false woman: vowed he'd never enter a bed again with her, and, to show he was in earnest, slept all night upon the sofa. He said it was the dearest secret of his life; said she had told me; and that I had told you; and that's how it had come out. What do you say? *Badgerly was right? I did tell you?* I know I did; but when dear Mrs. Badgerly mentioned the matter to me and a few friends, as we were all laughing at tea together, quite in a confidential way—when she just spoke of her husband's whiskers, and how long he was over 'em every morning— of course, poor soul! she never thought it was to be talked of in the world again. Eh? *Then I had no right to tell you of it?* And that's the way I'm thanked for my confidence. Because I don't keep a secret from you, but show you, I may say, my naked soul, Caudle, that's how I'm rewarded. Poor Mrs. Badgerly—for all her hard words—after she went away, I'm sure my heart quite bled for her. What do you say, Mr. Caudle? *Serves her right—she should hold her tongue?* Yes; that's like your tyranny— you'd never let a poor woman speak. Eh—what, what Mr. Caudle?

"That's a very fine speech, I dare say; and wives are very much obliged to you, only there's not a bit of truth in it. No, we women don't get together, and pick our husbands to pieces, just as sometimes mischievous little girls rip up their dolls. That's an old sentiment of yours, Mr. Caudle: but I'm sure you've no occasion to say it of me. I hear a good deal of other people's husbands, certainly; I can't shut my ears; I wish I could: but I never say anything about you,—and I might, and you know it—and there's somebody else that knows it, too. No: I sit still and say nothing; what I have in my own bosom about you, Caudle, will be buried with me. But I know what you think of wives. I heard you talking to Mr. Prettyman, when you little thought I was listening, and you didn't know much what you were saying—I heard you. 'My dear Prettyman,' says you, 'when some women get talking, they club all their husbands' faults together; just as children club their cakes and apples, to make a common feast for the whole set.' Eh? *You don't remember it?* But I do: and I remember, too, what brandy was left, when Prettyman went. 'Twould be odd if you could remember much about it, after that.

"And now you've gone and separated man and wife, and I'm to be blamed for it. You've not only carried misery into a family, but broken my confidence. You've proved to me that henceforth I'm not to trust you

with anything, Mr. Caudle. No: I'll lock up whatever I know in my own
breast,—for now I find nobody, not even one's own husband, is to be re-
lied upon. From this moment, I may look upon myself as a solitary woman. Now, it's no use your trying to go to sleep. What do you say? *You
know that?* Very well. Now, I want to ask you one question more. Eh?
*You want to ask me one?* Very well—go on—I'm not afraid to be cate-
chised. I never dropt a syllable that as a wife I ought to have kept to myself—no, I'm not at all forgetting what I've said—and whatever you've got
to ask me speak out at once. No—I don't want you to spare me; all I want
you is to speak. *You will speak?* Well, then, do.

"What? *Who told people you'd a false front tooth?* And is that all?
Well, I'm sure—as if the world couldn't see it. I know I did just mention
it once, but then I thought everybody knew it—besides, I was aggravated
to do it; yes, aggravated. I remember it was that very day, at Mrs. Badgerly's, when husbands' whiskers came up. Well, after we'd done with
them, somebody said something about teeth. Whereupon, Miss Prettyman—a minx! she was born to destroy the peace of families, I know she
was: she was there; and if I'd only known that such a creature was——
no, I'm not rambling, not at all, and I'm coming to the tooth. To be
sure, this is a great deal you've got against me, isn't it? Well, somebody
spoke about teeth, when Miss Prettyman with one of her insulting leers,
said, 'she thought Mr. Caudle had the whitest teeth she ever *had* beheld.' Of course, my blood was up—every wife's would be; and I believe
I might have said, 'Yes, they were well enough; but when a young lady
so very much praised a married man's teeth, she perhaps didn't know
that one of the front ones was an elephant's.' Like her impudence!—I set
*her* down for the rest of the evening. But I can see the humour you're in
to-night. You only came to bed to quarrel, and I'm not going to indulge
you. All I say is this, after the shameful mischief you've made at the Badgerlys', you never break my confidence again. Never—and now you know
it."

Caudle hereupon writes—"And here she seemed inclined to sleep. Not
for a moment did I think to prevent her."

# LECTURE XXXII.

MRS. CAUDLE DISCOURSES OF MAIDS-OF-ALL-WORK AND MAIDS IN
GENERAL. MR. CAUDLE'S "INFAMOUS BEHAVIOUR" TEN YEARS AGO.

"THERE NOW, it isn't my intention to say a word to-night, Mr. Caudle. No; I want to go to sleep, if I can; for after what I've gone through to-day, and with the head-ache I've got,—and if I haven't left my smelling-salts on the mantel-piece, on the right-hand corner just as you go into the room—nobody could miss it—I say, nobody could miss it—in a little green bottle, and——well, there you lie like a stone, and I might perish and you wouldn't move. Oh, my poor head! But it may open and shut, and what do you care?

"Yes, that's like your feeling, just. I want my salts, and you tell me there's nothing like being still for a head-ache. Indeed? But I'm not go-ing to be still; so don't you think it. That's just how a woman's put upon. But I know your aggravation—I know your art. You think to keep me quiet about that minx Kitty,—your favourite, sir! Upon my life, I'm not to discharge my own servant without—but she shall go. If I had to do all the work myself, she shouldn't stop under my roof. I can see how she looks down upon me. I can see a great deal, Mr. Caudle, that I never choose to open my lips about—but I can't shut my eyes. Perhaps it would have been better for my peace of mind if I always could. Don't say that. I'm not a foolish woman, and I know very well what I'm saying. I sup-pose you think I forget *that* Rebecca? I know it's ten years ago that she lived with us—but what's that to do with it? Things arn't the less true for being old, I suppose. No; and your conduct, Mr. Caudle, at that time—if it was a hundred years ago—I should never forget. *What? I shall always be the same silly woman?* I hope I shall—I trust I shall always have my eyes about me in my own house. Now, don't think of going to sleep, Caudle; because, as you've brought this up about that Rebecca, you shall hear me out. Well, I do wonder that you can name her? Eh? *You didn't name her?* That's nothing at all to do with it; for I know just as well what you think, as if you did. I suppose you'll say that you didn't drink a glass of wine to her? *Never?* So you said at the time, but I've thought of it for ten long years, and the more I've thought, the surer I am of it. And at that very time—if you please to recollect—at that very time little Jack was a baby. I shouldn't have so much cared but for that; but he was hardly running alone, when you nodded and drank a glass of wine to that creature. No; I'm not mad, and I'm not dreaming. I saw how you did it,—and the hypocrisy made it worse and worse. I saw you when the creature was just behind my chair, you took up a glass of wine, and saying to me, 'Margaret,' and then lifting up your eyes at the bold minx, and saying, 'my dear,' as if you wanted me to believe that you spoke only to me, when I could see you laugh at her behind me. And at that time little Jack wasn't on his feet. What do you say? *Heaven forgive me?* Ha! Mr. Caudle, it's you who ought to ask for that: I'm safe enough, I am: it's you who should ask to be forgiven.

"No, I wouldn't slander a saint—and I didn't take away the girl's character for nothing. I know she brought an action for what I said; and I know you had to pay damages for what you call my tongue—I well remember all that. And serve you right; if you hadn't laughed at her, it wouldn't have happened. But if you will make free with such people, of course you're sure to suffer for it. 'Twould have served you right if the lawyer's bill had been double. Damages, indeed! Not that anybody's tongue could have damaged her!

"And now, Mr. Caudle, you're the same man you were ten years ago. What? *You hope so?* The more shame for you. At your time of life, with all your children growing up about you, to—*What am I talking of?* I know very well; and so would you, if you had any conscience, which you haven't. When I say I shall discharge Kitty, you say she's a very good servant, and I shan't get a better. But I know why you think her good; you think her pretty, and that's enough for you; as if girls who work for their bread have any business to be pretty,—which she isn't. Pretty servants, indeed! going mincing about with their fal-lal faces, as if even the flies would spoil 'em. But I know what a bad man you are—now, it's no use your denying it; for didn't I overhear your talking to Mr. Prettyman, and didn't you say that you couldn't bear to have ugly servants about you? I ask you,—didn't you say that? *Perhaps you did?* You don't blush to confess it? If your principles, Mr. Caudle, ar'n't enough to make a woman's blood run cold!

"Oh, yes! you've talked that stuff again and again; and once I might have believed it; but I know a little more of you now. You like to see pretty servants, just as you like to see pretty statues, and pretty pictures, and pretty flowers, and anything in nature that's pretty, just as you say, for the eye to feed upon. Yes: I know your eyes,—very well. I know what they were ten years ago; for shall I ever forget that glass of wine when little Jack was in arms? I don't care if it was a thousand years ago, it's as fresh as yesterday, and I never will cease to talk of it. When you know me, how can you ask it?

"And now you insist upon keeping Kitty, when there's no having a bit of crockery for her? That girl would break the Bank of England,—I know she would—if she was to put her hand upon it. But what's a whole set of blue china to her beautiful blue eyes? I know that's what you mean, though you don't say it.

"Oh, you needn't lie groaning there, for you don't think I shall ever forget Rebecca. Yes,—it's very well for you to swear at Rebecca now,—but you didn't swear at her then, Mr. Caudle, I know. 'Margaret, my dear!' Well, how you can have the face to look at me—*You don't look at me?* The more shame for you.

"I can only say, that either Kitty leaves the house, or I do. Which is it to be, Mr. Caudle? Eh? *You don't care? Both?* But you're not going to get rid of me in that manner, I can tell you. But for that trollop—now, you may swear and rave as you like—*You don't intend to say a word more?* Very well; it's no matter what you say—her quarter's up on Tuesday, and go she shall. A soup-plate and a basin went yesterday.

"A soup-plate and a basin, and when I've the head-ache as I have, Mr. Caudle, tearing me to pieces! But I shall never be well in this world—never. A soup-plate and a basin!"

"She slept," writes Caudle, "and poor Kitty left on Tuesday."

## LECTURE XXXIII.

### MRS. CAUDLE HAS DISCOVERED THAT CAUDLE IS A RAILWAY DIRECTOR.

"WHEN I took up the paper to-day, Caudle, you might have knocked me down with a feather! Now, don't be a hypocrite—you know what's the matter. And when you haven't a bed to lie upon, and are brought to sleep upon coal-sacks—and then I can tell you, Mr. Caudle, you may sleep by yourself—then you'll know what's the matter. Now, I've seen your name, and don't deny it. Yes,—the Eel-Pie Island[25] Railway—and among the Directors, Job Caudle, Esq., of the Turtle-Dovery, and—no, I won't be quiet. It isn't often—goodness knows!—that I speak; but seeing what I do, I won't be silent. *What do I see?* Why, there, Mr. Caudle, at the foot of the bed, I see all the blessed children in tatters—I see you in a gaol, and the carpets hung out at the windows.

---

25 Eel-Pie Island, near Twickenham Ferry, a favorite resort of boating parties and pleasure-seekers.

"And now I know why you talk in your sleep about a broad and narrow gauge! I couldn't think what was on your mind,—but now it's out. Ha! Mr. Caudle, there's something about a broad and narrow way that I wish you'd remember—but you're turned quite a heathen: yes, you think of nothing but money now. *Don't I like money?* To be sure I do; but then I like it when I'm certain of it; no risks for me. Yes, it's all very well to talk about fortunes made in no time: they're like shirts made in no time—it's ten to one if they hang long together.

"And now it's plain enough why you can't eat or drink, or sleep, or do anything. All your mind's allotted into railways; for you shan't make me believe the Eel-Pie Island's the only one. Oh no! I can see by the looks of you. Why, in a little time, if you haven't as many lines in your face as there are lines laid down! Every one of your features seems cut up,— and all seem travelling from one another. Six months ago, Caudle, you hadn't a wrinkle; yes, you'd a cheek as smooth as any china, and now your face is like the map of England.

"At your time of life, too! You, who were for always going small and sure! You to make heads-and-tails of your money in this way! It's that stockbroker's dog at Flam Cottage—he's bitten you, I'm sure of it. You're not fit to manage your own property now; and I should be only acting the part of a good wife, if I were to call in the mad-doctors.

"Well, I shall never know rest any more now. There won't be a soul knock at the door after this, that I shan't think it's the man coming to take possession. 'Twill be something for the Chalkpits to laugh at when we're sold up. I think I see 'em here, bidding for all our little articles of bigotry and virtue, and—what are you laughing at? *They're not bigotry and virtue; but bijouterie and vertu?* It's all the same: only you're never so happy as when you're taking me up.

"If I can tell what's come to the world, I'm a sinner! Everybody's for turning their farthings into double sovereigns and cheating their neighbours of the balance. And you, too—you're beside yourself, Caudle,— I'm sure of it. I've watched you when you thought me fast asleep. And then you've lain, and whispered and whispered, and then hugged yourself, and laughed at the bed-posts, as if you'd seen 'em turned to sovereign gold. I do believe that you sometimes think the patch-work quilt is made of thousand pound bank-notes.

"Well, when we're brought to the Union,[26] then you'll find out your mistake. But it will be a poor satisfaction for me every night to tell you of it. What, Mr. Caudle? *They won't let me tell you of it?* And you call

[26] In the workhouses (unions) husband and wife were separated.

that 'some comfort?' And after the wife I've been to you! But now I recollect. I think I've heard you praise that Union before; though, like a
fond fool as I've always been, I never once suspected the reason of it.

"And now, of course, day and night you'll never be at home? No,
you'll live and sleep at Eel-Pie Island! I shall be left alone with nothing
but my thoughts, thinking when the broker will come, and you'll be
with your brother directors. I may slave and I may toil to save sixpences;
and you'll be throwing away hundreds. And then the expensive tastes
you've got! Nothing good enough for you now. I'm sure you sometimes
think yourself King Solomon. But that comes of making money—if, indeed, you have made any—without earning it. No: I don't talk nonsense:
people *can* make money without earning it. And when they do, why, it's
like taking a lot of spirits at one draught; it gets into their head, and
they don't know what they're about. And you're in that state now, Mr.
Caudle: I'm sure of it, by the way of you. There's a tipsiness of the pocket as well as of the stomach,—and you're in that condition at this very
moment.

"Not that I should so much mind—that is, if you *have* made money—
if you'd stop at the Eel-Pie line. But I know what these things are;
they're like treacle to flies: when men are well in 'em, they can't get out
of 'em: or if they do, it's often without a feather to fly with. No: if you've
really made money by the Eel-Pie line, and will give it to me to take care
of for the dear children, why, perhaps, love, I'll say no more of the matter. What! *Nonsense?* Yes, of course: I never ask you for money, but
that's the word.

"And now, catch you stopping at the Eel-Pie line! Oh no, I know your
aggravating spirit. In a day or two I shall see another fine flourish in the
paper, with a proposal for a branch from Eel-Pie Island to the Chelsea
Bun-house.[27] Give you a mile of rail, and—I know you men,—you'll take
a hundred. Well, if it didn't make me quiver to read that stuff in the paper,—and your name to it! But I suppose it was Mr. Prettyman's work;
for his precious name's among 'em. How you tell the people 'that eel-
pies are now become an essential element of civilisation'—I learnt all
the words by heart, that I might say 'em to you—'that the Eastern popu-
lation of London are cut off from the blessings of such a necessary,—and
that by means of the projected line eel-pies will be brought home to the
business and bosoms of Ratcliffe-highway,[28] and the adjacent depen-

27 Chelsea Bun-house, a shop at the bottom of Jews' Row, near the Compasses, once
famous for its homemade buns.
28 Ratcliffe-highway, noted for its numerous marine shops, runs from East Smithfield to Shadwell High Street.

dencies.' Well, when you men—lords of the creation, as you call yourselves—do get together to make up a company, or anything of the sort,—
is there any story-book can come up to you? And so you look solemnly
in one another's faces, and never so much as moving the corners of your
mouths, pick one another's pockets. No, I'm not using hard words, Mr.
Caudle—but only the words that's proper.

"And this I *must* say. Whatever you've got, I'm none the better for it.
You never give me any of your Eel-Pie shares. What do you say? *You
will give me some?* Not I—I'll have nothing to do with any wickedness of
the kind. If, like any other husband, you choose to throw a heap of money into my lap—what? *You'll think of it? When the Eel-Pies go up?* Then
I know what they're worth—they'll never fetch a farthing."

"She was suddenly silent"—writes Caudle—"and I was sinking into
sleep, when she elbowed me, and cried, 'Caudle, do you think they'll be
up to-morrow?' "

# LECTURE XXXIV.

MRS. CAUDLE, SUSPECTING THAT MR. CAUDLE HAS MADE HIS WILL,
IS "ONLY ANXIOUS AS A WIFE" TO KNOW ITS PROVISIONS.

"I ALWAYS said you'd a strong mind when you liked, Caudle; and what
you've just been doing proves it. Some people won't make a will, because they think they must die directly afterwards. Now, you're above
that, love, arn't you? Nonsense; you know very well what I mean. I
know your will's made, for Scratcherly told me so. What? *You don't believe it?* Well, I'm sure! That's a pretty thing for a man to say to his
wife. I know he's too much a man of business to talk; but I suppose
there's a way of telling things without speaking them. And when I put
the question to him, lawyer as he is, he hadn't the face to deny it.

"To be sure, it can be of no consequence to me whether your will is
made or not. I shall not be alive, Mr. Caudle, to want anything: I shall
be provided for a long time before your will's of any use. No, Mr. Caudle; I shan't survive you: and—though a woman's wrong to let her affection for a man be known, for then she's always taken advantage of—
though I know it's foolish and weak to say so, still I don't want to survive you. How should I? No, no; don't say that: I'm not good for a hundred—I sha'n't see you out, and another husband too. What a gross idea,

Caudle! To imagine I'd ever think of marrying again. No—never! What? *That's what we all say?* Not at all; quite the reverse. To me the very idea of such a thing is horrible, and always was. Yes, I know very well that some do marry again—but what they're made of, I'm sure I can't tell.—Ugh!

"There are men, I know, who leave their property in such a way that their widows, to hold it, must keep widows. Now, if there is anything in the world that is mean and small, it is that. Don't you think so too, Caudle? Why don't you speak, love? That's so like you! I never want a little quiet rational talk, but you want to go to sleep. But you never were like any other man! What? *How do I know?* There now,—that's so like your aggravating way. I never open my lips upon a subject, but you try to put me off. I've no doubt when Miss Prettyman speaks, you can answer *her* properly enough. There you are, again! Upon my life, it *is* odd; but I never can in the most innocent way mention that person's name that—*Why can't I leave her alone?* I'm sure—with all my heart! Who wants to talk about her? I don't: only you always will say something that's certain to bring up her name.

"What was I saying, Caudle? Oh, about the way some men bind their widows. To my mind, there is nothing so little. When a man forbids his wife to marry again without losing what he leaves—it's what I call self-ishness after death. Mean to a degree! It's like taking his wife into the grave with him. Eh? *You never want to do that?* No, I'm sure of that, love: you're not the man to tie a woman up in that mean manner. A man who'd do that, would have his widow burnt with him, if he could—just as those monsters, that call themselves men, do in the Indies.

"However, it's no matter to me how you've made your will; but it may be to your second wife. What? *I shall never give you a chance?* Ha! you don't know my constitution after all, Caudle. I'm not at all the woman I was. I say nothing about 'em, but very often you don't know my feel-ings. And as we're on the subject, dearest, I have only one favour to ask. When you marry again—now it's no use your saying that. After the com-forts you've known of marriage—what are you sighing at, dear?—after the comforts, you must marry again.—Now don't forswear yourself in that violent way, taking an oath that you know you must break—you couldn't help it, I'm sure of it; and I know you better than you know yourself. Well, all I ask is, love, because it's only for your sake, and it would make no difference to me then—how should it?—but all I ask is, don't marry Miss Pret——There! there! I've done; I won't say another word about it; but all I ask is, don't. After the way you've been thought of, and after the comforts you've been used to, Caudle, she wouldn't be the wife for you. Of course, I could then have no interest in the matter—you might marry the Queen of England, for what it would be to me then—I'm only anxious about you. Mind, Caudle, I'm not saying anything against her; not at all; but there's a flightiness in her manner—I dare say, poor thing, she means no harm, and it may be, as the saying is, only her manner after all—still there *is* a flightiness about her that, after what you've been used to, would make you very wretched. Now, if I may boast of anything, Caudle, it is my propriety of manner the whole of my life. I know that wives who're very particular, arn't thought as well of as those who're not—still, it's next to nothing to be virtuous, if people don't seem so. And virtue, Caudle—no, I'm not going to preach about virtue, for I never do. No; and I don't go about with my virtue, like a child with a drum, making all sorts of noises with it. But I know your principles. I shall never forget what I once heard you say to Prettyman: and it's no excuse that you'd taken so much wine you didn't know what you were saying at the time; for wine brings out men's wickedness, just as fire brings out spots of grease. *What did you say?* Why, you said this:—'Virtue's a beautiful thing in women, when they don't make so much noise about it; but there's some women, who think virtue was given 'em, as claws were given to cats'—yes, cats was the word—'to do nothing but scratch with.' That's what you said. *You don't recollect a syllable of it?* No, that's it; when you're in that dreadful state, you recollect nothing: but it's a good thing I do.

"But we won't talk of that, love—that's all over: I dare say you meant nothing. But I'm glad you agree with me, that the man who'd tie up his widow, not to marry again, is a mean man. It makes me happy that you've that confidence in me to say that. *You never said it?* That's nothing to do with it—you've just as good as said it. No: when a man leaves all his property to his wife, without binding her hands from marrying again, he shows what a dependence he has upon her love. He proves to all the world what a wife she's been to him; and how, after his death, he knows she'll grieve for him. And then, of course, a second marriage never enters her head. But when she only keeps his money so long as she keeps a widow, why she's aggravated to take another husband. I'm sure of it; many a poor woman has been driven into wedlock again, only because she was spited into it by her husband's will. It's only natural to suppose it. If I thought, Caudle, you could do such a thing, though it would break my heart to do it,—yet, though you were dead and gone, I'd show you I'd a spirit, and marry again directly. Not but what it's ridiculous my talking in such a way, as I shall go long before you; still, mark my words, and don't provoke me with any will of that sort, or I'd do it—as I'm a living woman in this bed to-night, I'd do it."

"I did not contradict her," says Caudle, "but suffered her to slumber in such assurance."

## LECTURE XXXV.

MRS. CAUDLE "HAS BEEN TOLD" THAT CAUDLE HAS
"TAKEN TO PLAY" AT BILLIARDS.

"YOU'RE very late to-night, dear. *It's not late?* Well, then, it isn't, that's all. Of course, a woman can never tell when it's late. You were late on Tuesday, too: a little late on the Friday before; on the Wednesday before that—now, you needn't twist about in that manner; I'm not going to say anything—no; for I see it's now no use. Once, I own, it used to fret me when you staid out; but that's all over: you've now brought me to that state, Caudle—and it's your own fault, entirely—that I don't care whether you ever come home or not. I never thought I could be brought to think so little of you; but you've done it: you've been treading on the worm for these twenty years, and it's turned at last.

"Now, I'm not going to quarrel; that's all over: I don't feel enough for you to quarrel with,—I don't, Caudle, as true as I'm in this bed. All I want of you is—any other man would speak to his wife, and not lie there like a log—all I want is this. Just tell me where you were on Tuesday? You were not at dear mother's, though you know she's not well, and you know she thinks of leaving the dear children her money; but you never had any feeling for anybody belonging to me. And you were not at your Club: no, I know that. And you were not at any theatre. *How do I know?* Ha, Mr. Caudle! I only wish I didn't know. No; you were not at any of these places; but I know well enough where you were. *Then why do I ask if I know?* That's it: just to prove what a hypocrite you are: just to show you that you can't deceive me.

"So, Mr. Caudle—you've turned billiard-player, sir. *Only once?* That's quite enough: you might as well play a thousand times; for you're a lost man, Caudle. Only once, indeed. I wonder, if I was to say 'Only once,' what would you say to me? But, of course, a man can do no wrong in anything.

"And you're a lord of the creation, Mr. Caudle; and you can stay away from the comforts of your blessed fireside, and the society of your own wife and children—though, to be sure, you never thought anything of them—to push ivory balls about with a long stick upon a green table-cloth. What pleasure any man can take in such stuff must astonish any sensible woman. I pity you, Caudle!

"And you can go and do nothing but make 'cannons'—for that's the gibberish they talk at billiards—when there's the manly and athletic game of cribbage, as my poor grandmother used to call it, at your own hearth. You can go into a billiard-room—you, a respectable tradesman, or as you set yourself up for one, for if the world knew all, there's very little respectability in you—you can go and play billiards with a set of creatures in mustachios, when you might take a nice, quiet hand with me at home. But no! anything but cribbage with your own wife!

"Caudle, it's all over now; you've gone to destruction. I never knew a man enter a billiard-room that he wasn't lost for ever. There was my uncle Wardle; a better man never broke the bread of life: he took to billiards and he didn't live with aunt a month afterwards. *A lucky fellow?* And that's what you call a man who leaves his wife—a 'lucky fellow?' But, to be sure, what can I expect? We shall not be together long now: it's been some time coming, but, at last, we must separate: and the wife I've been to you!

"But I know who it is; it's that fiend, Prettyman. I *will* call him a fiend, and I'm by no means a foolish woman: you'd no more have thought of billiards than a goose, if it hadn't been for him. Now, it's no use, Caudle, your telling me that you have only been once, and that you can't hit a ball anyhow—you'll soon get over all that; and then you'll never be at home. You'll be a marked man, Caudle; yes, marked: there'll be something about you that'll be dreadful; for if I couldn't tell a billiard-player by his looks, I've no eyes, that's all. They all of 'em look as yellow as parchment, and wear mustachios—I suppose you'll let yours grow, now; though they'll be a good deal troubled to come, I know that. Yes, they've all a yellow and sly look; just for all as if they were first-cousins to people that picked pockets. And that will be your case, Caudle: in six months, the dear children won't know their own father.

"Well, if I know myself at all, I could have borne anything but billiards. The companions you'll find! The Captains that will be always borrowing fifty pounds of you! I tell you, Caudle, a billiard-room's a place where ruin of all sorts is made easy, I may say, to the lowest understanding,—so you can't miss it. It's a chapel of ease for the devil to preach in—don't tell me not to be eloquent: I don't know what you mean, Mr. Caudle, and I shall be just as eloquent as I like. But I never can open my lips—and it isn't often, goodness knows!—that I'm not insulted.

"No, I won't be quiet on this matter; I won't, Caudle: on any other, I wouldn't say a word—and you know it—if you didn't like it; but on this matter, I *will* speak. I know you can't play at billiards; and never could learn—I dare say not; but that makes it all the worse, for look at the money you'll lose; see the ruin you'll be brought to. It's no use your telling me you'll not play—now you can't help it. And nicely you'll be eaten up. Don't talk to me; dear aunt told me all about it. The lots of fellows that go every day into billiard-rooms to get their dinners, just as a fox sneaks into a farm-yard to look about him for a fat goose—and they'll eat you up, Caudle; I know they will.

"Billiard-balls, indeed! Well, in my time, I've been over Woolwich Arsenal—you were something like a man then, for it was just before we were married—and then, I saw all sorts of balls; mountains of 'em, to be shot away at churches, and into people's peaceable habitations, breaking the china, and nobody knows what—I say, I've seen all these balls—well, I know I've said that before; but I choose to say it again—and there's not one of 'em, iron as they are, that could do half the mischief of a billiard-ball. That's a ball, Caudle, that's gone through many a wife's heart, to say nothing of her children. And that's a ball, that night and day you'll be destroying your family with. Don't tell me you'll not play! When once a man's given to it—as my poor aunt used to say—the devil's always tempting him with a ball, as he tempted Eve with an apple.

"I shall never think of being happy any more. No: that's quite out of the question. You'll be there every night—I know you will, better than you, so don't deny it—every night over that wicked green cloth. Green, indeed! It's red, crimson red, Caudle, if you could only properly see it—crimson red, with the hearts those balls have broken. Don't tell me not to be pathetic—I shall: as pathetic as it suits me. I suppose I may speak. However, I've done. It's all settled now. You're a billiard-player, and I'm a wretched woman."

"I did not deny either position," writes Caudle, "and for this reason—I wanted to sleep."

# LECTURE THE LAST.

### MRS. CAUDLE HAS TAKEN COLD; THE TRAGEDY OF THIN SHOES.

"I'M NOT going to contradict you, Caudle; you may say what you like—but I think I ought to know my own feelings better than you. I don't wish to upbraid you neither; I'm too ill for that; but it's not getting wet in thin shoes,—oh, no! it's my mind, Caudle, my mind, that's killing me. Oh, yes! gruel, indeed—you think gruel will cure a woman of anything; and you know, too, how I hate it. Gruel can't reach what I suffer; but, of course, nobody is ever ill but yourself. Well, I—I didn't mean to say that; but when you talk in that way about thin shoes, a woman says, of course, what she doesn't mean; she can't help it. You've always gone on about my shoes; when I think I'm the fittest judge of what becomes me best. I dare say,—'twould be all the same to you if I put on ploughman's boots; but I'm not going to make a figure of my feet, I can tell you. I've never got cold with the shoes I've worn yet, 'tisn't likely I should begin now.

"No, Caudle; I wouldn't wish to say anything to accuse you; no, goodness knows, I wouldn't make you uncomfortable for the world,—but the cold I've got, I got ten years ago. I have never said anything about it—but it has never left me. Yes; ten years ago the day before yesterday. *How can I recollect it?* Oh, very well: women remember things you never think of: poor souls! they've good cause to do so. Ten years ago, I was sitting up for you,—there now, I'm not going to say anything to vex you, only do let me speak: ten years ago, I was waiting for you, and I fell asleep, and the fire went out, and when I woke I found I was sitting right in the draught of the key-hole. That was my death, Caudle, though don't let that make you uneasy, love; for I don't think you meant to do it.

"Ha! it's all very well for you to call it nonsense; and to lay your ill conduct upon my shoes. That's like a man, exactly! There never was a man yet that killed his wife, who couldn't give a reason for it. No: I don't mean to say that you've killed me: quite the reverse: still, there's never been a day that I haven't felt that key-hole. What? *Why won't I have a doctor?* What's the use of a doctor? Why should I put you to expense? Besides, I dare say you'll do very well without me, Caudle: yes, after a very little time, you won't miss me much—no man ever does.

"Peggy tells me, Miss Prettyman called to-day. *What of it?* Nothing, of course. Yes; I know she heard I was ill, and that's why she came. A little indecent, I think, Mr. Caudle; she might wait; I sha'n't be in her way long; she may soon have the key of the caddy, now.

"Ha! Mr. Caudle, what's the use of your calling me your dearest soul now? Well, I do believe you. I dare say you do mean it; that is, I hope you do. Nevertheless, you can't expect I can lie quiet in this bed, and think of that young woman—not, indeed, that she's near so young as she gives herself out. I bear no malice toward her, Caudle,—not the least. Still, I don't think I could lay at peace in my grave if—well, I won't say anything more about her; but you know what I mean.

"I think dear mother would keep house beautifully for you, when I'm gone. Well, love, I won't talk in that way if you desire it. Still, I know I've a dreadful cold; though I won't allow it for a minute to be the shoes—certainly not. I never would wear 'em thick, and you know it, and they never gave me cold yet. No, dearest Caudle, it's ten years ago that did it; not that I'll say a syllable of the matter to hurt you. I'd die first.

"Mother, you see, knows all your little ways; and you wouldn't get another wife to study you and pet you up as I've done—a second wife never does; it isn't likely she should. And after all, we've been very happy. It hasn't been my fault, if we've ever had a word or two, for you couldn't help now and then being aggravating; nobody can help their tempers always,—especially men. Still we've been very happy, haven't we, Caudle?

"Good night. Yes,—this cold does tear me to pieces; but for all that, it isn't the shoes. God bless you, Caudle; no,—it's *not* the shoes. I won't say it's the key-hole; but again I say, it's not the shoes. God bless you once more—But never say it's the shoes."

The above significant sketch is a correct copy of a drawing from the hand of Caudle at the end of this Lecture. It can hardly, we think, be imagined that Mrs. Caudle, during her fatal illness, never mixed admonishment with soothing as before; but such fragmentary Lectures were, doubtless, considered by her disconsolate widower as having too touching, too solemn an import to be vulgarised by type. They were, however, printed on the heart of Caudle; for he never ceased to speak of the late partner of his bed but as either "his sainted creature," or "that angel now in heaven."

## POSTSCRIPT.

Our duty of editorship is closed. We hope we have honestly fulfilled the task of selection from a large mass of papers. We could have presented to the female world a Lecture for Every Night in the Year. Yes,—three hundred and sixty-five separate Lectures! We trust, however, that we have done enough. And if we have armed weak woman with even one argument in her unequal contest with that imperious creature, man—if we have awarded to a sex, as Mrs. Caudle herself was wont to declare, "put upon from the beginning," the slightest means of defence—if we have supplied a solitary text to meet any one of the manifold wrongs with which woman, in her household life, is continually pressed by her tyrannic task-master, man,—we feel that we have only paid back one grain, hardly one, of that mountain of more than gold it is our felicity to owe her.

During the progress of these Lectures, it has very often pained us, and that excessively, to hear from unthinking, inexperienced men—bachelors of course—that every woman, no matter how divinely composed, has in her ichor-flowing veins, one drop—"no bigger than a wren's eye"— of Caudle; that Eve herself may now and then have been guilty of a lecture, murmuring it balmily amongst the rose-leaves.

It may be so; still, be it our pride never to believe it. NEVER!

THE END OF MRS. CAUDLE'S CURTAIN LECTURES.

# THE ENGLISH IN LITTLE.*

## BY GENERAL TOM THUMB.

THE GENERAL—we expected it all along—has written a book upon us. A small but very pithy volume. Ere this, men have written prayers and homilies in a space no larger than the circle of a silver penny. The General, with characteristic minuteness, has painted England and the English in little—so little that it might be contained in the round of a Pennsylvanian dollar. Of course, when the words enshrined in this delicate calligraphy—executed with pen from humming-bird—are reproduced in printer's type, they will make a small volume. The original manuscript has, in the handsomest manner, been forwarded by the General to Prince Albert to wear as a watch-paper. We therefore, as we humbly conceive, confer a national benefit in making that public which, otherwise, could only be accessible to the elect. Lords and ladies might, possibly, by privilege of their position, be enabled to gratify their intense and very natural anxiety to know what General Tom Thumb really thought of them. They might pray an audience of the Prince, to read his watch-paper. But are there not thousands—millions, who like those far-seeing women, the Weird Sisters, could as soon "look into the seeds of time"[1] as behold the literary treasure consigned to the royal chronometer? Therefore, for the millions we clothe Tom Thumb's thoughts with printer's inky suit.

We knew the General must become an author. He could not do otherwise, from the contact of the society he daily suffered, than conceive a book. We saw him—small flesh and blood dot of humanity—ere he was

---

* *Punch*, XI, 195, 199, 211, 219, 235, 239–240, 257–258, 264; XII, 1–2, 19, 39–40, 63, 95, 162.

1 "If you can look into the seeds of time / And say which grain will grow and which will not . . . ." (*Macbeth*, I, iii, 58–59.)

bronzed, or rather gilt, by public exhibitions. We had the honour to pre-
cede, ay, royalty and nobility, in our introduction to General Thumb.
We were admitted to his privacy; and shall never forget the artless manner with which he played with certain five shilling pieces, accidentally
left upon the table: shall never forget the innocent looks and tones of
silver thread with which he assured us that "when he'd got enough of
them dollars, he'd buy a watch with 'em; tarnation smart." Ingenuous
homunculus! But then, not a thorough courtier, he had not trod the
floors of palaces, and therefore was not inordinately proud of his littleness.

A golden change came on. The General sang and danced hornpipes to
the smiles of royalty, and—like Sinbad's lumps of flesh—was stuck about
with precious jewels: gifts of the lords and ladies of the land. And then,
we say, Thumb grew, and rapidly, into an author.

Did the reader ever watch the daily progress of a gosling? When it has
chipped the shell—the kindly wall of lime that for weeks has kept it from
a troublous world of spits, and sage and onions—and finds its feet upon
a treacherous earth, waddling like an animated lump of flannel—or
swimming, as a ball of worsted would swim upon the waters—beautiful
and innocent is that fleecy hosiery-look of the small, faintly whistling
new comer! Nothing so innocent. A victim to the English climate, it may
be struck with sudden cramp; when with no ado at all, Sarah the maid,
will carry the little sufferer in her bosom, warming back its damnified activity. A week, a fortnight, and the gosling-flannel takes a coarser texture; its woolliness subsides, at the best, into flannel much worn. Another and another week, and you see—plainly behold them—the insidious
pen feathers begin to shoot from either wing. That seeming innocent
thing is already a terrible magazine; it begins to grow quills, instruments, that in due season, may make men weep, and laugh; and like the
*plectrum* touching the lyre, awaken sleeping harmonies in human heart-
strings.

Reader, that gosling—that innocent, flannel gosling—*was* Tom
Thumb. That quill-bearing animal *is* now the General. He has written
a book. He has achieved—"The English in Little!"

The world may be surprised at this. We are not. We were sure it
would come. The inspiration was the natural influence of the circumstances that environed the General. He saw so much, his little heart
could not contain it; and so all ran out upon paper. No wonder: what
he saw was enough to turn a giant into a human cuttlefish, and make
Goliah flow with ink.

It is a very curious fact—too curious, perhaps, to obtain due consideration of a nation of gold-washers—that authorship did certainly stop Tom Thumb's growth. His parents and guardians were, naturally enough, becoming a little uneasy at the expansion of their charge. The General's tailor looked grave. Buttons had to be advanced almost the sixteenth of an inch; betokening growing abdomen. Trowsers had to be lowered, as the tailor graphically had it, "about the blackness of his nail." We say it:—Tom Thumb's dearest well-wishers felt very uncomfortable. It was suggested by one anxious friend, that if the General's trowsers were fitted with stout, strong, leather straps, they might possibly stop his growth—for with him to grow was to be lost; even as to puff a bubble too much is to burst it.

We repeat it: it was an anxious time for the parents and lovers of the curious. Who could say? As boys who seem dwarfed dunces at school, when unconfined, rapidly grow into men of genius,—so contrarily, might Tom Thumb, making up for lost time, take a fatal start and lose his genius as a pigmy, by becoming merely a common man. With this thought, he was rarely permitted to sit or stand by a window; lest light through glass should act upon him as upon a cucumber, and draw him rapidly to his fullest length.

At this critical time, Tom Thumb sat down to his book. Not only was his growth checked from that very moment, but—surely an uncommon case—his book completed, he was really a smaller creature than when he took up his quill. Possibly, there might be something in the contents of the book that accounted for this; for, be it known, the General tells all his experience. We think this a little ungallant; and yet—no, we cannot say. For if ladies will crowd and scuffle with one another, and almost snap stay-laces to kiss the smallest of a gentleman in public—merely because he is the smallest—loving lap-dogs for no less reason; why, human vanity cannot be expected to go to its grave with its finger on its lip. It will publish its nectarine triumphs!

The General's book, however—and we propose to give a chapter every week until the whole shall be published—has much graver matter than kissing in it; grave as that sometimes is, in this weak world of lips. The General, in his "English in Little," discusses everything dear to the bosom of a free-born Briton. Our constitution, our government, our social institutions, our virtues, our vices, our literature, our drama—and here the General is a great authority, for did he not act with the feminine pillars of the modern theatre—(pillars in the very best silk stockings?)— our fashionable life, or rather, as it is called, "*the* world!" And when it is remembered that this very select world is carefully made out of a huge world—in the same way that, having made a marble out of an eighteen-inch globe, all but the chosen taw should go for waste, nothing—the reader may expect from the General's book the most delicious revealings.

However, we will no further anticipate. The English have idolised a dwarf; and the pigmy, duly returning the compliment, paints "The English in Little."


## TOM THUMB IN PRIVATE LODGINGS—
## INVITED TO THE PALACE.

WHEN I was first brought to England, Governor Barnum showed me on the stage of a playhouse for two or three nights; just, as he said, to give the stupid Britishers such a tarnation small taste of me, that they should be all the hungrier for it.

And then the Governor kept me so private in private lodgings, that not above a hundred of his private friends came every day to see me. "And where did you get the General?" asked everybody. And then, Governor Barnum putting one of his hands in his pocket, poked out the t'other at full length, and said—"The General, when I first found him, was a drug in the family, quite a drug." Whether the Governor meant salts or senna—for I guess I've taken both—I can't say. But if I've remained a drug, considering how the Britishers have swallowed me, they must have been tarnation physicked.

And after a good many days, the Governor having writ a letter to Mrs. Victoria—the Britishers call her—yes, poor critters! they do—Her Gracious Majesty; but I, who am a citizen of the smartest nation of all creation, I who look upon—— Well, I'm smart, I calculate, and so will say Her Gracious Majesty. Well, the Governor having writ his letter, went, every time there was a knock at the door, to the winder, to see if Mrs.— I mean if Her Gracious Majesty hadn't sent her best coach for him and me, that is, for the kit of us. Many days went over, and there was no royal knock, and no coach with the royal cream and curds-and-whey horses. At last, Governor Barnum being terrible riled to be sure, said to me—"General," says he.

"Governor," says I.

"Mrs. Victoria," says he—he always called her 'Gracious Majesty' afore Britishers, though he always winked tarnation at me as he did it—"Mrs. Victoria," says he, "has not answered the letter I writ her."

"P'raps," says I, "poor critter, she can't write,"—for, being a true American, I like to take Queens down a peg. "Poor critter!" I said agin, "p'raps she can't write."

"Gen'ral," said Governor Barnum, "she *can* write: it's provided by the British Constitution and the law that all critters with crowns upon their heads must be taught to write; or the Government would stop still—go down—as though run upon a snag. They *must* write, or how could they sign death-warrants?"

Well, this brings me up; stiff as a dead nigger. "General," says Barnum to me, looking a bowie knife in each eye: "you wouldn't sleep easy, I guess, upon your goose-down"—(I didn't think it *was* goose; I calculated it was cock and hen; I mean—what am I saying?—rooster and hen.)—"You would not sleep easy if you thought any critter of a Queen insulted the star-spangled banner?"

"I should think not," said I; and as I said it, I alarmed the Governor; for I looked as if I'd growed an inch.—"I should think not," said I—and I sunk down softly again, and saw the Governor was a little easy.

"Well, then," said he, "you are the greatest, brightest star of that banner; and she was not writ an answer; she has insulted *you*."

Well, I do confess it: my blood begin to bile; and I felt like a little copper tea-kettle that I've seen the Britishers put upon the table with a lamp under it, for grog; I felt a lamp under me at that moment,—my inside a wobbling, and the steam a coming out of my mouth. "I am a star, Governor," said I: "I know my brightness, and feel myself twinkle."

"Well, then," said the Governor, "what a wife does, her husband must also answer for."

"To be sure," says I; "that's why the weddin'-ring's made round to hoop 'em both."

"Well, then," said the Governor, "as we're insulted, I shall write to Mr. Albert to satisfy me as a gentleman. I never travel without the necessaries of life, and I've brought my Kentucky rifle."

"You're a beauty, Governor," says I: "you have brains enough to set up a forest o' monkeys on their hind legs as shopkeepers, and make 'em cheat one another like Christians."

"None o' your soft sawder, General," said the Governor: "my stomach's weak, and can't stand it. I shall write to Mr. Albert in the name o' the star-spangled banner, to come out with me, in his wife's own Hyde Park,[2] for early bullets."

"You *are* a beauty," I said agin. "You *are* a beauty. If the Falls could be turned into sherry-cobbler, Congress ought to give you the right of a free straw for all your mortal days."

"Only grant me one request," said the Governor, as he set down afore the paper, and dipt his pen in the ink, "If I should fall, General"——

"There'll be a war," said I.

"Of course," said he. "My ghost would haunt both countries at the same time if there wasn't. But that's not it: if I should fall, you'll have nobody to direct you; for you'll be left all alone with nothing but your innocence. Therefore, *if* I should fall, always recollect the price I'd set upon you—think of the honour of your country—remember the dignity of human natur—and don't be shown for halfpence."

I could say nothing, but I climbed up the calf of his leg, and kissed his little finger!

The Governor had put his pen in the ink, when—"*Rap*—RAP—RAP!"

There was the Royal Knock at the door!

Barnum run to the winder; looked out, and bobbed his head in agin as if he'd seen a flash of lightning. *It was the gold on the Royal livery!*

A card was brought up, from Her Most Gracious Majesty. There were these words, in her own hand-writing, upon it:—"Her Majesty the Queen of England would feel herself particularly honoured by the company of General Tom Thumb and that of his Guardian this evening to tea. N.B. Muffins. Please to ring the Back-stairs Bell."


TOM THUMB GOES TO THE PALACE—THE
"BACKSTAIRS"—THE MAIDS-OF-HONOUR.


"I DON'T much like going to the Palace up the backstairs," said Governor Barnum. "Shouldn't much like Congress to know it. 'Tisn't doing the thing by the star-spangled banner. However, just to see what crowned heads is made of, we'll go."

"In course," said I, for already I felt my teeth in the royal muffins. "In course."

Barnum set down, and writ a short note to the Queen, civilly telling

2 Hyde Park, a municipal park of over three hundred acres in West London; formerly the manor of Edward Hyde, Earl of Clarendon.

her, that as we had no other engagement for that night, we'd come. Barnum was going to seal the letter with wax.

"Governor," says I, "no wax: think of the independence of the model republic, and seal with a wafer."

Well, at seven o'clock, for the Queen dined very early that day to see us, we druv from our private lodgings in Grafton Street[3] to Buckingham Palace. We took nothing more than a cab, to show American independence.

"If Mrs. Victoria," said Barnum to me, "had asked us in at the front-gate, where the flag is flying, we'd have gone, General, in a coach-and-six. As it is, we'll match the back-stairs with a cab."

Well, we druv up, and hadn't need to ring the bell; for the door was opened in a minute, and a dozen critters in crimson—with railroads of gold running up and down their coats, and their heads as if they'd come out of a snow-storm, were waitin for us. I hadn't then time to make a meditation; or I should have said something about happy Columbia, where our helps are free citizens, and not tattooed by the tailors, as they are among the Britishers. However, I did say to Governor Barnum very softly, "I'd rather be a Red Man than a Man in Crimson." Whereupon, the Governor half-shut his eye, like a slit in a money-box, and held up his finger.

"General, this is the back-stairs," said one of the helps in crimson.

P'raps, my countrymen—for I write to Americans—you may have heard of the back-stairs of palaces. You never saw sich a thing, and for the sake of our happy republic I hope you never will. At Washington there is no back-stairs. When we want Mr. Polk, we don't stand knocking at the door; but just turn the handle and walk into the drawing-room; and, if he's not there, into any other place in the house; and we should just like to catch him putting a bolt to any door on the premises. 'Tisn't so at the court of the Britishers.

"This is the back-stairs," said the help. And first, to begin with, they are so tarnation small, and so cruel crooked, that I'm certain no really great man ever could go up and down 'em. Howsomever, the Governor and I mounted and mounted—feeling ourselves walking up a cork-screw—and we both thought there would be no end to it. How I did pity the poor critters of palaces, obligated to run up and down a twisting, twirling, back staircase, fitterer for eels and snakes to go up and down, and in and out—much fitterer than for two-legged humans.

[3] Grafton Street, between Old Bond Street and Dover Street; the residences of Admiral Earl Howe and Lord Brougham were here.

Well, at last we got up the back-stairs, and though I am lovely small, when I'd got to the end I never did feel so little in my life. "Governor," says I, "if they don't let us out at the front gate, I shall stay here for good. There is no back-stairs in a Free Republic, and my dander is up at the thoughts on it."

Agin the Governor puts up his finger, as much as to say "bus'ness." So I says nothin, but stands still to get my wind. "You must stay here till Her Majesty shall be pleased to command your presence," said the help.

I was a little riled at this, but with "bus'ness" uppermost in my mind, I said nothing. Well, in a few minutes, what they call a Lord-in-waitin comes to us, and says we must follow him. You should have seen the critter. He was dressed in a sky-blue satin coat, with amber-coloured very-smalls[4] and a pink-waistcoat, with silver periwinkles crawling all about it. There was bunches of silk sunflowers and hollyhocks worked in his skirts—and silk convolvuluses a running round his cuffs. He wanted nothing but a tight-rope and a balance-pole to be set up for life.

And I dare say, now, you want to know what is meant by a Lord-in-waitin. Why, it's jist a lord a waiting for whatever he can get to better himself. They all belong to what is called, noble families, and go to the palace to learn to be humble to their own helps at home. And you may be sure they are. For when a lord stands upon his two legs for hours behind the Queen—and carries Prince Albert's fowling-piece when he goes a gunning—and holds his horse for him to get up and down agin—and brings him his hat, and gloves, and stick, and all that—why, you may be sure that sich a lord has all the starch taken out of him by the time he gets back to his own house. It's only nat'ral.

Well, this Lord-in-waitin took us through one room and then through another and another—and if I wasn't reminded of them boxes, that go on holding a box inside a box, until there's no end on 'em,—I'm a 'possum, that's all.—At last, he said, "You'll stay here." I began to rile agin—but agin the Governor held up his finger.

By-am-by comes a whole cloud of Maids-of-honour. Oh, such walking nosegays of lilies and roses! I felt my heart bein' cut up like an apple—and a slice being served out all round.

Well, if I didn't think they'd eat me! Yes; I'm a sea-serpent, if I didn't think my time was come; for they all run at me—with their arms out—like a flock of fowls at corn. "I'll kiss him," says one—"No, me first," says another—"Don't you think it," said a third—"I'll kiss him, if I die for it," screeched a fourth; and so they pulled me from one to another—and

4 very-smalls, tight knee breeches.

kissed, and kissed, and kissed—you would have thought there was a thousand cart-whips a smacking altogether.

I have been a good deal about the world; and have been kissed by the ladies in all quarters. It is therefore my intention to write you a geographical account of kissing; beginning with our own dear Yankee Doodle girls, and ending with the Britishers. But to do this—and while Queen Victoria is a waitin to receive me—I must take another sheet of paper.

## TOM THUMB PHILOSOPHIZES ON KISSES—IS INTRODUCED TO THE ROYAL PRESENCE.

AN AMERICAN as I am—a free citizen of the smartest nation of creation, 'tisn't for me to find fault with the gals of free Columbia. Nevertheless, truth is mighty, and with fair play will whip her weight in wild cats. Therefore, I cannot say much for the kissing of America. Governor Barnum tells me that I oughtn't to give my 'pinion of the matter till I get back again, with all my snuff-boxes and tooth-picks, and pencil cases of crowned heads about me; when the kisses will be a different matter, as the royalty of Europe will be saluted through me. But this I must say; the kissing of America, of my own countrywomen, was terrible cautious; nothing more than what you might call respect with the chill off. But then, Barnum says, I was nobody; and gals don't kiss nobodies like somebodies. For all that, I'm a little riled when I think of it. For I remember, how at New York they used to look at me, and mince round and round me, and put their hands under my chin, as if I warn't a human cretur, but a gooseberry bush, and they were afraid of their fingers. And then the boldest on 'em kissed me short and not at all satisfactory; for all the world as if they thought they was doing me a service, and not themselves an honour. They'll find me rayther different when I get back, I calculate; so they'd better practise a little afore I come among 'em.

Now in England kissing is mighty hearty. The gals arn't a bit ashamed on it. I shall say no more here about the Maids-of-Honour as kissed me a million times in the Palace, but speak of the 'Gyptian Hall, where I was kissed four thousand times a day, which is only allowing eight kisses a piece for every female: some on 'em took more—some less, but I'm striking the averages. I had when I was first shewed there, tarnation pretty dimples; and in a month, my cheeks was as smooth as an apple. The dimples was kissed out; run away with by the lips of the ladies. I often said to Barnum, "Governor, this is by no means the Cheshire. I feel my face is wasting away with so much kissing; melting slick like a sugar-plum in a baby's mouth. Tell you what it is: if I'm to lose my cheeks, I ought to make something by 'em. Therefore, it's my opinion you should alter the price, in this way. 'Them as only looks, a shilling; them as kisses, eighteenpence.' Once or twice—for to be kissed eight different ways by five hundred females is nation hard work—once or twice, I thought I'd have a notice writ, and hung about my neck; sich a one as I seed at a flower-show, with these words—"Admire, but touch not." I confess it: now and then I used to be riled; used to say to myself, "Have you nobody at home to kiss; that you will put on your bonnets and patterns to come and kiss a little gentleman in public?" But as I said afore; take the people altogether, English kissing is mighty pleasant.

In Scotland I was only kissed outright at private parties. Of that, as a man of honour, I say nothing. In public, the ladies used to blow kisses at me through their fingers.

Was kissed tarnation in France. Rayther disagreeable in one particular, as the ladies so very often left the paint upon my nose.

Talking of France, it's a wonder I'm a single man. For when the King of the French heard from Barnum that I had got the fortin I have, I'm darned if he didn't say he must have me for one of the Princesses. Now, being a true republican, that didn't suit my book at all. "No, no," says I to Barnum; "don't mind the Princesses kissing me now and then, when I'm in a good temper, but I'd as soon run upon a snag as upon the marriage service. Seen too much of life, and been kissed a little too much round the world for that." So I escaped—cut slick from the Tuileries—going off in Barnum's hat-box.

Well, I did think that I should give a whole account of all the kissing I've gone through, but on second thoughts it can't be done here, no how. The subject is so full—as Barnum says—that I can't do it justice in a little book, so I intend to make it a big history, by itself, with pictures of the ladies, with their lips made up jest as they attacked me; made up now peaking like rose-buds, and now as if I was a cake at a pastry-cook's, made for nothing but to be eaten. It's wonderful to a man with my experience of lips to know what mouths can be made on 'em. Nobody would believe it, but they will when they see my book. And so to get back to Queen Victoria's palace.

When the Maids-of-Honour had done kissing me, and stood—like flustered Birds of Paradise—a taking breath, the Lord-in-Waitin comes in agin, and says, "General, Her Majesty the Queen will be very happy to see you." All the Maids-of-Honour fell back, and I following the lord, and—Barnum following me—walks into the presence of the Queen of the British Isles. I'd made my mind up to show my independence, to go in whistling "Yankee Doodle," or "Star of Columbia," but somehow I found my voice had departed—gone slick, and not even left its ghost behind—and Barnum, too, I shouldn't ha' known him; he shook all over, and his face looked as if it had been dabbed with a powder-puff. I thought to myself, the British Lion must be somewhere, under some sofa p'raps, in the 'partment, and the Governor sees him, and shakes and is pale accordin'.

I walks up to the Queen, who was a sittin' by the tea-things. "I'm very happy, General," said Her Majesty, "to see you here. Genius, though ever so small—if it *is* genius, General—is welcome to this fire-place."

Upon this, I bowed, as any gentleman would do to any lady.

"General," said Gracious Majesty, "allow me to introduce my husband." Whereupon, Prince Albert said in the most affable manner—

"I hope to improve the acquaintance of the General, when we go a gunning together," and then Royal Highness went on with his tea.

"Do you take sugar, General?" said Gracious Majesty with tongs in her hand.

"I do, madam," said I; for I found my voice a coming back agin.

"Which do you prefer?"—said Gracious Majesty, with a smile that seemed to turn me into a lump of honey—"which sugar do you prefer, white or brown?"

"Either," said I, "but if it isn't slave-grown, I'm a true republican, and won't touch a tarnation morsel."

ELL, I sot a stirrin and a stirrin my cup, and afore I'd tasted the smallest grain of tea I felt myself as snug in the Royal Back Room—and a mighty pretty location it was—as though I'd been raised there. "Gen'ral, is your tea to your likin?" says Gracious Majesty, smilin like a pictur. Now, to say the truth, the tea was first chop, but as a citizen of the freest nation on airth, it wasn't for me to say so. I should think not. Therefore, puckerin my mouth like a button-hole, and givin my head a shake as if I'd swallowed pison, I said, "Jist the smallest notion more gun-powder." Whereupon Gracious Majesty smiled agin, and spooned out the green. Then a Maid-of-honour give me another cup, and another Maid brought me the cream-jug, and another Maid the sugar-basin. And as they stood about me, they kept so lookin down upon me, and poutin their pretty lips, and sighing for all the world as if they'd straws in their precious mouths and I was sherry-cobbler that they was drinkin up. "It's a little warm, gals," said I, by way of a small hint, for in a minute I thought I shouldn't breathe. I thought my life would be strained away through white muslin.

"Ladies," said Gracious Majesty, "I'm afeard you're troublesome to the Gen'ral."

"Not at all, Gracious Majesty," said I, for I'm naterally tender to the critters; tho', to say the special, I don't like 'em swarmin about me at all times. Everything in its place, as Uncle Phil said when he threw aunt in the horse-pond.

Well, I got on pretty smart, and was mighty pleased to be sure; tho', for the honour of the Republic, I wouldn't diskiver it. "No," said I to myself, "I'll take the best they can give me, as if I was born to it, like an American citizen. I'm determined nothin shall surprise me. If Gracious Majesty gives me the crown of England to hold my marbles in, why, I'll keep a stiff upper lip; praps I'll say 'thankee,' praps I won't." As for Governor Barnum, I never seed a man so starched on a sudden. He seemed froz with royalty, like a dead hog in a Nova Scotia winter. But for me,—well, I sot in my chair like any ostrich feather in the Maids' heads—as easy, and, for all the world, as handsum.

"Gen'ral, what do you think of our muffins?" said Gracious Majesty.

Afore I could answer, I could see Barnum's eye burnin on me like a blue-light. "Steady, Gen'ral; mind what you're about. Muffins is a leadin question. Steady; or she has you high and dry upon the Corn Laws." Though the Governor only scrooged and quivered his eye a little, I could see he meant all this. Whereupon, I jist bobbed my tongue agin my cheek, as much as to say to him, "Of all the days I was born, it wasn't yesterday."

"What do you think of our muffins?" again axed Gracious Majesty.

Whereupon, I smiled down the corners of my mouth into my waist-coat pockets, and answered by asking, "What, Gracious Majesty, do you think of our Hominy Cakes?"

"Hominy cakes, Gen'ral! I never heerd of 'em," said Gracious Majesty.

I was jist going to cry out, where was you born?—when I remembered, in Kinsington Gardens.[5] So I only said—"Never heerd of Hominy Cakes! You never say so?"

"Upon my honour, Gen'ral," says Gracious Majesty, laying her white hand solemn on the tea-caddy.

Whereupon I clears my throat, as if I was goin to speak in Congress, and stretchin out my right hand—for an Honour Maid near me run for my cup and sarcer—and said—"Get a pint of small Hominy grits: a pint of sifted Indian meal; a teaspoonful of salt; three table-spoonfuls of fresh butter; three eggs; three table-spoonfuls of strong yeast; a quart of milk; a salt-spoonful of pearl-ash or salaratus"—and here I stopt short.

"Well, Gen'ral," said Gracious Majesty, "and when I have got these, what then?"

"Why, then, Gracious Majesty,"—said I—"my mother will show you how to mix 'em. The dear old critter's in London, and any arternoon is at your service; providin always with the compliment of a coach-and-six to bring her, where the flag flies, at the front gate," for I was determined to have no more of the back-stairs.

Upon this Gracious Majesty larfed so hearty, and showed sich rows of pearls, they'd have shined better in her crown than the rael ones, I'm certain. "Gen'ral, you're very good, I'm much beholden to you," said Gracious Majesty, and agin she larfed; and the Honour Maids larfed too,

[5] Queen Victoria was born on May 24, 1819, in Kensington Palace; Kensington Gardens, originally the grounds of the Palace, adjoin Hyde Park.

though in course, smaller than their missus. And now, seein I was making my way like any liner, I thought I'd give the republic a turn, and do
no harm neither to the British. So I said,—"Gracious Majesty, if you'd
like to eat the real Hominy Cake in airnest, I allot that you had better
eat it at Uncle Sam's fireside. You've a nice little steamer, and in the summer go paddlin' about the sea, to blow away the cares of state; and take
out the marks that etarnally wearin that heavy crown must bring upon
your tender forehead." And here, I thought to myself, crowns ought to
be well lined with bank-notes to make 'em fit at all easy. "Yes, Gracious
Majesty, you and your husband—and I will say this to his face, a very
fine young man he is, and I doubt not, a tarnation good shot with a rifle
—you go to France, and eat frog-pies with Louis-Philippe, and it's only
my hope that that cunnin critter (for he'd skin a weasel without wakin
him) won't some day eat up all the molasses, and give you nothin but the
basin"—(if I'd said Spanish liquorish instead of molasses, could I ha'
been a grain nearer the truth?)—"You go and visit the King of the
French, and the Duke of Cobourgers,[6] and the King of the Prushys, and
sich like, why not some summer get up the steam, and jist run over to
take a bite of Hominy Cake with the Yankees?"

Well, Gracious Majesty looked for all the world as if I'd hit at one
blow the very nail her mind had long been hammerin' on. So I follows
it up.

"We've plenty of room in the States," says I, "for your husband and all
the dear children at Astor House.[7] And there, I guess, the dear critters
won't be cramped up, as I larn they are here, but may grow and expand
like corn cobs. Bless you," said I, for I got sudden familiar, "dear critters!
There's somethin like air! Send their royal highnesses to bed at night,
and they'd grow so, you'd disown 'em in the morning."

"And, Gen'ral," said Gracious Majesty, "you think they'd make me
welcome in the States?"

"Welcome!" cried I, "they'd make you up a bed of Pennsylvanian
bonds[8]—and you know how tarnation sound the critters have slept upon
*them*—and, for a counterpane, kiver you with the star-spangled banner."

6 Prince Albert's father.

7 Astor House, in New York, was a forerunner of Astor family hotel properties that
much later included the Astor Hotel and the Waldorf-Astoria; built by John Jacob
Astor (1763–1848), an American merchant and one of the richest men in the United
States.

8 In the early 1840's the public debt of the Commonwealth of Pennsylvania was
so great that there was no money in the treasury to pay the interest due on state
bonds.

# THE GENERAL MEETS THE GENIUS OF BRITAIN
## AT THE PALACE, AND DANCES HIS HORNPIPE;
## SINGS "YANKEE DOODLE,"
## AND IS ROYALLY REWARDED.

HERE was nothin more said at that time about Gracious Majesty's goin to New York; but I could see she sot thinkin on it; and I could see now and then she looked tenderlike at the corner of her beautiful bright eyes at Prince Albert, who did seem a leetle streaked—for I've heerd he's not so good a sailor as a sea-gull—jist a leetle streaked at the notion of crossing the Atlantic. So kinder like to relieve him, I thought I'd change the conversation. Givin my cup and sarcer to an Honor-Maid, I sot with one knee across the tother—I could see Governor Barnum was a trifle ryled at this, and kept shakin his head and pussin up his mouth like a rabbit's, while I kept a pattin my right calf—not mindin him a grain. I sot, and said to the Prince—"Royal Highness," ses I, "anything doin at the Playhouses?" Well, I could see in a minute I'd put my foot into the milk-pan. All the Honor-Maids looked, on a sudden, as if they'd lost their week's pocket-money: and as for Barnum, he lifted up his eyebrows for all the world like the arches of Waterloo Bridge.[9] Well, I seed that somehow I'd taken the wrong turnin; and therefore, being an independent American, it wasn't for me to go back. In course, I repeated the question. "Anything doin at the playhouses?" ses I.

Whereupon, a Maid-of-Honor, a makin believe to cross behind me for the kittle-holder or toasting-fork, I can't say which, ses in my ear—"If you love me, Gen'ral, not a word about them low places. We never think about playhouses here. If you love me"—this she ses twice, and the words seemed to run for the first time like melted butter over my heart—"if you love me, ax about the Opera."

I was a leetle streaked at this, as I know'd nothin of the Opera; and should have liked to obligate the pretty critter that looked down, like a nosegay of flesh, upon me. Howsomever, jist as I was goin to start something, she ses—"Hush! here's the company comin."

The door was thrown open, and the Lord-in-Waitin—him as I spoke of, with the flower-beds worked upon his coat skirts—showed in sich a crowd of ladies and gentlemen; and Gracious Majesty smiled, and curt-

---

9 Waterloo Bridge, over the Thames, between Wellington Street, Strand, and the Waterloo Road.

seyed in the affablest way to every one on 'em. "Who are these critters?" ses I, in a whisper, to Lady Dorcas—for I'd pinched her arm, and she'd told me her name was Dorcas—"Who are these?"

"They are all of 'em authors, and artists, and musicians, and players, and philosophers, and people of that sort," ses Lady Dorcas. "They all come to see us once a week: but then they're smuggled up the backstairs, and so the mob, that is, the people, you see, Gen'ral, never know nothing of the matter."

"Why not?" ses I. "Gracious Majesty aint ashamed of 'em, eh?"

"Not exactly ashamed," ses Lady Dorcas. "Still, you see, in the station that we hold, we must keep up appearances." Well, I was goin to make answer; but the handsum critter looked so knowin at me, and made sich a cherry-bob with her lips, that, I felt it—I hadn't a word to throw at a dog.

Well, I sot for at least ten minutes, and not a soul of 'em said a syllable to me. At last my blood began to bile, and I ses to Lady Dorcas, ses I—"My dander's risin. The authors and painters, and philosophers, as you call the critters, think no more of me, than if I was one of theirselves."

Whereupon Lady Dorcas smiled so, my heart opened at it, and said, "Envy, dear Gen'ral, nothing but envy."

Well, Gracious Majesty was smilin and talkin to all of 'em by turns, and I thought I'd ax some of their names, that I might put down all about theirselves and families, and make a book on it—as I'm doin—to sell. "Who's that good-tempered looking gen'lman," says I, "talking to Gracious Majesty?"

"That," ses Lady Dorcas, "is Mr. Edwin Landseer;[10] he's our domestic painter. He's a great favourite here; always paintin' some of us, specially the lapdogs and parrots."

Well, I guess I should have known that, if Lady Dorcas hadn't told me so. For there was two or three of the Queen's spanels, that no sooner seed him, than they run yelping away from him; they thought—cunnin critters!—he'd come for a sittin.

"Look," ses Lady Dorcas, and she pinted to a China cat,[11] that went rubbin herself aginst Landseer's leg, like an old acquaintance. "Only look at that—there's sagacity."

"Why," ses I, "does she want to be painted? The dogs, on the contrairy, run away."

"Very true," ses Lady Dorcas; "dogs don't make good sitters; but, I

[10] Sir Edwin Landseer (1802–1873), noted for the sentiment and drama he brought into his paintings of dogs, cats, stags, and other animals.
[11] China cat, a "Siamese."

don't know how it is, cats like it. Look at that darling!"—the China cat still a rubbin herself—"she's been in three exhibitions; and—I know it as well as I know my own thoughts—she's standin on her hind legs, a begging of Landseer for a fourth full-length."

"Who's that?" ses I, as a tallish, slimmish gen'leman came in, and the Queen shook him by the hand very hearty. "Who's that?"

Lady Dorcas lowered her voice, and putting her rosebud mouth to my ear—I thought my heart would have beat through my busum—she said, in a sort of solemn whisper, "That's the imminent tragedian, Mr. Macready."[12]

Well, I'd heerd a good deal of him, and as we'd both been on the stage, I felt a kinder sort of curiosity in him. "A very pleasin sort of human," ses I; "introduce him."

"Bye-and-bye," says Lady Dorcas. "When Gracious Majesty's done with him."

"And does Macready come often here?" ses I.

"Bless you, Gen'ral! every week," ses her Ladyship. "He comes to read Shakspeare to the Queen and the Prince; but"—here Dorcas looked solemn agin—"you mustn't say I told you; it would be as much as my place is worth."

"Why not?" ses I.

"Why, the fact is, Gen'ral, it's agreed in the Palace that we should vote the English drama and English players low; but—natur will prevail, Gen'ral—we can't help lovin Shakspeare, and them as plays him best. We've tried to get the better on it, but we can't; therefore, as Lady Morgan said here the other night, we enjoy private drama-drinking, and keep up appearances."

"And who is that plain-mannered, thoughtful-looking republican?" ses I, pintin to another.

"That," says Lady Dorcas, "is Mr. Thomas Carlyle. A particular friend of the Prince's. He teaches the Prince German and English from his own books, and both together. He's now in the middle of *Oliver Cromwell*."[13]

Well, Lady Dorcas tells 'em all off, one by one, to me; all the authors, and painters, and genius—as she called it—of the country; come, as they always come (but up the back-stairs, be it remembered), once a week to a sworry with Her Gracious Majesty.

I sot a few mintes longer, when as nobody took no notice of me, I

---

[12] William Charles Macready (1793–1873), actor-manager at Covent Garden (1837–1839) and at Drury Lane (1841–1843).

[13] Carlyle's *Oliver Cromwell's Letters and Speeches* appeared in three volumes in 1845.

thought I'd ryle 'em all for the night, and whittle my stick. I'd jist given the wink to Barnum, when Gracious Majesty comes up to me, and, askin a thousand pardons, introduced all the company. Knowin my place, I sot in my chair, while all the genius of Britain—as Lady Dorcas called 'em—was ordered to make their bow, and pass afore me. When this was over, Gracious Majesty, with one of her own smiles, ses—

"Gen'ral, would it be at all aginst the grain, to ask you to obleege me and my husband, and the company, to honour us with the College Horn-pipe?"

Well, I didn't say yes, slick. No: I thought of the model republic, and of American independence. So I sot a minute, jist as if I was thinkin whether I would or wouldn't. At last, when I'd wound 'em all up to the agony pint of expectation, I ses—"I don't care if I do. But, for fear I should slip, jist let one of the helps brush them crumbs off the table;" for the genuises had been goin into the pound-cake and macaroons, like lightnin into a gooseberry-bush. Sartin some of 'em hadn't dined that day.

I think I've seen a leetle too much of life to brag, and so I won't say nothin of my hornpipe; only jist this,—as soon as I'd done it, Gracious Majesty ses "Charming!" And all the Maids-of-Honor—Lady Dorcas in special—cried softly, "What a angel!" "What a pet!" "What a animated sugar-plum!" And then the Queen unlocked a bracelet from her arm, with a little watch in it, and Governor Barnum locked it round my neck. And then didn't the geniuses look as if they'd ground glass in their stock-ings—and I—I pitied 'em.

Arter the hornpipe, I sung *Yankee Doodle*, whereupon Prince Albert was so affected, that he took his four diamond studs out of his shirt, and puttin 'em in my hand said—"Though they can add no lustre to you, Gen'ral, your genius may impart a brilliancy to them."

Arter that, I did the Greek Statues.[14] And didn't some of the Maids-of-Honor squeal at my "Ajax defyin the Thunder and Lightnin!" At this pint, however, Sir James Clarke[15]—shaking his head, and looking a little alarmed—begged I should be removed off the table.

And I was removed accordin.

---

[14] did the Greek statues, that is, in a series of tableaux vivants Tom Thumb, dressed in appropriate costumes, depicted on stage famous statues of antiquity.

[15] Sir James Clarke (1788–1870), appointed physician in ordinary on Queen Vic-toria's accession.

# THE GENERAL AND HIS GOVERNOR TAKE A CATALOGUE OF PRESENTS BESTOWED AT THE PALACE.—AN ARITHMETICAL AND PHILOSOPHICAL CALCULATION.

"You jist look here! I am thunder-smitten," ses I, trying to fling down the *Morning Post* as I spoke.

"What's the matter, Gen'ral?" axed Barnum, chipping his fourth egg —for he sucks 'em like a weazel, that he may soften his voice to talk small to the women. "What's the difficulty?" ses Barnum.

"If these Britishers arn't all froth and bang, like ginger-pop, I'm a varmint, and not the wonder of the airth, that's all. Don't they crow about their Freedom of the Press, like twenty thousand game-cocks"—

"Roosters," ses Barnum, solemn; "remember you're a pure American citizen, Gen'ral, and never forget to say roosters. I should never forgive myself if I'd brought you from the most enlightened nation of the airth to be contaminated by the vulgarity of Europe. Roosters," and he went on with his egg.

"Well, I am so ryled," ses I, "taint a wonder what I said. Here's the *Mornin Post* with the *Court Circlar* in it—as full of lies as Philadelphy's full of Quakers. Jist read it." Whereupon Barnum reads:

"Last night the Duke and Duchess of Ermine, the Marquis and Marchioness of Strawberryleaf, his Excellency the Cannibal Islands' Minister and Lady, dined at the Palace. In the evening there was a distinguished party of the nobility and *corps diplomatique.*"

"Not a word about me!" ses I. "Won't you go slick to our Ambassador —won't Mr. Everett"[16]—for it was afore Bancroft's[17] time in course— "won't he call Mr. *Court Circlar* out? Ain't it an affront to the flag?"

" 'Tisn't his fault, poor critter," ses Barnum; "*Court Circlar* only puts in the paper what's handed out to him chalked on a slate. One of the Honor Maids or Waitin Lords gives it him; and he only puts it in his best English, and then sends it to the papers."

"And they talk of a pure, inlightened press! I wonder if our own *Mornin Airthquake* would belittle itself by such doings! I have heerd of printers' devils; and for sartin they must write such bamboozlin with their pinted tails. 'Tisn't at all clear grit, Barnum"—ses I—"to be left out

---

[16] Edward Everett (1794–1865); senator, governor of Massachusetts, and president of Harvard University; minister to England from 1840 to 1845.

[17] George Bancroft (1800–1891), historian, secretary of the navy, and diplomat; minister to Great Britain from 1846 to 1849.

for Dukes and Marquises and such critters. I could not ha' thought it of Gracious Majesty."

"Gen'ral," says Barnum, in his soft way—and he'd gammon a whole bed of spinach by only winkin at it—"Gen'ral, we mustn't be too hard upon Gracious Majesty; dear lady, she can't help it. John Bull, the beast"—

"That's right, Governor," ses I, "swear at him, and make me happy."

"John Bull doesn't care a munch of oil-cake for all the genius of the 'varsal airth.—And if he was to know that painters, and players, and poets, and such cattle, went once a week—as they do—to spend a sworry with Gracious Majesty, why, it's much to be feared he'd look down upon her. And so, whenever Gracious Majesty has a private party of geniuses to tea with her, why, jist for the sake of appearances, and peace and quiet, she's obliged to put 'em off upon the public as Dukes and Airls, and Ambassadors. In like way, you see, as coiners gild pocket-pieces, and pass 'em for pure gold."

"If genius isn't the rael Cheshire here"—ses I, a leetle streaked—"what's to become of *me*?"

"We shan't show you as a genius, Gen'ral; *that* wouldn't pay for the candles. No; we shall sink the genius—for you are a wonderful critter, that's a truth as plain as chalk—and puff the dwarf."

Still I wasn't to be smoothed round and round like a beaver hat, and I ses—"if I'd ha' been up to that deceivin varmint, *Court Circlar*, you don't think I'd have flung away my hornpipe and our national melody! No: they should have sent me to the Tower first."

"Now, Gen'ral," ses Barnum, "don't let your dander rise. And for the weakness of the Britishers, don't despise it, for we shall turn it into ready money. If they cared for what's called genius, they wouldn't suit us. I'm told that a man at the 'Gyptian Hall was able to set up his carriage for life upon a baboon's-head and a salmon's tail."

"Lor!" ses I—for I *was* 'stonished—"as how?"

"Why, he put 'em both together, and called 'em a mermaid. The shillins fell in showers. There was no keeping out the people of quality. One old baronite was flung down in the mob, and broke his leg; but he warn't to be discountenanced; for the very next day he come upon crutches."

"And set up his carriage upon a false mermaid?" ses I, quite bewondered.

"And more than that," ses Barnum, "he sold her rael comb and glass fifty times over for a swinging sum—but all private, in course—to dowagers of the nobility. By the way," ses Barnum—and he looked on a sudden as bright as though he'd wiped his face with the tail of a comet—"by the way, Gen'ral, you didn't happen to be born with a caul—eh?"

"I don't know; mother can tell you," ses I.

"Because, if you was, I've no doubt it would sell agin and agin to the Lords of the Admiralty. That pint must be thought of," ses Barnum, seriously. "Howsumever, if your name isn't yet in the *Court Circlar*, you was gilt and jewelled last night at the Palace tarnation. Look here;" whereupon Barnum took out such a heap of gold and glitter, from a drawer, I thought to myself, "I'm as fine as a new weathercock."

"Let us catalogue 'em, reg'lar," ses Barnum, and he got pen and paper. "Call 'em out, and I'll write."

—A gold bracelet, from Gracious Majesty, with a watch a tickin still in the middle of it.

"Barnum," ses I, "I did feel a leetle like a dog with this about my neck last night. Couldn't it be taken in for my leg, kinder Order of the Garter-like?" Barnum nodded, and I went on.

—Four diamond shirt-studs out of Prince Albert's own busum.—

"Well, they're nation genteel, but a leetle small; not much bigger than big peas. Howsumever, I'll wear 'em till bigger comes, and then they'll serve for counters at cards."

—Two large emerald brooches, from two Duchesses.

"I tell you what I shall do," ses I. "Yes; with these brooches I'll give trade a lift. I'll wear 'em for buckles, and stick 'em in my shoes. And so," ses I, "like a true republican, look down upon the aristocracy." Barnum didn't speak, but grinned, as much as to say, "Gen'ral, bless you!"

—Three gold chains, given from the necks of three Countesses.

"Two of 'em jined," ses I, "will make me a skippin rope; and the third will go round my waist to tie my dressin-gown."

—Five-and-twenty pearl and diamond and ruby rings, warm from the fingers of several ladies of nobility.

I didn't know what to make of them; but I seed that something was wriggling in the mind of Barnum; for he sot bitin the end of his pen, like a rabbit at a cabbage-stalk. At last—his face lightin' up like gas—he ses, "I tell you what, Gen'ral. Them rings—when you get more of 'em—and by-and-by you'll have as many as a thousand rattlesnakes—them rings may be made a great feature. We'll have 'em all linked together, and made a kinder chain of; and then, when you go agin upon the stage, you may dance a hornpipe in the fetters; and the name of every lady's ring may go into the play-bills."

"Governor," ses I, "that will be very handsum; besides, it will ryle the men, and that gives me special satisfaction. For I could see 'em, last night, while some of the pretty critters was kissin me—not but what I could have done with half the allowance I got, for I *have* seen flies killed with treacle—I could see 'em a lookin' at me, as if they could have swallowed me like a mint-julep. And 'specially the geniuses, as they called themselves, looked in that fashion;—and they needn't; they never give me nothin."

"Genius, my dear Gen'ral," ses Barnum, "never does. Don't expect it. It may be, that genius has seldom anything to give—but, however—it is to gifted critters like myself, Gen'ral, genius is always shabby. Howsumever, to proceed with the catalogue."

—A silver thimble!

Well, I *was* streaked! Who *could* have insulted me with that dirty bit of metal! And then I recollected, jist as I was lifted into the carriage, it was flung in at the winder, no doubt by one o' the house-maids of the Palace. I was so ryled, I was going to climb up the leg of the table, and catch hold of the thimble, and fling it in the fire, when the Governor put his hand upon me.

"Gen'ral," ses he, "I guess your thoughts. Arter you were in bed last night, I thought much of that thimble. I know a little of arithmetic and morals, and they are linked tarnation close together. Well, I find that allowin one housemaid out of fifty that comes to see you gives you a silver thimble, and of course she will"—

"Why of course?" ses I.

"If Gracious Majesty gives a watch, in course the housemaid will give a thimble. It's example in high places that makes the true vally of monarchy. Well, I calculate that every housemaid out of fifty presenting you with her thimble, we shall have at least two thousand bushels, three hundred pecks, two quarts, of silver thimbles."

"Lor!" ses I. "And what, Governor, shall we do with 'em?"

"Send 'em to the Mint," says Barnum, "and melt 'em into dollar pieces."


THE GENERAL UPON EXETER HALL
AND THE EGYPTIAN HALL.

BARNUM having hired a location at 'Gyptian Hall, ses to me, "Well, Gen'ral, when do you feel disposed to show yourself to these English critters? If tainte done soon, they'll tear the door off the hinges." For Barnum had put it about in all the papers, consarnin my visit to Gracious Majesty to the Palace, sinkin, in course, the slight of the back-stairs, for he didn't want to get up a war atween the two countries afore we'd plucked the Britishers. "If tainte awful to hear the smashin of carriage-poles and pannels in the street right under our winders; the aristocracy do so crowd to catch a glimpse on you." The aristocracy of England, be it understood, is sich a critter for the true grit; the rael thing, special if it comes from anywhere across the sea.

"Barnum," ses I, "I do feel a little streaked that you should bamboozle me about the baboon and the salmon, that made a mermaid atween 'em; there never was nothing o' the sort; father has been and inquired; and only that they saw his dander was up considerable, they'd have kicked him out of the 'Gyptian Hall, slick."

Barnum ses nothin to this; but I could see he was ryled tarnation, for he stroddled like a pair of compasses across the room, and pulled and pulled at the bell, as tho' he was payed for pullin it. "Ax the Gen'ral's father," ses Barnum to the help when he come, "to do me the leetle favour of steppin up here." And afore you could ring a dollar, father was in the room.

"So, I hear you've been to the Hall," ses Barnum; "now which way did you go to it."

"Out o' the house, down Bond Street, along Picadilly, past Charin-Cross—where the king, whose head they cut off, tho' he looks perkin enough jist now, is sittin a horseback—then right up the Strand, and on the left to a purty big stone house up steps."

Somethin I could see was ticklin Barnum; but he only said, "You never heerd, Mr. Strelton, I s'pose, of Exeter Hall?"[18]

"Never," ses father; and Barnum shakes his head, as much as to say "Poor forlorn sheep." However, in a minute he kinder smiled, and ses, "What did you see at the Hall, Mr. Strelton?"

"Why," ses father, "I see a good many people, most on 'em in black, with white cloths twisted 'bout their throats; and a good many on 'em lookin as though they'd jist lost a dollar and not found a cent; and there was a good many she critters—a lot on 'em with steel and tawtey-shell spectacles on their noses, and some of 'em lookin as if they'd jist come from picklin inions, and had a leetle of the vinegar in their faces."

I could see Barnum screw his mouth, as tho' he was suckin up a julep. However, he ses, "Go on, I beg, Mr. Strelton."

[18] Exeter Hall, in the Strand, was used for annual meetings of religious societies.

"Well," ses father, "I followed them as was going up, and after twistin and turnin I found meself in a sort of horse-shoe place, filled with black coats, and white cloths, and tawtey-shell spectacles. Afore me was a large platform, very full of these critters. 'Tarnation,' ses I to meself, 'how on airth can they show the mermaid on that stage, if it is so full of humans? 'Taint givin the poor critter fair play.' Well, they put a solemn-faced, straight-haired human in a big chair, and the people clapt and halloed; and I heerd more than one tawtey-shell woman say 'That's Sir Randrew[19]—that's the blessed Baronite!' and others screech'd 'What a lamb of a man!' "

Barnum wriggled and twisted, and then cried, smotherin a larf, "Go on, Mr. Strelton, go on."

"Well," ses father, "the chairman got upon his legs, and said 'It was a delightful sight to see what he did see afore him, so many fellar countrymen and women,'—here one tawtey-shell began to sob,—'and more, so many foreigners.' Well, thinkin this was nothin more than a purty compliment to the flag, I cries out 'Columbia thanks you, stranger,' whereupon the meetin—sich was their manners to the freest citizen on airth,—screeched out 'Shame!' 'Turn him out!' but I only screwed meself tighter to the seat and grinned like a thousand wild cats at 'em. 'We are here assembled,' ses the Chairman, 'to cut off another inch from the tail of Satan! We have put down that sinful ingine the Sunday muffin-bell, and we will not pause, or falter, or bate a jot of heart or hope, before we see the day when the grass will grow in Lunnun streets on Sundays—when people will go with their eyes upon the stones to church and back again; and not a soul—no, nothin but the benighted sparrows—to be heerd in this wicked metropolis; and the Thames—so full of steamers—be as the Dead Sea.' And then the people halloed, and the Chairman sot down; and other critters got up, and talked in the like way. So at last, I gets up and goes out, and so down stairs, till I come to a feller with a long stick in his hand, and goold upon his collar, and goold about his hat. 'When are they goin to show the mermaid?' ses I. 'What do you mean?' ses he, looking a leetle afire. 'The critter,' ses I, 'that's half woman half fish.' 'No woman o' the sort here,' ses the goold band, mighty short. And then he turned agin upon me, and ses, 'You poor lost sheep—go, show your humbleness, and crawl to home upon all fours.' Well, I was too tickled by his airnestness to be at all ryled, so I ses, 'Well, if I can't see the mermaid, can I see the sarpents? I spose you know what a sarpent is, here to the Hall.' 'I should think so,' ses Goold Band; 'they're smitin him now

19 Sir Randrew, Sir Andrew Agnew, ridiculed by Jerrold as a notorious Sabbatarian.

upstairs. The baronite has got him by the throat, and I wouldn't be him for tuppence.' I was in a bit of a fog; still it was such a curious critter, that I kinder humoured him. 'And where,' ses I, 'did the Jibbeways show theirselves? where did they do the war dance? and where's the Battle of Waterloo modelled in biscuit?—and where'—but afore I could say any more, Goold Collar lays his hand upon me and calls up one of the Perlice. 'You will take this wretched heathen to the station—and then afore the magistrate—and then to the treadmill, where they'll cut his hair, and larn him to be a Christian.' 'I come here,' ses I, 'to see the Mermaid, and have got my shilling ready, if anybody had axed me for it.' 'Go away, you great fool, and don't make a noise,' ses the Perlice, smilin like, and givin me a good-natured shove down half-a-dozen steps. Well, the American Eagle did a little expand his wings in my busum, but I smoothed him down, and holdin my fist up at Goold Band, I whistled Yankee Doodle —as loud as ten thousand canaries—and walked on."

Here Barnum bust into sich a fit of laughter, the fire-irons danced agin. "Mister Strelton," ses he, when he'd come a leetle to, "you must understand that in Lunnum there is two Halls—one is Exeter, and one is 'Gyptian. Now, you have been to Exeter, and not to 'Gyptian."

And so it turned out. Howsomever, as I am writin to Americans, it's only proper in me to warn 'em aginst the mistake; otherways, from what is sometimes done and said at Exeter Hall, strangers might sartinly believe they were at the 'Gyptian.[20]


## AFTER A PARENTHESIS, THE GENERAL DISCOURSES UPON CHRISTMAS IN ENGLAND.

BEFORE I go on with this little account of the Britishers, I may jist sot down two or three lines in answer to a cloud of letters that has come upon me from citizens of America, located in this country. Many on 'em —and Mr. Bancroft in special, our ambassador—fault me for what they call the imperfect use of my mother tongue. Well, I can't say; praps they're right, and praps they're wrong. But the truth is, they do speak the wust English in London—and in special about the squares—that any critter ever heerd on this airth. And when it's remembered, as it ought

20 A typical anti-clerical remark of Jerrold's, suggesting that the business of the clergy was on the same level as that of Tom Thumb's sideshow, then appearing at Egyptian Hall.

to be, how much I have mixed in high life—that is, how many tables of the aristocracy I've danced my hornpipe at evenin parties upon—some allowance, I think, might be made for any error or so of a mistake in, what Barnum has told me to call, "the hurry of composition." Howsumever, when I'm once clear of these British critters, and am agin under the wings of the Columbian eagle, my English—Barnum is ready to wager it—will come agin purer than ever. Shouldn't wonder.

As I do not belittle meself to write to the English, but to the citizens of inlightened America, I shall break off for a leetle bit from my 'count of my first appearance at the 'Gyptian Hall, to talk about the way in which the Britishers pass their Christmas; a day which has jist turned round the corner.

In the first place, long afore Christmas, every family begins to fatten its own bullock—its own sheep—and its own pig. They don't feed the critters upon corn and peeches, as in the model republic, but cram 'em with almond cakes, and pine-apples, which, thanks to the West Indies—that will be soon annexed to America, being, in fact, only bits broken off her by an airthquake or somethin o' the sort, and therefore our rightful property,—which pine-apples, I was about to say, are as plenty as periwinkles, and plentier. Well, all the beasts are druv near to Portman-Square;[21] where Prince Albert, as a patron of the fine arts, and the Duke of Cambridge, as the friend and adviser of all the cooks in London, and therefore a mighty stout judge of what jintes of all sorts are—come with a band of music belongin to the Horse Guards—(and you should see how their silver kittle-drums sparkle!)—and give away silver meddles for first prize beef, and bunches of horse-radish for the second.

And after the prizes are given out, all the masters of the workhouses—they are called Unions out of joke, acause they break the weddin-ring in 'em, and part man and wife—all of 'em buy the cattle, and puttin green boughs about their horns, and collars and bows of ribbons round about and all over 'em, drive 'em to the workhouse; and for the pigs and sheep as can't walk, they hire cabs and hackney-coaches. This very Christmas as is gone, the fattest ox was druv to the Union of St. Pancras;[22] but I don't know what for—and when I axed Barnum he wouldn't tell me—the St. Pancras ox was dressed in black ribbons; and so was an ox that was druv to St. Marrowbone.[23]

There will, next Christmas, I have heerd, be a sort of poultry show—kinder fancy fair like—for ladies; so that the lords of the airth, as the men critters call themselves, mayn't have the fat all their own way at the Portman. The ladies and young gals will show their turkies, and their ducks, and their geese, and roosters and hens, and be prized accordin. Only right and proper this. Why should great, big, hulkin men carry away all the meddles for fat beef—(and after all, when they think they're growin meat, they're only makin tarnation dear candles)—and the dear little pussey critters not have so much as a silver thimble for a plump rooster? 'Taint the straight line by no means; when the airth was made,

21 Portman-Square, between Orchard St., Oxford St., and Baker St.; Mrs. Montagu and the Duke of Hamilton had resided here.

22 St. Pancras, metropolitan borough of London, known for its large railway terminals and for St. Pancras Church, named for the martyred patron saint of children.

23 St. Marrowbone, St. Marylebone, metropolitan borough of London, near Regent's Park; here are located the zoological and botanical gardens, and Mme. Tussaud's waxworks.

woman was to have half of it; but the truth must be said; we have
wronged the pretty critter precious. And how kind she always was and
is to us! Never keepin nothin wholly to herself; for as I said to Barnum
the other day, who only larfed and couldn't say nothin in answer—when,
poor soul, she hadn't no more than one apple, didn't she give Adam
half of it?

And so the ladies' poultry show—as Lady Dorcas said to me yesterday
—only proves a leetle more of the spirit of the times, and the growin
rights of women. (Dear critters! since I've been kissed as I have been, you
can't think how I take 'em all to heart.) Lady Dorcas tells me that she's
goin to fatten ring-doves upon peppermint-drops; whilst a great agricultural Duchess as she knows, has already got a pen of turkies crammin on
custards, tipsy-cake, and blank-mange. I'll wager one of my dimond
studs, that Royal Highness giv me, that the women's poultry, with fair
play to back 'em, will beat the cattle. "Tipsy-cake against ile-cake," ses
I, and not a doubt on the matter.

However, as I'm upon Christmas, I'll tell you all about it—I'll shake
you all the flour out of the bag, and more than's in it, as the miller said
down east, to Cob, the miser, who was buried in a flint-skin waistcoat.
Their beef—'xceptin always the prize, which does railly make one think
of a candle-stick—is first chop; and their plum-puddin is somehow gathered from all the best eends of the varsal airth. But they have a custom
which is terrible to think on, 'specially for young single fellars like me
with their hearts to let, and so many pretty critters wantin to take the
lodgins.

It is this.—The gals go out on the last moonlight nights afore Christmas, and—now, I've had all this story from Lady Dorcas, and, in course,
it's as true as a thunderbolt—and searchin up and down the woods
about Lunnun, Highgate, and Hornsey, and Saint John's Wood[24] in
particular—they climb up the oak and apple-trees, and cut off branches
of mistletoe; a thing that, as a free Republican, I am proud to say does
not grow in smart America. Well, they bring home the mistletoe and
hang it up wherever it *will* hang in their houses; and there—as Lady
Dorcas ses to me—it is no sooner hung, than one Cupid at least goes and
perches in it, like a sparrow in a bird's-eye maple; and there he sits, a
fingerin his bow and his arrow, awaitin for his prey, like a hunter of old
Kentuck for a 'possum.

Well; when a young fellar enters the house, one of the gals lookin as

[24] Saint John's Wood, residential section, bordering on St. Marylebone metropolitan borough; location of Lord's Cricket Ground.

if she wouldn't drink dove's milk, she is so innocent—sidles and sidles right under the mistletoe, and a half-larfin, and a half-poutin, without sayin a word axes the young fellar to come under the 'dentical branch also; and when there—he can't help it; twenty thousand giants couldn't hold him from doin it—he kisses the gal smack; and at the very moment twang goes the bow-string in the mistletoe, like the fiddle-string of Ole Bull[25]—and the young fellar is hit right through his waistcoat, without a drop of blood a showin the wound. Well, now you may larf at me or not, as you like; but in six months that young fellar's that gal's husband. It was never known to fail. With mistletoe-berries, they make bird-lime —ses Lady Dorcas to me—and with mistletoe they make bride-lime too.

One thing, however, is special good in English Christmas; and it has been specially attended to this Christmas as is jist over. It is this. All the money that was won at cards—from pounds to half-pence—was the very next morning sent to buy small comforts for the poor of the parish. "Barnum," ses I, for I'd been very lucky, "Barnum, take this leetle fifty."

## THE GENERAL DISCOURSES ON ENGLISH CUSTOMS—NEW YEAR'S DAY AND TWELFTH-CAKE[26] ART. BARNUM DEFINES MODESTY.

ON THE LAST occasion I told you a leetle about the Britishers' Christmas, and might fill a letter-sheet with the 'count of New Year's Day, and Twelfth-Cake Day, and sich like; but tainte my notion. No; I shall at once go on with the greatest subject on airth—meself. However, as I'm a writin at a charitable time of the year, I don't mind settin down two or three matters afore I begin with 'Gyptian Hall.

In the first place, for New Year's Day. The Queen and the Prince are very charitable at the Castle. All the oldest and forlornest Members of Parliament meet in the Quodrangle; and then the Lord Chancellor and the Archbishop of Canterbury distribute, as the papers call it, Her Majesty's bounty to the poor critters; consisting of law-books, writ to the meanest understanding, and sermons, the tracts, and sich like things, to

25 Ole Bull (1810–1880), a widely-acclaimed Norwegian violinist.
26 Twelfth-cake, a large cake used at the festivities of Twelfth-night, usually ornamented with frosting, and with a bean introduced to determine the king or queen of the feast.

teach 'em the strait line towards their deluded constituents when the House of Commons 'sembles. There is also another very pretty custom—terrible affectin, I can tell you. It is this:—

There is three kings,[27] they say, reigning at a place they call Somerset House. Kings of the Poor. I've never seen their crowns and robes, but, thinking of their subjects, suppose 'em to be crowned with straw, and robed with tatters. Well, Barnum tells me that these kings—kinder like the Pope in Rome, Barnum ses—go every New-Year's Eve to some West-End workhouse—they went to St. James's this year—and wash the feet and hands of all the poor with Windsor soap, and dry 'em on damask towels. This is only to show what the Kings of the Poor, in this country, think of the Poor. But they're always doin somethin with 'em.

The Twelfth-cakes, at this season, are monstrous beautiful. The figures are mostly Lord John Russell[28] and the rest of the ministers in the very best sugar; that the children may fill their leetle bellies with principles, Barnum ses, without knowin it. The Britishers have high notions of art for Twelfth-cakes; but are easy pleased with out o' door statues. Anything, they think, will do in bronze or stone, but they are mighty particklar in art when it comes to sugar. Barnum ses they succeed better with Twelfth-cakes 'cause all the confectioners set their faces against Royal 'Cademicians. I haven't the smallest crumb of doubt upon it,—that's it.

And now about 'Gyptian Hall. Barnum had got it put about in the papers, that Gracious Majesty had asked me to muffins; and moreover, had got some wood-cuts, I think he called 'em, in the *Ulcerated News*,[29] and other pictur papers, showing how I *didn't* dance a quadrille with Gracious Majesty, and how I did lick his Royal Highness at a game of billiards, standin on the table and givin him five. And, moreover, there were picturs of the dimond studs, and rings, and all the gifts, down to the royal housemaid's thimble flung in at the carriage, at Buckinham Palace. Well, as the *Ulcerated News* goes into the busums of all families, —and there's nothin like pictures for teachin the true grit of politics,— all the world soon knowed about Tom Thumb; and I'm a sinner, if it didn't take a body of police, with Colonel Rowan sittin in his saddle always at their head, to keep the Britishers clear of our door, that was always obleeged to be opened with the chain up, in fear they'd break in

---

[27] Possibly the Exchequer, the Probate Office, and the Legacy Duty Office, all of which were contained in Somerset House.

[28] Lord John Russell (1792–1878), prime minister and first lord of treasury from 1846 to 1852.

[29] *Ulcerated News*, the *Illustrated News*, noted for its sensational journalism.

upon us. Once or twice Barnum thought he'd write to the Horse Guards, to have half-a-dozen sogers with shiny breastplates and drawn swords at at the door, in disguise as a guard of honour, but raelly to protect us. " 'Twould be only doin the handsome thing to the star-spangled banner," said Barnum; and he'd sit a bitin his pen, and then, like an independent citizen of the freest nation on airth, he'd fling it away with a kinder toss, as much as to say, "No, Gen'ral, we won't be obleeged to the critters."

Well, with all this shindy a goin on, I ses one day to Barnum—"How is it, Barnum," ses I, "that these Britishers do make sich a tearin noise about everything that's stranger-like? Everything that's not of theirselves and their own country?"

Whereupon Barnum looking solemn upon me, and putting his forefinger erect up the side of his right cheek—for I like to be particlar in this sort of thing, it gives a finish to writin, in the like way as it does to paintin. In proof of which at this moment, there's a Royal 'Cademician who'll get a hundred pound note for a pictur of a cabbage-leaf, when another painter can't sell his Jupiters, Alexanders, and sich things for the price of ile-cloth table mats. And wherefore? Why, the cabbage-leaf, everybody cries, is so rael. To be sure it is: how could it miss? For doesn't the 'Cademician go to Covent Garden and buy a rael leaf, and count all the leetle stalks and veins, and paint every one on 'em? How then can it miss being rael and natural? Whereas for the pictur of Jupiter, whoever seed the original to judge by? And so, in course, the cabbage-leaf carries it; and so a good-sized summer cabbage is, whenever he likes, a hundred pound note at least, in the pocket of that 'Cademician. The rael afore the ideal—the substance afore the shadow any day!

Well, Barnum puts his fore finger up his right cheek, and ses—"Why does John Bull like foreigners afore his own Britishers? I'll tell you; it all comes of his modesty."

"What's that?" ses I, for I'm wus nor a caterpillar if I'd ever heerd him name the thing afore.

"Why, modesty," ses Barnum "is"—and then he did look in a tarnation fix. "Modesty, Gen'ral, is," ses Barnum; and then he stopt agin; no, he couldn't get it out: it seemed to stick like a leetle fishbone in his throat; and the more he hummed and hawed, the more it wouldn't come. At last, he takes a turn or two in the room to hide his ignorance; and then ses with a kinder determined manner, "Look you here, Gen'ral, I'll explain this leetle question to you, by money. I'll illustrate what modesty raelly is, by what is called the coin of the realm."

"Is that possible?" ses I, "Gov'nor."

"Gen'ral," replies Barnum, solemn, "there is nothing—no moral pinte on the airth that money will not illustrate, if you only know how to set about it. Well, modesty is jist as stupid a thing as this; it is for all the world as if a full weight goolden sov'reign was to insist upon going for only nineteen shillins, and not a farden more. That is modesty; by which you will understand that modesty is always a thing that a man loses by. Deny your full weight, though it be but a thousandth part of a grain, and though you're put in a pair of scales, and balanced, the world will swear that you don't weigh half you raelly do. Modesty! Why, it's as if a whole hog should beleettle himself down to a suckin pig."

"What you've said about the goolden suv'reign, Governor," ses I, "has sunk into my heart. I'll fancy meself that precious coin, and never go for half-a-cent under it."

"My dear Gen'ral, that won't do at all. By no means. No: the true wisdom of this airth is for a man who thinks himself a goolden suv'rain, to get twenty-seven—twenty-eight—aye, thirty shillings for his goold; and what's more, never—when he can get 'em—never to refuse the extra ha'-pence."

Barnum was goin on, when at the moment a thousand trumpets seemed to blow on a sudden in the street—drums and clarinets struck up —and the Gov'nor, with all his hair one end, run to the winder.


THE GENERAL GIVES AUDIENCE TO LORD MAYOR
AND ALDERMEN—FREEDOM OF THE CITY—
THE GENERAL'S MUTTON CHOP.

"O Gen'ral," ses Barnum, drawin in his head from the winder, and his face all alight and red, like the Lunnun sun in a fog, "Gen'ral," ses he, "here's a percession come to take you down to the 'Gyptian Hall. There's the Lord Mayor in his goold coach, and the sheriffs, and men in brass and steel armour, and the aldermen, and a band o' trumpets and kittle-drums, and crowds of women in rainbow silks and sattins, and I think— but I'll not be sure—a leetle sprinklin of bishops, and all, as I say, to tend you in state to the Hall. I must say it, Gen'ral; it's very handsome of the critters."

"Is our Ambassador—is Everett among 'em," ses I; for I own it—I did feel a leetle streaked that my own representative at the British Court should hang back at the eend. 'Twasn't doin the right thing afore strangers.

"Gen'ral," ses Barnum, "tainte to be expected. The fact is—oh there's no doubt on it—that Everett is a leetle ryled at your tarnation success afore Gracious Majesty. Then, agin, Everett is a literary critter—"

"What's a literary critter," ses I, for I'd never heerd of it by that name.

"Oh, a critter"—ses Barnum, smilin sour, with his mouth like a vinegar cruet—"a critter that wriggles in ink, upon foolscap."

"I see! Making marks like a snail upon a cabbage leaf," ses I.

"Jist so," ses Barnum. "And such critters are special catawampious at the rael thing—the true grit, like you. You know, Gen'ral, you saw a lot of 'em at the Palace with Gracious Majesty, eatin muffins with the Prince, and helping themselves to cream and sugar, as if they'd been born with royal tongs twixt their fingers. Well, you're the nat'ral true thing—a fortin in your own littleness; and they can't abide that you should have come into the world like a human dimond as you are—the brightest gem in the crown of America, if she had one. It's all summed up in this, I tell you. They can't abide that anybody's littleness should make a fortin, when what they call their greatness can hardly make both eends meet."

"I think it's only belittleing ourselves to talk of the critters," ses I. "Howsumever, I'm not goin to the Hall, afore I've had somethin to eat. And I *do* think, Barnum, 'twould be only acting like the freest citizens of the airth if we axed the Mayor and Aldermen to take a julep, and sent some bread and cheese to the men in brass and steel outside."

"You're right, Gen'ral," ses Barnum. "Our country can't expect no less on us." Whereupon Barnum was goin down stairs, when he stopt. "What will you take, Gen'ral?"

"Oh, a mutton chop—done in paper,—what d'ye call it?" ses I, for I'd seen the sort two days afore.

"A cutlet *a lar Maintenon*," ses Barnum. "And do you know—for its my dooty, as your guardian, while you fill my pocket, to fill your mind—do you know why a mutton chop cooked in that fashion is called Maintenon? No, you don't: well, it's this. Henry the Fourth had a sweetheart called Marmselle Maintenon; and he was so tarnation fond on her, that when he was away at the wars, he always had her curl-papers sent to him, and in them dental papers they always cooked his mutton chops. Pretty, isn't it?"

"More pretty than nice," ses I; "but Kings are strange critters." And then a thought hit me.—"Barnum," ses I—"when the Mayor and Alder-

men come, and taken their julep, let 'em serve me my chop. And—jist
to ryle 'em a bit, and to show 'em the glory, and wealth, and independence of the freest nation of all creation—let them cook *my* chop in a
twenty pound Bank o' England note." Whereupon Barnum larfed and
nodded, and goes down stairs; and in a minute or two, I heerd sich a
shufflin and a scrapin of feet, and then the door was flung open, and
Barnum backed into the room, a bowin like a poplar in a high wind, and
arter him came the Lord Mayor in a velvet gown, with a goold chain—
like a ship's chain cable round his neck—and the Sheriffs and the Aldermen in dark blue gowns, trimmed with cat-skins. Whereupon, lookin at
'em bold, but kindly like, I put out my right hand to be kissed. Well,
arter that leetle ceremony, the Lord Mayor seemed to take heart a bit,
and began to speak; or, rayther to read off a piece of vellum or ass's skin,
tainte for me to say which. "Gen'ral"—ses Lord Mayor—"it is the old and
ancient custom of the Lord Mayor of the fust commercial city of the
airth"—

"New York excepted," ses I.

"New York excepted," ses he, coloring a leetle about the nose, "to welcome genius of any sort, and of any size, to the sile of England. The city
of London is the appinted seat of all the Arts."

"I'm very glad to hear it," ses I, "and hope they have all taken their
places."

Whereupon Lord Mayor coughs, and goes on. "London, proud of her
merchant princes—crowned as they are with bank paper—London,
proud of Temple Bar, and Alderman Gibbs,[30] and Bow bell, and her
giants—London is still more proud of the genius she has fostered. Look
at Shakspeare: it isn't for me to say how many hundred pounds London has given for his signitur or oughtograff (though London won't
let his plays be acted, for fear of corruptin her prentices)—London,
through me, offers you the freedom of the city."

"Much obleeged," ses I. "What's it good for?"

" 'Twill permit you, Gen'ral," ses Lord Mayor, "to open a shop in the
City, or to work as a coal-porter. And whereas, Gen'ral, at the door of
our noble cathedral, St. Paul's—that beautiful edifice, that we're so fond
on that we've smothered it round about with houses, just like killin a
critter with kindness—wherein no free and inlightened citizen can enter that sacred buildin before he puts down tuppence, the City of London offers you, through me, a free admission for the season."

[30] Henry Hucks Gibbs (1819–1907), merchant and scholar, joined the family firm
of bankers in 1843 and later became director of the Bank of England.

"For one," ses I.

"For two," ses Lord Mayor, "yourself and Barnum. And now it is for you, Gen'ral, to appint the day when you will receive the freedom; and pray obleege us with a long notice, that Guildhall may be scrubbed and whitewashed, and the giants gilt and painted for the 'casion."

"Lord Mayor," ses I, without ever getting up, "I shall be happy to take the freedom—any freedom, in fact—with this leetle bargain, that you allow me also to appinte the size, and weight, and make of the goold box that is to hold it." Whereupon Lord Mayor and Aldermen puckered up their mouths and nodded their heads, kinder to say, "you've fixed our flints, anyhow."

Well, the mint julep and the cobblers went round, and mighty pleasant it was. "Gen'ral," ses Lord Mayor, his nose getting like any babby's coral; "Gen'ral, I'll give you a toast. Here is to the intimate relations atween England and America; and may General Tom Thumb prove a link—a goolden link—to the two countries."

"Lord Mayor and Aldermen," ses I, "as the freest citizen in airth, I thank you. Doubtless you mean well, poor critters! by the toast aforesaid. But if I am to be the link atween the two countries, don't you think it will a leetle bit hurt the shippin interest, seein how tarnation short it will make the passage?"

You never heerd sich larfin as there was at this. And Barnum larfed—and I could see it—wos as proud of me as a monkey of a new jacket. And then in his sly, soft, and buttery manner he ses, "Don't, Gen'ral, don't;" all the while meanin "Do, Gen'ral, do."

Well, still they handed round the cobblers and sandwiches, and still Lord Mayor and Aldermen ate and drank, and still the British public —inlightened critters!—waited, with their toes a coolin on the stones outside—and the ladies, pretty, pussy things! with their noses gettin as blue as vi'lets, in the carriages. At last, Lord Mayor ses to me, "Gen'ral, when will it quite soot you that we should attend you to the 'Gyptian Hall? It's the leetlest favor we can do you—the smallest ceremony upon airth, and we've come to do it. Never shall it be said that the City of London doesn't encourage art—you hain't seen our staty of the Dook[31]—and foster genius. When, Gen'ral, will you go?"

"When I've swallowed Marmsell Maintenon," ses I.

"The Gen'ral means"—ses Barnum, with his face shinin as gay as any coffin-plate—"the Gen'ral means his *cotelette a lar Maintenon*."

---

[31] Sir Francis Legatt Chantrey's equestrian statue of Wellington was erected in front of the third Royal Exchange in 1844.

"And here it comes," ses I; for at the minute it came in, smellin beautiful. Well, you should jist have seen the Lord Mayor and Aldermen. They all left off eatin and drinkin, and made a ring round me to see me eat, jist as if I'd been a boa constrictor, and was goin' to swallow a buffalo, horns and all. Well, I ses nothin; but with the eend of my knife, I takes the bank note off the chop, and throws it into the silver dish. Then I heard a whisperin and a rustlin—for I didn't look at 'em—and at last one of the Aldermen—I think his name was Gibbs—ses, "Don't tell me: I think I ought to know a bank-note by this time. And that's one."

"To be sure it is," ses I. "Nothing like a bank-note to give a chop a true flavour; it's better than pickles."

"But it's a twenty pound note," ses Alderman Gibbs.

"In course it is," ses I. "That's because to-day I take my chop a leetle under-done; when I want it well cooked, I always have a fifty."

When I said this, the Mayor and Aldermen looked at me as if I warn't a critter of this world, and I thought every second they'd drop down upon their marrowbones afore me.

## THE GENERAL DEPARTS FOR THE EGYPTIAN HALL.—GREAT PUBLIC MANIFESTATION BY THE POPULACE.

"AND NOW, Lord Mayor," ses I—havin finished my chop, and takin no manner of notice of the Bank note that that critter, Alderman Gibbs, would still be a smackin his lips and lookin at—"And now, Lord Mayor, as I feel a little the true Cheshire, we'll jest go to 'Gyptian Hall, and you shall have the honour to 'scort me. 'Tainte every day," ses I, "the City of London has sich luck."

" 'Tainte," ses Lord Mayor; and then he begins to go back'ards out o' the room, a bowin and a bowin afore me, like a pigeon pickin up peas.

"Mind the stairs, Lord Mayor," ses I, "or you will find yourself a standin on your head on the door-mat." Barnum put on his cloak. "Barnum," ses I, "are you ready?" "Ready," ses Barnum: whereupon, I jumps upon a chair, and then jumps from it, sitting a stroddle on Barnum's right hip, and holdin the Guv'ner by the buttons; and then he put his cloak round me, and walked down stairs, and nobody, to have looked at Barnum, would have thought there was the least mite particular about him; never thinkin there was the greatest wonder upon airth sittin a stroddle on his leg. And in this way, Barnum always takes me in and out of the coach, that the critters in the street mayn't be for a minute on the free list, and see me without the shillin.

Well, the door was opened, and the Mayor and the Aldermen got into their carriages and wheeled off, and the men in armour began to trot, and the brass band to play "See, the Conquerin Hero comes!"—it's always played to me and Wellington—and the people hooraed as if they'd tear a hole in the sky above 'em. Then they began to screach for Tom Thumb. "Where's the Gen'ral?" they cried, "The Gen'ral—the Gen'ral!" for they never seed me get in the charot. "The Gen'ral!" cried the men—and the women, the dear critters, I could hear their voices, like the ringin of so many dollars, cryin out, "Where's the Darlin'?" "the Duck?" "the Cherub?" "the Angel?" "the airthly Bird of Paradise?" and I don't know what beside. For this is clear, I'd turned all the critters' heads afore they'd seen me; and after they'd seen me agin and agin, and kissed and kissed me, till my cheeks was wastin away like a cake of Windsor soap, their heads had another twist, and are goin on turnin and turnin at this present moment. How Barnum did larf!—I felt the critter grinnin in his very pockets as he heard the mob—and didn't I punch him with both my fists, and larf too! At last, there was sich a noise, and the bells did ring so, I wanted to look about me.

"It's impossible, Gen'ral!"—ses Barnum, " 'twould spile all. Don't you know, Gen'ral, what an unprincipled critter the public is. If I was only to show the leetlest piece on airth of you, they'd fancy the rest, and keep the shillins as close as oysters."

"Well, then, tell me all about it. Is there many o' the critters?" ses I.

"Many!" cries Barnum. "I should say—and Gen'ral, I never 'xaggerate; tainte my hook, by no means—but I should say, on a rough guess, a leetle above a million."

"And a million shillins," ses I—

"Never mind," ses Barnum: "I know all about that better than you, Gen'ral. Well, this is a mighty fine sight, to be sure. All the people with their holiday clothes on—all at the winders, and on the roofs of the houses—and some of the gals with your pictur, Gen'ral, from the *Ulcerated News*, pinned jest over their hearts."

"The pretty pussy critters," ses I.

"And Gen'ral," ses Barnum, "don't you smell nothin, kinder scent?" ses he.

"Nothin," ses I; and I didn't.

"Well, you ought: for they're throwin flowers from all the winders—

and—there—I'm a varmint if there isn't one lady in a squirrel tippet that's jest emptied a bottle of lavender—don't you smell it—on the roof of the coach. A great day, Gen'ral, this for Columbia," ses Barnum; and agin I felt his pocket beat and throb as if it was alive. "Well, this is as it should be. How d'ye do, Everett? Yes, Gen'ral, there's our ambassador jest turned out of Bond Street in his full dress, on a piebald horse, bearin the star-spangled banner, and carryin a goolden eagle in his hat. Well, this is only payin his countrymen proper respect. He won't lose nothin by it, at Washington. He's a good critter, after all, that Everett."

"Barnum," ses I, "what d'ye think? I've a thought. Suppose we was to ax Everett as the 'Bassador of the United States, jest for the first day, to give us a kinder glory-like, to take the shillins?"

"Gen'ral," ses Barnum, "ambassadors and politicians are good enough critters in their way; but never mix 'em up with your private shillins. Tainte the true grit, nohow. There! Do you hear that?"

"Why, they're firin the guns!" ses I; "yes, I can smell the powder."

"The Park and the Tower ninety-eight-pounders, I can tell 'em to an ounce," ses Barnum; "mighty civil of Gracious Majesty to have 'em fired; they don't do no more when she opens the Parliament—the Grand National Caucus. And now, Gen'ral, we're a-going to stop—for here's 'Gyptian Hall." Well, I might ha' known that by the screechin and hollorin of the people. And all the bells rung louder and louder—and the guns went on a-bangin—and the trumpets a-screaming, and in the middle of the shindy, Barnum steps out of the coach, and, with me still gripping him about the leg, and entirely kivered by the cloak, enters the 'Gyptian Hall. I felt him a-goin up a lot of stairs, and, at last, he went into a room. "Gen'ral," ses he, "you're welcome to home;" whereupon I climbs down his leg to the floor, and looked about me. The room was large and—what I special like in a room—was very high. "Yes, Gen'ral, this is what we may call our mint; here we'll strike a million or so of dollars out of the enlightened British public that is so humble of itself, it can't find nothin to run after at home; and so likes to have genius, like pine-apples, of foreign growth."

"Are we all alone in the Hall?" ses I.

"No," ses Barnum, "there's a poor critter that has made an Apollo in marble, and a Hebe, and a Venus, and half-a-dozen Graces, and things of that sort. All day yesterday—for I made inquiry special—there was only three people came to see the lot, and one o' them was a baby in arms."

"If you please, sir," ses Barnum's man, comin in, "if you please, sir, is the Gen'ral ready? There'll be murder if you don't open the doors; there's sich a crowd! Three ladies have been carried out faintin, and I've left two jist goin into asterisks!"

When Barnum heerd this he larfed, and rubbed his hands, and stroddled up and down the room, and put his hands in his pocket, and took 'em out, and rubbed 'em again. Then he stopt and drawed himself up, and said solemn-like to his man: "A crowd of ladies, eh! I tell you what, you must let 'em wait till they rise to bilin pint, and then—when I give the word—let 'em bust in."

## THE GENERAL IS SEVERELY KISSED, AND HITS UPON AN EXPEDIENT TO RELIEVE HIMSELF.

RE YOU READY, Gen'ral?" ses Barnum. "Quite ready," ses I. "You may let the critters in." With this Barnum waves his hand, Majesty-like, and the doors fly back. Well, never on airth did I see such a shoal of humans! If they didn't swim in—like herrins— over one another's shoulders, I'm a seahorse. I could see them through a leetle hole in the curtain; for I hadn't walked out upon the table yet. And there they was! Such a mighty sight of grandmothers, and mothers and daughters; ten women to two men, and one in. Well, I will confess it: I couldn't help saying agin to meself—"You hippopotamuses! haven't you got nothin o' your own at home to nurse—no babbies; or, if no babbies, not even a spaniel or a kitten, to make a screeching hubbaboo about, but you must come out o' your own houses, to break your stay-laces, and have your ribbons—that cost them honest critters, your husbands, so much—tore slick off your bonnets, scrouging to see the smallest piece on airth of human natur?" Yes; I will say it: I do have these thoughts that belittle me—all really great critters have, Barnum tells me; and the bigger they are, he says—in spirit, in coors, I mean—the leetler will they sometimes insist upon bein. "It's all in the brain," ses Barnum: "and the brain," ses he, "is jist for all the world like a bit of ingy-rubber; the further you pull it out, with the greater the force, and all the backwarder it will go back." However, about these female critters. When the room was quite full—and, with the fine clothes, and the ribbons, and all that the women had about 'em, you would have thought it had been a gen'ral meetin of all the rainbows, past and to come, of all creation—when the room was as full, and as noisy as a whole forest of cockatoos, I steps out.

Well, you should have heerd the shrekin! You should have heerd the precious names they called me—'twas enough to break the heart of a peacock with delight, as Barnum said to me afterwards. As for meself—you know I'm used to it, now—I was bashful, shamefaced like, they said sich things to me. If I didn't blush to that degree that my shirt was tinder, I'm a varmint. Well, I danced in course, and sung my songs, and all that; and the critters were all but faintin with pleasure. At last, when we got a leetle quiet, Barnum pinted out to the people the dimond ring that Gracious Majesty had given me—and the dimond studs, and the goold pencil-case, and all the jew'llry. I sartinly did think that some on 'em would have dropped upon their knees, when they looked at 'em. And then they stared at me agin, as if somehow—knowin how I'd been treated at the palace—they thought I'd brought somethin royal, precious like about me, when I came away. But there was one thing happened that whips the universal airth. And this is it.

These critters think that whatever comes from a palace must have kinder magic in it: and so, one old lady comes up to Barnum, with tears a runnin down her face like rain-drops down window-frames, and ses—"My dear Mister, could you do me the leetle favour to lend me the dimond ring that Gracious Majesty give to the Gen'ral."

"What on airth do you want it for?" ses Barnum.

"Why, jist for this," ses the old lady. "The fact is—my leetle boy—poor critter! has got a humpback."

"Well?" ses Barnum, as much as to say—"I havn't."

"And I'm mortal sure on it," ses the old lady, "that if a leetle pimple, or sty, is to be rubbed away by a plain goold ring—as it always is"—

"Well?" ses Barnum agin—"Allowin it—what then?"

"Why, that my leetle boy's humpback could be rubbed quite straight by the ring with the Queen's dimond in it."

Dreadful, isn't it, to think on the superstition of these poor critters? But so it is, or I'm worse nor a snake. Well, now I'm a goin to tell you the beginnin o' my troubles.

After I'd done my dance and my song, and the postures—the Erc'les a stranglin the Nimmim Lion[32] was, arter the 'Pollo, the special favorite—

32 The first of the twelve labors of Hercules was skinning the Nemean lion.

the critters, jist as if they was askin nothin, said they should like to kiss me. Well, not having any fear—being sure they wouldn't bite—I said, "Very well, you critters; come along." The young and the pretty ones, if I must tell the truth, did not go aginst the grain, by no means; but it is a leetle too bad to be left to have no choice. Well, they all, one arter the other, fell a kissin me; and the older they were, I do really believe the harder they kissed. I felt my face a goin away—a meltin like a peach; and I cried out, and screeched; and at last was obligated to jump slick into Barnum's coat pocket; and hold, I may say, a kinder parley like, afore I'd come out. "I tell you what," ses I, "I've no objection on airth to be kissed; but then I do like to choose my own lips. Now it's mighty cur'ous, but I ne'er could bear to be kissed by leetle gals in all my life. No: I don't think kisses come to their full growth and flavour till thirty—so here I am proud and happy to be kissed by any female critter that is risin thirty-one." You should have seen 'em: they all hung behind in a minute; and nobody would from that minute beg a kiss, 'xcept it was a pretty pussy critter that knew her lips, and eyes, and roses in her cheeks made it kinder joke to be thought even two-and-twenty. And after that fashion—for the first day—at least, I was only kissed by the young and tender.

And so the first day was over; and arter a time, I got home; well nigh, I may say it, kissed off my legs. My face was skinned again—(what the critters had to answer for!) and Barnum went for Sir Benjamin Brodie,[33] (he didn't live far from us,) and he recommended a poultice of cold cream and rose-water outside; with a mutton-chop and a julep—for he said the American constitution required a julep—a-goin to bed.

Well, next mornin, I rose like a giant clean shaved; and went agin private to the Hall. I must say it—it was beautiful to see Barnum with his ear a half-cock kinder listenin to the shillins dropping at the door—as he would say, such a tarnation shower of silver! And never since this airth began, did any duck or goose—not that Barnum's either, not he; quite as far from one as t'other—ever enjoy a shower as Barnum did them silver-drops.

Well, on the third day, I'd hardly got to the Hall, when Barnum's man comes runnin as if there was a ghost at the pay-place that wanted to come in for nothin—but it wasn't: quite the contrary.

"What's the matter?" ses Barnum.

"The Dook of Wellington's at the door," cries the man.

"Is he? Then I'll go and talk to him—kinder gammonin him—while

[33] Sir Benjamin Brodie (1783–1862), sergeant-surgeon to Queen Victoria.

you, like greased lightin, dress the Gen'ral as Napoleon. We can do no
less; and the Dook will take it handsome."


## THE GENERAL'S INTERVIEW WITH THE DUKE—
## THE GENERAL GOES ON THE STAGE—LEAVES
## ENGLAND—LETTER TO "PUNCH."

WAL, THE FACT IS, I've jest to ax your pardon; but as I never thought of
writin about these critters till I'd been a long time among em—like a
stupid 'possum as I was—Barnum made up his mind to go back to the
States at the very nick of my last letter. And what with packin all the
plate and jew'lry—there's five-and-twenty packages of watches, pencil-
cases, and diamond and ruby rings, if there's an ounce—what with makin
all smoothe and strait, I've had no time to take up my pen till now, when
I sits down agin with the sweat upon my brow, to catch up the thread
where afore I dropt it. You recollect, in coorse, the Dook of Wellington
was knockin to come in—but they kept him at the door, while I was a
dressin, out o' compliment like, for Napoleon. Bein quite the emperor,
I walks out, and motions for 'em to open the door.

Wal, the Dook comes in. I heerd him, for I heerd Barnum a scrapin
before him; but I wouldn't look up; acause I'd got my arms a folded,
and was standin with my eyes down on the green baize of the table, a
contemplatin the battle of Oysterlitz. Then the Dook—with a lady on
his arm, or his arm on a lady's, I wont swear which—come close to the
table; and I heerd him take out his spy-glass, for it clicked like, as he
shook it to put it over his nose. Wal, he stood a starin at me—and I
heerd him grunt a leetle laugh. On which, lookin up, I handed him my
snuff-box. The critter dabbed in the tip of his leetle finger, and agin
grunted another leetle laugh. Wal, I felt my dander rise, and looked
piercin. You should have seen the Dook. There was sich a whiteness
came over his face; and his hair jest the leetlest morsel in life did lift
his hat off his head; and then—as Barnum told me arterwards—I could
see what was a movin inside of him. I brought into his mind all the three
days of Waterloo at once. I could see it—as Barnum told me—I could see
that he seed in me whole squares of infants and battelions of horses. He
fit all the battle over agin, I was so cruel, so startlin like Napoleon. At
last, when he was jest at bilin pint, and the lady was takin out her
smellin bottle to give it him, at last the Dook slappin his leg screeched

out—"Up guards! and at em!" And then the Dook could say no more; but bust into tears, and was led by the lady out into the open air.

Wal, as for Dooks and Markesses, and critters o' that grit, there was so many come to see me, I got tarnation tired of 'em. Very sweet and flatterin at first, but 'twas like livin on molasses in the eend. However— 'xcept the Dook of Iron, as he's called—they all left with me their cards, in the shape of goold watches, and breast-pins, and chains, and sich like; and so, I can't speak o' the critters as perhaps I ought. More's the pity: but as Barnum ses, "If you want to gag Truth, you must put a gold pin in her mouth." Wal, I've as many pins as a porkipine.

Arter a time, when the bloom was a bein wiped off the plum—as Barnum called it—that is, when the 'ristocracy begun to look upon me as if I was not a bit better than theirselves—Barnum said I should go upon the stage. Father and mother lifted up all their hands and feet agin the notion, and with tears in their eyes, said they wouldn't have their child disgraced no how. Whereupon Barnum—oh, what a critter it is! he'd talk an oyster out of its pearls—Barnum ses, "Disgrace!" ses he, "why, the British stage is the glory of the 'varsal airth, and the glory of Britain in partiklar. Don't the Queen go to the theatre three times a week, with all her Court in ostrich feathers? Three times a week,"—ses Barnum, but he never said 'twas the 'Talian, not the British playhouse. Wal, father and mother was honied all over by Barnum, and it was agreed— though mother said it'ud shorten her life—that I should turn play-actor.

When this was known, you may be sure our house was beset by managers. For a whole week we were obleged to have two policemen to keep 'em off. At last, Barnum made his pick of 'em; and afore I knowed where I was, I was upon the stage. But upon that pint, you get no more out o' me. Else if I had a mind

*　　*　　*　　*　　*　　*　　*

*Radley's Hotel, Liverpool.*

I hadn't time to finish, and can now only say that we start by next packet but one, the *Cambria,* with jolly Captain Judkins. The Mayor's getting up what he calls a demonstration. I'm to go aboard the ship upon a elephant, and hold a levy on the quarter-deck. Bancroft, our 'bassador, has jest drov into the town, and will ride upon the head o' the animal. The Miss Cushmans[34]—one on 'em as *Romeo*—and an American citizen, will drop rosebuds in our way.

[34] Charlotte Saunders Cushman (1816–1876) and Susan Webb Cushman (1822– 1859), American actresses and sisters, toured England together between 1845 and 1849. Charlotte was known for her role as Romeo.

I would say more, but Radley's come up to tell me I must go and meet that tarnation Bancroft.

GENERAL TOM THUMB TO *Punch.*

YOU CRITTER PUNCH,                              *The Astor, New York, March 15.*

Here I am, once agin among the smartest nation. Since I've had these presents from kings and queens, you can't think how the free American citizens do like me. They look upon me like a copper spoon that was sent to Europe to be plated, and come back more twinklin than ever they looked for.

As you save me—you critter—sich a world of postage by printin my letters, I intend to make myself (*gratis* for nothin) your 'Merican correspondent.

Yours,

THUMB.

P.S. POLK is gettin so low in public 'pinion, 'twill take pickaxes and shovels to dig him up again.

Private and confidential—I start for President next 'lection.

# THE COCKNEY.*

"My lot might have been that of a slave, a savage, or a peasant," says the grateful Gibbon; "nor can I reflect without pleasure on the bounty of Nature, which cast my birth in a free and civilised country, in an age of science and philosophy, in a family of honourable rank, and decently endowed with the gifts of fortune." In his heart, the true Cockney has a kindred gratitude to that of the author of "The Rise and Fall," though it may happen he shall never express it; nay, shall be almost ignorant of its existence. Yet, notwithstanding, it is the unknown cause of his self-complacency, the hidden source of his pride, the reason of his compassionate consideration of original deficiencies of his rustic brethren. He might have been born at the Land's-End;¹ he might have spoken broad Cornish; he might have never seen St. Paul's Church, or the wax-work in Westminster Abbey. Hence, in the meaning of the classic historian, he must have been a slave, a savage, or a peasant. He is, however, none of these—but a cockney; and therefore a person, to his own satisfaction at least, conversant with all London science and philosophy; and, by virtue of such advantage, justified in the wickedness of his jokes upon bacon, smock-frocks, and hob-nails.

We believe that, despite much antiquarian research, the term Cockney has never been satisfactorily traced to its origin. Should we regret this? No; we ought rather to rejoice that what has been familiarised by—shall we say, contempt—is indeed of an antiquity

Mysteriously remote and high.²

* *The Writings of Douglas Jerrold* (8 vols.; London, 1851–1858) , V, 264–271.

¹ Land's-End, promontory in Cornwall, forming the westernmost extremity of England; of wave-carved granite, it has cliffs one hundred feet high.

² ". . . yet of ancestry / Mysteriously remote and high." (Wordsworth, "Vernal Ode," ll. 116–117.)

The Cockney, like the forty centuries apostrophised by Bonaparte, may, from the height of time, look down upon the present fleeting generation.[3] Whence Cockney? *Unde derivatur?* Antiquarians have dreamt dreams about it; have, indeed, written their pages in sand: but we have nothing certain—nothing to quench curiosity thirsting for a draught of truth. With these premises, we may safely touch upon the fables imagined by the ingenious men who have, as we think, vainly sought to bring the Cockney from the dim realm of shadows into "the light of common day."[4]

[3] Speech in Egypt, July 21, 1798: "Soldiers, from the summit of yonder pyramids, forty centuries look down on you."

[4] [*Jerrold's note*] One historian relates, that a gentle dweller in London, having incautiously wandered at least three miles from Bow Church, was suddenly astonished by the crowing of a cock. In the artificial life in which he had passed his early days, he had, of course, never listened to the clarion of Chanticleer; he had only seen him smoking in the dish, or exposed to the critical thumb and finger of chaffering housewives in the Poultry. Hence, our Londoner, when somewhat recovered from his astonishment, exclaimed, "the cock *neighs!*" From this, the antiquarian, with an ingenious boldness not uncommon with his tribe, has declared the word Cockney a word of reproach—a blot—a shame—a brand; a nick-name illustrative of the grossest ignorance of the susceptible and astute citizens of London. We should not have spoken of this antiquarian morsel, considering it as merely a thing for the nursery, were not trifles of a like consistency every day made up by commentators and glossary mongers, to be swallowed by men.

Chaucer, in his "Canterbury Tales," makes John, the gamesome clerk, say—

> I shall be holden a daffe or a *cokenay*;

a fool, a cokenay—using the term as one of foulest reproach for a man of sense; upon which Mr. Tyrrwhit expressed his belief that it is a term of contempt borrowed originally from the kitchen. In base Latinity, *cook* is *coquinator*— hence *cokenay,* opines Mr. Tyrrwhit, is easily derived. The critic supports his opinion by a citation from Hugh Bigot:—

> Were I in my castle of Bungay,
> Upon the river of Wavenay,
> I would na care for the King of *Cokeney.*

Here London is called Cokeney, in allusion to an imaginary country of idleness and luxury, anciently known by the name of *Cokaigne,* or *Cocagne,* still derived by Hickes from *coquina,* the kitchen, the place of brawn and sweetbread; a derivation that would have been most satisfactory to Rabelais himself. Hickes published a poem, "The Country of Cokaigne," probably, thinks Mr. Tyrrwhit, translated from the French, who have had the same fable among them. Boileau says,

> Paris est pour un riche *un pais de Cocagne.*

There is also a Neapolitan festival, called *La Cocagna*; and in a mock-heroic poem, in the Sicilian dialect, called *La Cuciagna Conquistata* (1674), the most noble city of Cuccagna is described as being seated on a mountain of grated cheese, and crowned with a huge cauldron of maccaroni.

[*Editor's note*] "And fade into the light of common day." (Wordsworth, "Ode: Intimations of Immortality," l. 76.)

The Cockney has, within the last half century, declined from his importance in the eyes of his rustic brethren. When London was to York a city almost as mysterious as Timbuctoo, the Cockney, in his individual character, was invested with higher and more curious attributes than are awarded to him in these days. When he was only to be approached in his metropolitan fastness, by a week's tedious journey in the quickest-going waggon; when folks, two hundred miles away, shut up their shops and made their wills ere they girded up their loins, and corded their trunks, that they might see the animal in its natural state in Fleet Street[5] and in Bishopsgate;[6] he was, when at length through many dangers looked upon, a creature of no small interest—no passing wonderment. His dress, his air, his look of extraordinary wisdom—all things presented him to the Arcadian from Lancashire or the county of Dorset, as a person of considerable importance. Stage-coaches were started, railroads were laid down, and Timbuctoo (we mean Cockaigne) was no longer a mysterious city, but a common rendezvous for graziers, button-makers, dairy-maids from Devon, and pitmen from Newcastle. The pavement of Bond-street,[7] almost sacred to the shoes of the Cockney, became sacrificed by the hobnails of all the counties.

Besides the more favourable claims of the Cockney upon the curiosity and homage of Corydon,[8] he had, in the legends told at farmers' firesides of his less estimable qualities, a dangerous interest in the eyes of his rustic beholder. All white-headed men, who in their youth had made one pilgrimage to London, would tell fearful histories of the wiliness of ring-droppers—of the miraculous faculty of Cockaigne pick-pockets. Hence, Lubin from Shropshire, who crawled from the waggon to Cheapside,[9] had a new source of interest as he surveyed the gold-laced coats of the fine people about him: they might be thieves and sharpers in their working suits, and they might be only gentlemen!

And when the Cockney quitted London—yes, when he would condescend to visit his mother's relations in the wilds of Leicestershire! "My

---

5 Fleet Street, one of the most famous thoroughfares of London, between Ludgate Hill and the Strand; Madame Tussand's wax museum was located here.

6 Bishopsgate, originally one of the city gates (so called after Erkenwald, a seventh-century bishop of London); the gates were removed in the eighteenth century and the site marked by two tablets on the houses at the corners of Camomile and Wormwood Streets.

7 Bond-street, in Westminster, famous for its fashionable shops and such residents as Boswell, Swift, and Lord Nelson.

8 Corydon, a conventional name for a shepherd in a pastoral poem.

9 Cheapside, street in London running from St. Paul's Church-yard to the Bank of England.

cousin from London!" Was he not a something—a bit of the great, mysterious city? Was he not shown as the very choicest and most certain sample of the great Babylon? Even as the pedant showed the one brick as the sample of the house, so was Whittington Simmons, from Lad Lane, exhibited as a veritable fragment of marvellous London. And then what humours of Cockaigne did the said Whittington Simmons put forth, to his own present glory, and to his memory for twenty years afterwards, at the rural fire-side! How the farmer laughed! And how deliciously Whittington, with a joke from the playhouse or with the last flash phrase east of the Bar, how triumphantly did he silence the unconquerable exciseman!

Why dwell upon the glories of a departed age? Why, to present mortification, touch upon the raptures of the past? What is now the Cockney in the eyes of Corydon—what London to York?

'Tis distance lends enchantment to the view![10]

And there is no distance where there is a railroad. The Cockney is no longer stared, wondered at, upon his native pavement; but unceremoniously jostled by Melibœus Mugs, from the Potteries. And then, for the Cockney's reputation of cheat, among the pastoral swains! How rarely do we find him triumphant over the cunning of a Smithfield bullock driver? How seldom, in these common-place days, doth he drop a ring? Lastly, for the glory of his rural visits, what is the Cockney now in Staffordshire?—only to imitate the phrase of Louis XVIII., only one Englishman more. He walks the street of a country place, and is no more the object of curiosity than the town-pump. He visits the farmer's fire-side; is he there the indomitable wit? doth he talk and jest, the wonder of some, the fear of many, and the admiration of all? Alas! it is most probable that he claims no more attention than the sides of bacon hanging about him; or, like the bacon, only keeps his place—so has the rustic won upon the Cockney—to be the further smoked. The inventors of railways have much to answer for.

However, albeit the revolution of things has lessened the importance of the Cockney in the eyes of all the world out of London, he himself remains, in his own assurance, the same clever, knowing, judicious, sprightly, witty fellow that he ever was. He knows life in its varieties. He was born and bred in Bishopsgate Within; and, for that unanswerable reason, is in no way to be cozened. He is a part and parcel of the

---

[10] " 'Tis distance lends enchantment to the view, / And robes the mountain in its azure hue." (Thomas Campbell, *Pleasures of Hope*, Part I, ll. 7–8.)

greatest city upon earth; a piece of the very heart of the empire. The Mansion House,[11] the Monument,[12] and Guildhall,[13] are to him more ancient than the pyramids. Gog and Magog, to the real Cockney, stand in the remote relation of ancestors: he is wood of their wood. Politics to him are most familiar matters; he can discuss state questions as easily as he could play at push-pin;[14] and displace a ministry with the same readiness as, in the days of his apprenticeship, he could take down the shutters. The Court, with all its wonders, is to him no *terra incognita*: not it; for he has seen her Majesty, drawn by the cream-coloured horses, go down to Parliament; and once a week, or oftener, takes off his hat to the Queen in her rides from the palace. Hence, there is no state ceremony with which he is unacquainted; no divinity, "hedging" the royal person, which he has not, with increasing familiarity, doffed his beaver to. In his business hours, the Cockney is worthy of the attention of any reflecting cart-horse. He is the genius of labour; the willing serf to those worse than Egyptian taskmasters, "£. s. d." Consider him when working for his daily bread; and man, the paragon of animals, appears a creature expressly fashioned to toil for shillings, and for—nothing more. His very soul seems absorbed in the consideration of the coin of the realm; his mind hath no greater range than that of his shop; and his every thought, like every omnibus, runs to the Bank.

But the Cockney has his festive hours, his day of pleasure; and, perhaps, his peculiar genius for pleasantry is never more characteristically exerted than at the masquerade. Here the Cockney is, indeed, in fullest feather. His animal spirits are so abundant that they, incontinently, make him knock off hats; deal body-blows; and send him playing leapfrog over the heads of his fellow revellers. If the Cockney be somewhat dull at a repartee, he has the acutest sensibility for a row; and though he shakes his ears and looks doggedly at a thrust of wit, he can, with the liveliest promptitude, make play for a black eye. These, however, are the enjoyments of his more sportive—his more youthful season. The middle-aged Cockney has severer pleasures, calm meditative hours, when his soul makes holiday from the business of the week, and spreads its wings and soars, unburdened by the weight of the shop. Sunday comes; and in

11 Mansion House, the residence of the lord mayor during his term of office.

12 the Monument, in Monument Yard, Fish Street Hill, a fluted column of the Doric order, erected to commemorate the Great Fire of London, 1666; designed by Christopher Wren.

13 Guildhall, a public building in central London used for the lord mayor's banquets and other municipal functions.

14 push-pin, a child's game in which each player pushes his pin with the object of crossing that of the other player.

tavern bower, or humbler tea-garden, with one eye upon his pipe, and the other on a bed of marigolds, the Cockney will sit and smoke, and smoke, and drink an unconsidered quantity of British brandy; and satisfactorily consider his own virtues, complacently taking for himself the very highest rank for true piety, and earnest, downright, Sabbath-keeping, above all the other sinful nations of this sinful earth. It may be, that both his tongue and his foot trip a little on his way home; and his wife, if she be with him, is not addressed in that soft, captivating strain that first won her virgin heart. It has, too, happened that, arrived in his bed-chamber, there has been some difficulty on the part of the mistress and maid in getting off the good man's boots; though, sometimes, he has imperiously waived the ceremony by insisting to go to bed in them. And what of this? hath he not spent his seventh day without whistling; without singing? Did ever the sinful wish rise within him of a fiddle? did he, like a heathenish foreigner, ever dream of a dance? No: he enjoyed himself like a Christian and an Englishman; ten pipes of tobacco, and eight glasses of very black brandy and water, making but a small part of his nobler recreations.

We have seen the Cockney on his own ground. He is, however, to be viewed to greater advantage when away, not from London merely, but from England. What a delicious fellow is the real Cockney in France! How delightful at the Hague! What a positive blessing is one of the true London breed on the Rhine! All his finer qualities, like Madeira, improve wonderfully by a sea-voyage. His self-importance increases with the distance from Bow church,[15] and he lands at Calais or Boulogne, with an overwhelming sense of his nationality. He wanders up and down two or three streets, and see—he enters a shop, kept by "John Roberts, from Fish Street Hill,"[16] to make his foreign purchases. The inn at which the Cockney puts up—it is his boast—is kept by an Englishman; the dinners are English; the waiter is English; the chambermaid is English; the boots is English; and the barber who comes to shave him, if he be not English, has, at least, this recommendation—he has, in his time, lived five years in Saint-Mary-Axe,[17] and is *almost* English. More! when

[15] Bow church, St. Mary-le-Bow, in Cheapside; traditionally only he who is born within the sound of the Bow Bells is a true Londoner, a Cockney.

[16] Fish Street Hill, the main thoroughfare to old London Bridge. As befitted its name, the street was pervaded by a strong smell of fish. Writing from Paris, the poet Campbell describes his lodgings "in a street which makes me long for the silence of the Strand, and the smell of Fish Street Hill." (Henry B. Wheatley, *London Past and Present* [London, 1891], II, 47.)

[17] Saint-Mary-Axe, a street and parish in Lime Street Ward; the south end was mostly rented for offices; toward Houndsditch it was chiefly inhabited by Jews.

the Cockney—his heart set upon a little smuggling—buys a splendid French tea-pot, with a picture on each side of it; the very tea-pot which, from the moment that the Custom House officer comes aboard, puts our hero, who has the utensil in his hat, in the coldest sweat—that tea-pot, purchased as a *"souvenir"* for Mary Anne, though the innocent Cockney suspect it not, is, ten times out of twenty, English too.

Although he is in France, the Cockney is at a loss to conceive why there should be French manners—French feelings—French prejudices. We once witnessed a droll illustration of this astonishment. A real Cockney having stalked up and down the room of an hotel, where were hung several prints—the subjects, Napoleon's victories; and having stared, somewhat sulkily, at every picture, turned himself round, and, with a look of pitying wonder, exclaimed, "Well, I declare, upon my word, they seem to think a good deal of this Bonaparte here!"

Follow the Cockney to Paris. See! he is in the garden of the Tuileries! What can he be doing near the statue of Diana? Ha! the sentry calls to him, and the Cockney, with thunder in his brow, looks savagely at the foreigner. Our indignant countryman is, however, ordered away, and, swelling with national greatness, he moves on. What could he be doing at the statue? Let us see. Oh, here it is! The Cockney—poor fellow! it is an amiable weakness, he cannot help it—the Cockney has written in pencil his address in full on the right leg of Diana: here it is, *"John Wiggins, Muffin-maker, Wild Street, Drury Lane,*[18] *was here on the 20th of July,* 1839." A most important fact, thinks Cockney Wiggins, and one that ought to be disseminated amongst the visitors of the gardens of the Tuileries.

We have seen how the Cockney blesses himself on his Sunday proprieties when at home: abroad, however, it is another matter. "When at Rome, you know," he observes wittily, "we must do as Rome does. Eh?" The Cockney disdains not to illustrate the proverb. It is the Sabbath-night: we are at the theatre, Porte St. Martin. Who is that gentleman and party in the front box? Can it be? Yes, it is no other than the Englishman who, at "The Adam and Eve," every summer Sunday, virtuously smokes his pipe, and, with a fine sense of self-respect, confines himself to eight glasses of brandy-and-water. There he is, happy as a duck in a shower, with his wife, his sons, and his daughters. Next day, near one of the Barriers, a horse is to be baited by dogs: there is also to be an interesting fight between an ass and a muzzled bear. There, at the show,

[18] Wild Street, Lincoln's Inn, Drury Lane, end of Great Queen Street to Sardinia Street.

is the Cockney; there he is: only, however, to express his vehement disgust at the brutality of the French. He returns to England; and having profanely enjoyed his Sundays abroad, thinks it his duty to sign every petition for the better observance of the Sabbath at home. John Bull is no hypocrite—not he!

The Cockney in his travels, like a mackerel in water, cannot turn without displaying a new beauty in a new light. He is not to be thoroughly known when rooted to London soil. See him bound for the Rhine. He is for the first day or two all anticipation of the coming glories of his voyage; yet, do not wonder if, from Coblentz to Mentz, he remained below, in the cabin, playing cribbage with a congenial fellow-tourist.

"And what place is that?" asked a Cockney who, coming upon deck, suddenly beheld the stupendous fortress of Ehrenbreitstein.[19]

"That, sir, is supposed to be one of the largest fortresses in the world—Ehrenbreitstein."

"God bless me! very large indeed, very. Enormous! I——" and he turned his head to his friend, "I wonder how many beds could be made up there?"

The speculation revealed the calling of the travellers; they were Cockney innkeepers—"The Blue Lion"[20] out upon a jaunt with "The Bag-o'-Nails."[21]

Even on our English shores, the Cockney is an animal of interest. There is infinite fun and humour in him when, escaped from the counter, and carefully put up in a continental Strand-made *blouse,* he sauntereth dreamily along, picking up star-fish on Ramsgate[22] sands; or takes his post on Margate pier, with—prudent man!—a paper of shrimps under one arm, and in one hand, ready like Van Tromp,[23] to "sweep the Channel," the best of telescopes!

The Cockney is a good fellow at heart; and would be a much better, certainly a much more agreeable animal, had he not the crotchet in his head, that he was not only the cleverest, the wittiest, but, at the same time, the most decent, and the most moral, of all earth's many-favoured children.

[19] fortress of Ehrenbreitstein, in Rhineland Palatinate, West Germany, on a high cliff across the Rhine from Coblenz.

[20] "The Blue Lion," a tavern in St. Pancras.

[21] "The Bag-o'-Nails," a public house at the corner of Arabella Row and Buckingham Palace Road. Its sign was a satyr with a group of bacchanals.

[22] Ramsgate, municipal borough on the Isle of Thanet, Kent; a resort and fishing port; Queen Victoria lived here as a young princess.

[23] Van Tromp, Maarten Harpertszoon Tromp (1598–1653), a famous Dutch admiral. Legend has it that during the Anglo-Dutch War he sailed up the Channel with a broom at his masthead to symbolize his ability to sweep the seas.

# THE UNDERTAKER.*

No MAN (that is, no tradesman) has a more exquisite notion of the outward proprieties of life, of all its external decencies, luxuries, and holiday show-making, than your Undertaker. With him, death is not death;
but, on the contrary, a something to be handsomely appointed and provided for; to be approached with the deference paid by the trader to the
buyer, and treated with an attention, a courtesy, commensurate with the
probability of profit. To the Undertaker, death is not a ghastly, noisome
thing; a hideous object to be thrust into the earth; the companion of
corruption; the fellow of the worm: not it! Death comes to the Undertaker, especially if he bury in high life, a melancholy coxcomb, curious
in the web of his winding-sheet, in the softness of his last pillow, in the
crimson or violet velvet that shall cover his oaken couch, and in more
than all, particular in the silver gilt nails, the plates, and handles, that
shall decorate it. A sense of profit in the Undertaker wholly neutralises
the terrible properties of death; for, to him, what is another corpse but
another customer?

"Of course, sir," says Mandrake, taking orders for a funeral,—"Of
course, sir, you'll have feathers?"

"Indeed, I—I see no use in feathers," replies the bereaved party, whose
means are scarcely sufficient for the daily necessities of the living; "no
use at all."

"No feathers, sir!" says Mandrake, with a look of pitying wonder.
"Why, excuse me, sir, but—really—you would bury a servant without
feathers."

"Well, if you think them necessary," ——

* The Writings of Douglas Jerrold (8 vols.; London, 1851–1858), V, 201–208.

"Necessary! No respectable person can be buried without feathers," says Mandrake; and (wise dealer!) he touches the chord of worldly pride, and feathers make part of the solemnity. "Then, sir, for mutes: you have mutes, doubtless?"

"I never could understand what service they were," is the answer.

"Oh, dear sir!" cries Mandrake; "not understand! Consider the look of the thing! You would bury a pauper, sir, without mutes."

"I merely want a plain, respectable funeral, Mr. Mandrake."

"Very true, sir; therefore, you must have mutes. What is the expense, sir? Nothing, in comparison with the look of the thing."

"I always thought it worse than useless to lavish money upon the dead; so, everything very plain, Mr. Mandrake."

"I shall take care, sir; depend upon me, sir: everything shall be of the most comfortable kind, sir. And now, sir, for the choice of ground;" and hereupon, Mr. Mandrake lays upon the table a plan of the churchyard, probably divided into three separate parts for the accommodation of the different ranks of the dead. "Now, sir, for the ground."

"Is there any choice?"

"Decidedly, sir. This is what we call the first ground; a charming, dry, gravelly soil: you may go any depth in it, sir,—any depth, sir: dry, sir, dry as your bed. This is the second ground; a little damper than the first, certainly: but still, some respectable persons do bury there." On this, Mr. Mandrake folds up the plan.

"Well, but the third ground. That is, I suppose, the cheapest?"

"Clay, sir; clay. Very damp, indeed;—you wouldn't like it—in winter extremely wet."

"Still, if the price be much lower than either of the others,"—

"Very true, sir; it is, and properly so; or how would the very poor people be able to bury at all? You may, of course, sir, do as you please; but nearly all respectable families bury in the first ground. If it were my own case, I should say the first ground—such gravel, sir!"

"Well, I suppose it must be so."

"You wouldn't like any other; depend upon it, sir, you wouldn't. The first ground, then, sir;" and Mr. Mandrake departs, self-satisfied that, for the look of the thing—for merely the sake of his customer's respectability—he has induced him to order feathers, mutes, and the first ground.

And in all this dealing what part of it has death? Alack! the feathers are not borne before his cold, white face; the mutes march not with solemn step to do him reverence: the fine, dry, gravelly bed is not for the ease of death's pithless bones; they would rest as well in the third ground as the first. No; the trappings of the defunct are but the outward dressings of the pride of the living: the Undertaker, in all his melancholy pomp, his dingy bravery, waits upon the quick, and not the dead. It is the living who crave for plumes, for nails, double gilt; for all the outward show of wealth and finery. Pride takes death, and, for its especial purpose, tricks it out in the frippery of life. "Man," says Sir Thomas Browne, "is a noble animal, splendid in ashes, and pompous in the grave; solemnising nativities and deaths with equal lustre; nor omitting ceremonies of bravery in the infamy of his nature."[1] Hence the Undertaker.

Let us, however, follow Mr. Mandrake through his daily solemnity. Let us attend him to the house of mourning; let us go with him on the day when he who was the very heart of that house is to be carried forth to the churchyard. For a time, the Undertaker takes possession of the miserable homestead. He is the self-created lord of its hospitality. It is he who stands the master of the mansion, and does its melancholy honours. With what grim urbanity he hands about the cake and wine! How he presses refreshment upon the heart-broken; how, as merely a matter of business, he proffers it to the mourners by invitation! His words, few and significant, come in whispers, and he treads the carpet as though he walked on flowers. Nor are his attentions confined to the relatives and friends of the dead: no, he has a keen anxiety for the wants of his vassals. The mutes, two breathing, half-crown images of deepest woe at the door, must, to support their load of sorrow, be plied with cake and alcohol; the coachmen cannot look sufficiently serious without their customary fluid; and the bearers, that they may stand manfully beneath their burthen, must nerve their hearts with potent gin.

The funeral is over, the cloaks are gathered up, the hatbands adjusted, the Undertaker and his servants have departed, and nought remains of the solemnity save—the bill! That is, in due time, presented; and—happy is the Undertaker above all the race of trading men—his commodities, as provided and supplied, defy the voice of cavil. His articles, six, eight, ten feet below the earth, are not to be questioned. He boldly charges for the "best mattress and pillow;" for the grass has begun to grow above them, or the mason has built them over, and who shall doubt their quality? The "best mattress!" What a melancholy satire in the superlative, when we think of the head of clay, the limbs of earth disposed upon it! And then, "To a stout, handsome elm coffin"; its durability and beauty

1 *Urn-Burial,* Chap. V.

insisted upon with a flourish, as if it were a thing made and adorned to endure for ever; a precious chest provided for the Judgment. Then follows, "To the use of the best black silk velvet pall," and the "feathers," and the "cloaks," and the "hearse," and the "coaches," and all that may be truly said to belong to the living; the mattress, the shroud, and the "handsome elm," being, indeed, the only things that can be honestly charged to the account of the dead.

But we are speaking of the funerals of the rich, or, at least, of those to whom death is not made more ghastly, more bitter, more agonising, by poverty. Such shows are made impressive by the worldly cunning of the dealer in coffins. How black, and fat, and shining, the horses! how richly caparisoned! what fine heavy, massive plumes! How the hearse nods from its roof! What an army of pages! And then, after the twenty mourning coaches, what a line of private carriages, sent by their owners as representatives of their love and respect to the departed. All this makes a touching sight; we are profoundly moved by this union of earth's wealth and earth's nothingness; this meeting of human glory and human meanness; this shaking hands of stark corruption and high-crested pride. Yes; there is in the sight food for meditation; serious matter suggestive of solemn thoughts; and yet, what are these brave shows of death to the miserable, squalid obsequies of the poor?

It is the Sabbath in London. Streams of people pour along the streets; everybody wears a brightened face; the whole metropolis makes cheerful holiday. All things move, and look, and sound of life, and life's activities. Careless talk and youthful laughter are heard as we pass: man seems immortal in his very ease. Creeping through the throng, comes the poor man's funeral train: look at the Undertaker marshalling the way. Is he the same functionary who handed cake and wine—who deferentially assisted at the fitting of the mourning gloves—who tried on the cloak; or, who noiselessly entered the room, and, ere the screws were turned, with a face set for the occasion, and a voice pitched to the sadness of his purpose, begged to know if "it was the wish,—before—before—" and then shrunk aside, as some one or two rushed in agony of heart to take a farewell look? Is it the same Undertaker—is it even a bird of the same sable feather? Hardly; for see how he lounges along the path: his head is cast aside, and there is in every feature the spirit of calculation. What is he thinking of,—the train he leads?—the part he plays in the festival of death? No: he is thinking of his deals at home—of the three other buryings his men are attending for him—of his chances of payment—of the people who have passed their word in security for part of the money for the present funeral—of the lateness of the hour—of his tea, that will be waiting for him ere the burying be done. How sad, how miserable the train that follows! The widow and her children: what efforts have been made—what future privations entailed, by the purchase of the mourning that covers them! Here is death in all his naked horror; with nought to mask his unsightliness—nothing to lessen the blow; here, indeed, he rends the heart-strings, and there is no medicine in fortune, no anodyne to heal the wounds. Follow the mourners from the church-yard home. Home!—A place of desolation; a cold hearth, and an empty cupboard. It is in the poor man's house that the dart of death is sharpest—that terror is added to the king of terrors. It is there that he sets up his saddest scutcheon in the haggard looks of the widow—in the pallid faces of the fatherless.

There is another funeral in which the Undertaker performs a double office. How often do we see him sauntering dreamily along, bearing on his shoulder the "baby bud"—the youngling that seemed born only to die. Noisy, laughing children play before and about him, as the Undertaker steadily pursues his way; the itinerant tradesman shouts at his ear, and all the noise, the stir, and bustle of unceremonious, working-day life, goes on around him, as, followed by the heart-broken mother, and some solitary friend, he carries to churchyard earth—what?—the last covering of an immortal spirit—the fleshly garment of one of God's angels.

The pauper's funeral has its Undertaker: an easy, careless, unpretending person; for at such a ceremonial, there is no need of even professional gravity. Rough, parish deals,[2] put in no equal claim with "fine elm, covered with superfine black cloth;" the rag that swathes the beggar has not the "magic in its web"[3] woven in the shrouds of corpses of respectability. No man puts on mourning for the pauper, nor should he. For, at his grave, humanity should rejoice—should feel a solemn gladness. Poor wretch! at length he has tricked the trickster, Fortune: he has shuffled off his worldly squalor, that, like a leprosy, parted him from healthy men; he is no longer the despised tatterdemalion—the outcast, the offal of the human kind. He has taken high promotion: he has escaped from the prison of this world, and is in the illimitable country of the dead. There he has rare companionship: he is with Solomon and Paul—with "the man of Uz"[4]—with Lazarus and Saint John! He, who, a week since, was a workhouse drudge, is now equal with any of the line

2 parish deals, charity coffins of unfinished pine.
3 "'Tis true; there's magic in the web of it." (*Othello,* III, iv, 75.)
4 "the man of Uz," Job.

of Pharaoh! Thus thinking, the rough-hewn deals of the pauper become rich as the cedar coffins of the royal dead: the beggar rots in his rags, yet shares he the self-same fate as spice-embalmed kings.

The Undertaker is sometimes called upon to make up by one great show—by the single pageant of an hour—for the neglect and misery shown and inflicted for years by the living to the dead. How many a poor relation has pined and died in a garret, disregarded by wealthy kindred, who profusely lavish upon clay what they denied to beating flesh and blood. How many a worthy soul, doomed, by the apathy of relatives, to a threadbare coat, has his coffin covered with superfine black cloth, at their most special request? He, who has been made prisoner to his wretched hearth by his napless hat, shall have plumes borne before him to his grave; and he, the penniless, who yearned for out-door air, yet had no limbs to bear him across the threshold, shall be carried in a hearse and four to his grave, with mourning coaches to follow. When death strikes the neglected relative—the poor man of worth and genius,—kindred and admirers send in the Undertaker to make amends for past coldness. Some of the money might have been better laid out with the vendors of creature-comforts; but no matter, let there be no stint of expense to the man who deals in hoods and scarfs, and the loan of the best pall. A few pounds might have soothed the last hours of the departed, stung, it may be, into death by the threats of creditors; the gentle process of the law.—That, however, is not to be thought of; there is now no fear of a prison for the defunct, so, Mr. Undertaker, be sure that his coffin is of the very best and stoutest elm.

> And bailiffs may seize his last blanket to-day,
> Whose pall shall be held up by nobles to-morrow.

The Undertaker comes in at the last to hush up all former indifference, all past neglect, to make all things even with a splendid funeral, and to bury the deceased, and the memory of his wrongs, handsomely together. Then comes the hypocrisy of the mourning, the outward sign of the inward heartbreaking, made manifest by many flounces, for one, if acknowledged at all, acknowledged as a family annoyance, whilst upon earth, though deeply regretted in many yards of crape and bombasin since he has been laid under it.

The Undertaker is now and then required to make due reparation to the self-wronged. When the muckworm who has starved his bowels, and kept bare his back, that he might die worth some darling amount, is called from the world he knew not how to enjoy, it is pleasant to see the

Undertaker lavish on the carcase of the miser all the sombre glories of his craft. We feel a kind of satisfaction at the expensive revenge taken upon his clay for all its former penury; we chuckle at the costliness with which the dead hunks is dished up for the worms; we acknowledge in the lengthy bill of the Undertaker a proper and piquant retribution on the money-clutching deceased. A few weeks ago was buried Mr. Skinpenny: he died worth half a million. A fortnight only before he was shovelled into the earth, he pathetically remonstrated with his profligate son on his reckless mode of poking the fire. No money could stand such an outlay for fuel.

"Well, but father," said the spendthrift, "the weather is extremely cold, and what am I to do?"

"Do, sir!" exclaimed the thrifty sire; "look here, sir, see what I do—see what I endure to save fourpence." On which Mr. Skinpenny twitched the wristband of his shirt from below his cuff, and showed that the garment had been vigilantly guarded from the hands of the laundress for many a week. The pleasant part remains to be told: the funeral of Skinpenny cost exactly one hundred pounds. We have only to add a wish, that, as his ghost seated itself in the boat of Charon, and after due chaffering paid its fare, the eternal waterman, ere he landed the thin shade, clapt into its hand the bill of Deathshead, Crossbones, and Company, for the burial of its flesh. To be doomed to read such a bill, and nothing but the bill, for a handful of ages, would, we conceive, be a very proper purgatory for the soul of a miser, who, shivering in rags whilst he lived, had been buried in fine linen and superfine black when a carcase.

There are some men, who, passing for dullards all their life, have had a joke at their funerals; they have, in anticipation, enjoyed their posthumous wit, and been content to live upon the humour of the future. It is only a short time since that we read of the funeral of an Italian wag, who gave it in strict charge, that certain torches, made under his own inspection, and carefully preserved for the ceremony, should be used in his funeral procession. The man died, the torches were lighted, the procession, composed of the sorrowing and the grave, was formed, and proceeded to the tomb. At a certain time, the torches having burned down to the combustibles, squibs, crackers, and other holiday fireworks, exploded from the funeral lights, to the fear and astonishment of the people. How often had the deceased, at the time a clod of clay, laughed and hugged himself at the explosion! How many times had he, in fact, enjoyed his own funeral! However, he must have died in good odour with the Church, or else, how easy for her cowled and bare-footed sons to have found in the squibs and crackers, a supernatural manifestation of the whereabout of the soul of the departed.

The Emperor Maximilian I. took, as we conceive, very unnecessary pains to show, when dead, the nothingness of human nature. He ordered his hair to be cut off, and his teeth to be ground to powder, and publicly burnt. He also ordered that his body, after due exposure, should be put into a sack of quicklime, covered with taffeta and white damask, laid in a coffin, and buried under the altar of St. George, in the church of the palace of Neustadt; the head and heart of the Emperor being so situated that the officiating priest should tread upon them. This is the very trick of bigotry: the tyrant, during his life, walks over living heads and hearts, and thinks he makes all quit with heaven if he give his dust to be trod upon by Mother Church.

As we have dealt with melancholy,—have written in the shade through several pages, we will wind up with a piece of humour which, were it generally followed, would, at least, have this good:—it would make needless funereal hypocrisy, and render burials ingenuous and truthful ceremonies. We quote from the "Choix des Testamens, Anciens et Modernes," this, the most wise and hearty last will of one Louis Cortusio, a doctor of Padua, dated 1418.

The testator forbids his friends to weep at his funeral on pain of being disinherited; and, on the contrary, appoints him who shall laugh the loudest his principal heir and universal legatee. Not a piece of black is to be seen in his house or in the church when he is to be buried; but both are to be strewn with flowers and green boughs on the day of his funeral. There is to be no tolling of bells; but his corpse is to be carried to church accompanied by fifty minstrels sounding their lutes, violins, flutes, hautboys, and trumpets; and "Hallelujah" is to be sung as at after Easter. The bier, covered with a shirt of different sparkling colours, is to be carried by twelve marriageable girls, clothed in green, and singing lively airs, to whom the testator leaves a dowry. Instead of torches, green boughs are to be carried by boys and girls wearing coronets of flowers, and singing in chorus. The clergy, with the monks and nuns (at least, those orders who do not wear black), to follow in procession. We have only to add (and we write it to the honour of the judicial powers of Padua), that the orders of the defunct were carried into effect. May the earth rest lightly on thee, Louis Cortusio!

We have but one quaint anecdote of an Undertaker: being, however, something in a kindred spirit to the humour of the doctor of Padua, it must be given. The Undertaker lost his wife. "I wear black," quoth he, "for strangers; how shall I show my mourning for the partner of my bosom?" A lucky thought fell upon the man of sables: he changed his garments of black for raiment of snowy white. From hat to shoes was the Undertaker clothed in candid array. We have heard of crows as white as whitest swans: can they be crows that have lost their mates?

# $\mathcal{S}$elections from "JENKINS" PAPERS*

## THE "POST" AT THE OPERA.

A WONDERFUL creature has made his descent upon *The Morning Post!* It is not generally known, but this paragon of animals, who "does" the Opera, is at the present moment a claimant for the long-dormant title of Bletheranskate[1]—yes, if he succeed, the man now known as nothing more than Peter Jenkins, will be the Earl of Bletheranskate. That he has the true aristocratic ichor in his veins, his writing (writing, do we call it?—inspiration, we should say)—sufficiently proves. Take the following burst:—

> Ever since the Italian lyrical drama crossed the Alps in the suite of the tasteful Medicis, its *vogue* has daily increased, it has become a ruling passion—it is *the quintessence of all civilised pleasures,* and *wherever* its principal *virtuosi* hoist their standard, *there for the time is* THE CAPITAL OF EUROPE, where the *most illustrious, noble, elegant, and tasteful* members of society *assemble.*

We do earnestly hope that Jenkins—(we must call him Jenkins until his claim is duly recognised)—will keep this profound truth from the knowledge of the singers and dancers. Only suppose that in a moment of irritation—and we have heard that such people really are at times a little given that way—only imagine them in a fit of the sulks to take ship for Sidney, or Adelaide, or Macquarrie Harbour: there immediately would be "the capital of Europe." Jenkins, be an Englishman. Would you destroy your country? Would you deprive us at once of the "most illus-

* *Punch,* IV, 126, 176, 196, 206, 216, 246, 249; V, 43; VI, 188.
   1 Bletheranskate, a word made from "blether" (foolish talk) and "skate" (contemptible fellow).

trious—noble—elegant—and tasteful?" For the sake of the nation scatter
not these firebrand truths.

Jenkins proceeds:—

> These *ornaments of society* are in general absent at the too early open-
> ing of her Majesty's Theatre—but on Saturday, as we surveyed the house,
> previous to the overture most of those *who constitute society* in England—
> those whom we *respect, esteem,* or *love,* rapidly *filled* the house.

We have always thought her Majesty's Theatre too small, and this
proves it. If only part of what "constitutes society" fills the theatre, what
is to become of the other section? But "society!" how beautifully the
Earl comes out here! With a fine aristocratic spirit, he melts down millions of Englishmen, and extracts therefrom—in the persons of about
two thousand people—"society!"

But let us proceed:—

> Every seat in every part of it was occupied, and if *those objectionable
> spectators were there*—those gentlemen of ambiguous gentility, the fash-
> ionable couriers, *valets, tailors,* and *shoemakers,* who obtain admission to
> the pit on the strength of knowing the measure of some actor or actress's
> foot—*they, and their frowsy dames,* were so *nailed to their benches as not
> to offend the eye.*[2]

Now, reader, can you not sympathise with the sufferings that have
produced this horror of tailors and shoemakers in the breast of Jenkins!
See him in the pit. He rises—looks airily about him, then falls, as though
shot, upon his seat. And wherefore? Alas! he has caught the eye of his
tailor in the pit—his long-suffering, unpaid tailor: he turns him round—
ha!—dreadful apparition! there is the very shoemaker whose trusted cor-
dovan of three years' wear still protects the feet of Jenkins. Thereupon,
great is the indignation of the Earl at tailors and shoemakers, and more
especially if accompanied by their "dames" in the pit of the Opera! Jenkins at length makes a rush for it: when—

> hastening through the corridors to procure a book of the opera, no where
> to be found, *we first encountered an illustrious and kind-hearted Prince,*
> and the next moment, in *our awkward haste, we stumbled upon* England's
> hero, moving along with a step as youthful and energetic as *his last speech*
> in the House of Lords.

Here the transcendent modesty of Jenkins shows itself; for he sup-
presses two incidents, for the truth of which we can vouch, having them

2 [*Jerrold's note*] *Morning Post,* March 13th.

from a witness thereof. The "illustrious Prince," when encountered, in the handsomest way begged to exchange snuff with Jenkins; and the Duke of Wellington "stumbled upon" in his "speaking step," took off his hat, and making the lowest bow to Jenkins, said,—"My very dear sir, I trust I have in no way distressed you. Will you do me the eternal honour of cutting your mutton with me at Apsley House?"[3] And all this the modesty of Jenkins has suppressed!

Glorious is Jenkins on an opera night, but how great the reverse! With the pride of birth (for that he is truly an earl who, from his style, can doubt) he lays out all his little income in gloves and eau-de-cologne, and becomes the next day merely Jenkins. Strange transformation! Touching contrast! Behold him in his glory in the opera pit—and then view him, as we a hundred times have seen him, creeping furtively from his three-pair back[4] to buy his herring, or the green luxury of water-cresses. Poor Jenkins! Poorer *Post!*

3 Apsley House, the London residence of the Duke of Wellington, at Hyde Park Corner, Piccadilly.
4 three-pair back, a third-floor lodging-room at the back of the house.

At this season of the year young nettle tops make an excellent table vegetable when boiled, and they are excellent as purifiers of the blood.—*Morning Post.*

JENKINS is so convinced of the truth of this, that he has already proposed to the lessee of the Opera the necessity of having a constant supply of "nettle tops" boiled, that the "shoemakers, tailors, and their *frowsy dames,*" who occasionally defile the Opera pit, may be compelled to eat of the vegetable at the pay-place, in order that their "blood" may be "purified" to something like patrician sweetness. Already Jenkins may be seen early in the morning, haunting Highgate[5] ditches.

5 Highgate, residential section of Hampstead metropolitan borough, London.

OUR READERS cannot forget that *The Morning Post*—(nay, *The Morning Jenkins*, for by such amended name, thanks to *Punch*, is that great diurnal now known to all men)—recently recommended a plentiful meal of "young nettle tops" as the very best thing for purifying the blood, and thereby purging all the land of what dear Jenkins would call its *canaille*. Great is Jenkins, whether he wield pasteboard thunderbolts, or, pant and dilate upon the glories of his own *virtuosi* and *ballerine!* Jenkins—like another most meek and most domestic animal—cannot open his mouth without being heard around. The prescription brayed by Jenkins has penetrated the recesses of Whitechapel—has struck upon the heart-strings of Shoreditch. *Punch* feels glorious that he can produce proofs of this, and here they are in grateful letters from correspondents.

Mr. Punch,—I am a tailor, sir, married, with a family of two sons and two daughters. I have, in my time, been called a very common-looking

Before taking the Nettles.

man, and my wife a ditto woman. Our children, sir, did also partake of the look of that sort of human mud, of which Mr. Jenkins would insinuate, common folks are made. Sir, the mud is gone—I, my wife, my sons and daughters, are now tip-top clay. The "frowsiness" of which Mr. Jenkins spoke is utterly evaporated, given place to a delicious smell of something between lavender-water and musk; this, as I am told, being the real odour of high life. Well, sir, and how do you think all this blessed change has been brought about? By nettle-tops, nothing but nettle-tops. There was a long-standing (though small) account between Mr. Jenkins and myself for turning an opera-waistcoat, and I therefore put myself and family under his treatment as a sort of set-off. For a whole week, sir, Mr. Jenkins came to Whitechapel, to superintend the boiling of the nettles; and the result is, my blood is purified to some-

After taking the Nettles.

thing very like the blood of a baronet—my wife's blood (as she herself declares) feels very like the blood of a baronet's lady, whilst my dear girls, Margarita and Sophinisba, full of nettles, consider themselves no less than the daughters of a marquess. My boy Ralph has changed his name into Alphonso, and Dick goes now to the Opera gallery as Ella, the door-keepers verily believing him to be the tenth in a zig-zag descent from a German prince!

And all this—all with Jenkins's nettles. The craving for the wondrous vegetable is getting very strong throughout the neighbourhood. If matters go on as at present for another week, all the blood of all Whitechapel will be of as fine a quality as the blood of May-Fair.[6]

All honour to Jenkins!
Your obedient Servant,
PETER GOOSETON, Tailor.

Whitechapel, May 8th.

Sir,—I was a shoemaker with a hump-back. I was 'prenticed from Shoreditch parish; but by the blessing of hard work and wax set up on my own account. Having for several years heel-tapped Mr. Jenkins's boots for the Opera, I got a taste for that place. Nevertheless, my visits to the pit (especially when I took my wife with me) were not without their sting, as I could not but feel that I was a shoemaker, and that my wife was—"frowsy."

Oh, sir, I shall always keep the return of the day with thanksgiving— that day, when I first read Mr. Jenkins's recipe of nettles. We have all

6 Mayfair, a fashionable section of London near Hyde Park.

lived upon their young "tops" for this past ten days, and the consequence is I have entirely lost my vulgar hump-back, feel myself as good
as any Earl, and believe my wife Margery to be as sweet as any perfume
as is.

I do, sir, but consider it a duty to make known this wonderful cure—
a duty of love towards my unfortunate fellow-creatures, and a duty of
gratitude towards the benevolent Mr. Jenkins.

I am, sir, your obedient Servant,

Shoreditch, May 6th.                    ALEXANDER NOBBY, Shoemaker.

Talk about the triumphs of vaccination! Why, only give Jenkins a
field of nettles, and he would in a trice make a House of Peers from a
body of costermongers.[7] We have the Order of the Thistle—there ought
to be the Order of the Nettle, and Jenkins—immortal Jenkins, for he
*shall never die*—should be its chancellor!


## JENKINS ON "SOCIETY."

HOMER sometimes donned a nightcap—Jenkins has, of late, slept a little.
Envy and malice have hinted that Jenkins has written himself out: this
we do not believe. Nevertheless, the *Morning Post* has of late been
dull as a dowager in her first mourning. On Monday, however, Jenkins
showed signs of returning consciousness; for he wrote as follows:—

> There was in the refined audience which assembled at the Opera on
> Saturday night a palpable increase of *spirit* and of *inclination* for the *ap-
> preciation* of the *sources of pleasure*. This animation confers a most essen-
> tial charm on the *reunions* at Her Majesty's Theatre—and on this occasion
> it was no doubt due *to the improved prospects of* SOCIETY.

This is tolerable; but still, very far below Jenkins at Jenkins' best. He
very properly looks upon the condition of Opera boxes as the barometer
of "society." If Duchesses turn out in their best diamonds and sweetest
smiles,—why, the weavers must be doing better at Bolton and Paisley: if
Marquesses rush to *Gazza Ladra*,[8] the agricultural interest must be looking up. There is true philosophy in this; albeit above the apprehension

---

[7] costermongers, hawkers of fruit, vegetables, fish, etc.
[8] *Gazza Ladra* (The Thievish Magpie), an opera by Rossini.

of common minds. But then Jenkins' is deep as his tailor's thimble—as deep, and as bottomless!

## SOMETHING FROM, AND OF, "JENKINS."

THE READERS of *Punch* are by this time aware that there is a print called *The Morning Post* (more commonly known of late as *The Morning Jenkins*), published every day, Sundays excepted, in London. At present this luminous sheet emanates from a modest brick building opposite Somerset-house,[9] in the Strand—the said building being surmounted by the statue of Mercury as Jenkins (as shown in *Punch*'s last). Well, Jenkins, like a plethoric footman who has outgrown his livery, has become

9 Somerset-house, a government office building in the Strand.

too big for his present building. Old bricks and mortar cannot contain
him, and so he is to be located in a new house built upon orders—between the Union Composite[10] and the Newgate Doric[11]—in Wellington-
street North. Well, Jenkins, who has his bricks at heart, nay, at head too,
has made a design for a beautiful piece of *alto relievo* to adorn the mansion; and has in the handsomest manner favoured us with the subjoined
early copy[.]

It will be seen at a glance that the vital principles of the *Morning
Post* are embodied in it. Great with his pen, Jenkins is no less great with
his pencil! We, however, are not to be mollified into the weakness of too
great tenderness towards Jenkins, by any little bit of overt liberality on
his part. Jenkins may be generous, but *Punch* must be just. Jenkins
says—

> *Cerito*[12] *ventured upon a great undertaking indeed; she danced the
> Cachucha.*[13] This was throwing down the gauntlet to Ellsler,[14] or rather
> attacking her at once in her stronghold. We confess, when we first heard
> of this intention, we were greatly alarmed: the struggles of Octavius and
> Antony, of Cæsar and Pompey, were mere *bagatelles* to this rivalry.

This appeared one day: mark what came out the next—yea, in Jenkins's own paper:—

> *Mdlle. Cerito requests us to state that she did not attempt to dance the
> Cachucha on Tuesday evening. The Gitana*[15] *was the dance performed by
> her on that occasion.*

Great was the concern, greater the perspiration of Jenkins when he
saw this. But man is weak. Had Jenkins not been at the Blue Posts, in
the Haymarket, playing all-fours[16] with the French Ambassador's footman—had he been in his place in the pit, and not given away his pass to
his tailor's one journeyman, he must have known the *Gitana* from the

---

[10] Union Composite, the workhouse, built, according to Jerrold, in the Roman style
of mixed Corinthian and Ionic architecture.

[11] Newgate Doric, the famous prison, of Ancient Greek architecture.

[12] *Cerito*, Francesca ("Fanny") Cerito (1817–1909), an Italian ballerina noted for
the brilliance, strength, and vivacity of her dancing. Her greatest role was in *Ondine,*
in London, 1843.

[13] *Cachucha*, a gay Andalusian solo dance, in three-four time, done with castanets.

[14] Ellsler, Fanny Ellsler (1810–1884), an Austrian dancer who made her London
debut in 1833 and appeared there again between 1838 and 1840. Her forte was folk
dancing, especially the cachucha, the cracovienne, and the tarantella.

[15] Gitana, a gypsy folk dance.

[16] all-fours, a card game for two, named from the four particulars by which it is
determined: high, low, Jack, and the game.

*Cachucha.* But seldom is it that Jenkins errs in this way, and we trust that by this time he is forgiven.

We have next a very private and particular account of the murders of Fanny Ellsler. Jenkins says—

> Cerito ventured on no slight undertaking when she came, alone, at the same time, to supply the place of the fairy Dumilatre,[17] and also *of that favourite who has triumphed both in the new world and in the old, and at whose feet expired in his youth the heir of an empire,* and in *his old age the greatest political writer of his times.* But Cerito has proved that nothing is above her power, and when she dances we forget all her rivals. [*and all her murders.*]

It is an historical fact (though not so well known as it ought to be) that the Duke of Reichstadt[18] was found dead at the feet of Ellsler, who, afterwards coming to England, in the most remorseless way, slaughtered "the greatest political writer of his times"—William Cobbett.[19] We only hope that Jenkins will not be her third victim.

We cannot, however, leave Jenkins without paying homage to his ubiquity. For on the very night he visited the opera—at the very hour— he was at Drury Lane, beholding *Athelwold.*[20] This is plain: for could any other pen save that of Jenkins put a sentence in such a delicious tangle?

> The chief defect of his drama is an utter want of the *chronological allocation of its tone,* which could only have been afforded *by that costumed thought* which is so rarely acquired by the dramatist.

What do you mean, Jenkins? "Costumed thought?" What is that? Thought in full-dress, of course. But, Jenkins, pray write to be understood—don't affect to write "too well"—condescend to be a man of the world—in a word, be a Man of the People, Jenkins!

## JENKINS ON COSTUMES—
## QUADRILLES—AND THE OPERA.

JENKINS, who writes as *Othello* loved, "not wisely," but, as he himself

---

17 Adèle Dumilatre (1821–1909), French ballerina.
18 Duke of Reichstadt, Napoleon II (1811–1832).
19 William Cobbett (1763–1835), essayist, politician, and agriculturist who fought for parliamentary reform in behalf of the poor, especially the agricultural laborer.
20 *Athelwold,* a play by Aaron Hill (1685–1750) based upon early English history.

assures us, "too well,"[21] has again favoured us with two or three samples of his superfine diction—samples so exquisite that it would be base in-

Punch frying Jenkins.

gratitude in *Punch* not to acknowledge them. And *Punch* does this the more readily, inasmuch as it is but too evident that poor Jenkins has, for some time past, been under a cloud. There has been a melancholy, a sombreness in his effusions, which would indicate the presence of some stern dictator—some prosaic writing-master, ready to rap Jenkins over

21 ". . . then must you speak / Of one that loved not wisely but too well. . . ." (*Othello*, V, ii, 345–346.)

the knuckles whenever he should coruscate about *le ballerine*—the *dilletanti*—the *virtuosi*, and, as he himself in his happiest moments would say, the other *raræ aves* of the opera. Jenkins has of late written with no champagne in his ink; no, not even with ginger pop. No Quaker could behave more demurely to a chambermaid, than has Jenkins of late comported himself towards the English language. We therefore hail the recent break-out; though justice to Jenkins compels us to state that it is very far below Jenkins' pressure.

Jenkins, discoursing on the "Fashions of the Court and High Life," says with a touching melancholy:—

> In the recent gloom, all preparations for toilettes *have been neglected*, and the anxiety to know what will be the ruling costume of the day is now at its full height.

Everybody can bear witness to this fashionable neglect of dress in the intensity of mourning. Marchionesses wore sackcloth, but then it was of the very finest texture; Countesses powdered their hair with ashes; but then they were ashes from the very best Wallsend:—[22]

> Having a *special access* to certain *high* councils of fashion, we think our fair readers will thank us for a few words of intelligence and advice.

Now, this is quite true. Jenkins has always been great with the dressmakers. By the way, his entry into toilette life was, we have generally understood, in a baby linen warehouse; his first attempt at composition was sticking "Welcome, little stranger" in minnikin pins in satin cushions.

Jenkins—let the reader see *The Morning Post*—continues:

> The ball given for the benefit of the Royal Academy holds a distinguished place amongst the *fêtes* in prospect, and *certain arbitrary mammas*, and *still more* arbitrary ladies of fashion, are already busily occupied in selecting the costumes of their daughters, who would, *we suspect*, in most cases, far prefer *choosing for themselves*. It must be owned that *they rarely fail in knowing* what is most advantageous to their youthful charms. Why should they not be allowed *this pleasure*, being *still aided* by *the experience* of the mammas? These, however, using their sovereign power, allow them *no voice in the matter*, and *occasionally choose* what is *positively disadvantageous*, by selecting costumes *not so much with regard to what is becoming as to what will obviate invidious comparisons of mere finery*; and we *have seen already* one or two incongruous instances of *this despotism*, such as making a timid retiring *blonde* wear a Spanish costume, &c., &c.

[22] Wallsend, a municipal borough in Northumberland; in a coal-mining region, Wallsend has given its name to a type of high quality coal.

If the reader be not weeping at this, it is not in the power of onions to move him. Again, mark the wondrous knowledge Jenkins hath of the female heart! Women, especially young women, prefer "choosing for themselves;" they absolutely "know what is most advantageous to their youthful charms!" True, Jenkins, very true. Did not your first love, who jilted you for the butler, who now keeps the Shoulder-knot and Trencher, at Penzance—did not she teach you this profound verity? How often, furtively glancing, Jenkins, have you seen her twitch a curl from under her bonnet, as though Zephyrus' self had blown it there? Go to, Jenkins! You know all the odd, winding ways of the female heart as well—aye, as well as all the ways of Seven Dials.[23]

Hear Jenkins on the philosophy of quadrilles:—

> Care should be taken, in order to give the quadrilles their full effect, that there should exist no great disproportion between the statures of the performers; and it should also be decided, that if the ball be really a fancy ball, the costumes should be such as can be easily recognised. For example, in the quadrille intended to represent the twelve months of the year, *why should they be represented alone, by the flowers worn?* This would make a very slight distinction and, besides, we have, alas! months in the year, when there are few, if any flowers even in our hot-houses.

We agree with Jenkins. Why should not every lady be honestly labelled from "January" to "December," carrying upon the head the months from *Punch's Almanack*, which *Punch* here solemnly promises to have printed on all variety of satins for the occasion.

We now return to Jenkins at the opera. Mark the consideration he has of—*himself*:—

> *We consider ourselves*, as journalists, in our reports bound above all things to *reflect* as exactly as possible the *impressions* of the public; however ephemeral they may be, they possess the deepest interest: for if *we ascend* from matters infinitely small, like those we treat of, to those works of intellect which are surpassingly great, we find that amongst historians those who produce the *deepest impression* are not such as reasoned at the distance of ages on long-past events—like a Niebhur, a Hume, and a Gibbon—but those who reported with *the sobered passions of the moment* the events they themselves beheld, *like* a Xenophon, a Davilla, a Guicciardini, and a Clarendon, &c.

[23] Seven Dials, an open area in the parish of St. Giles-in-the-Fields, from which seven streets radiate; characterized by crowded, lower-class dwellings, ginshops, and the haunts of ballad mongers.

Hang it, Jenkins! this is too modest. What! You write with "the sober-ed passions of the moment," and are therefore *like*—but let us give the list of your similitudes. Here it is!
"Xenophon—Davilla—Guicciardini—Clarendon[24]——Jenkins!"

## THE PERENNIAL JENKINS!

WE HAVE received a letter, which, with the characteristic justice of *Punch*, is herewith presented to the reader. It is a letter from Jenkins; but not from *the* Jenkins; not from the Man of the People, *i.e.*, Jenkins of the *Post*; but from Jenkins's namesake, who thus complains:—

> Cavendish Square, *July* 18.
>
> MR. PUNCH,—My name is, unhappily, JENKINS; I am a footman, and not ashamed to own it. But, sir, here is my grief. Go where I will, I am twitted with the authorship of certain articles, operatic and literary, in the *Morning Post*. The life I lead on opera-nights among my brethren of the shoul-der-knot is insupportable. Unless you do me justice, I shall be compelled to throw up a very excellent situation, change my name, and quit the country: Will you then, sir, oblige me by informing the world, that whoever the JENKINS may be who writes in the *Post*, it is not
>
> Your obedient Servant,
> NATHANIEL JENKINS.
>
> P.S.—Allow me to add, *Mr. Punch,* that I am rather surprised a man of your liberality should sneer at the condition of a footman. Is my namesake in the *Post* the worse for a livery?—I think not.

NATHANIEL JENKINS is a very decent, sensible fellow, and had his un-fortunate namesake written as good English as our correspondent, why, the critic Jenkins—poor cockchafer!—would never have been impaled upon the iron pen of *Punch*. But Nathaniel must not misunderstand us. We do not sneer at the livery that encases the corporal part of Jenkins. Not that his body, but that his soul is in livery, are we compelled to flog him with nettle-tops. Yes: his soul! Look, reader: peep in at the brain of Jenkins (you must use a glass, by the way, of great magnifying power). There, perched on *pia mater*, is what certain anatomists call the soul. With different men it takes different shapes. In the brain of Jenkins it

---

[24] Xenophon (434[?]–355 B.C.), Davila y Padilla (1562–1604), Francesco Guicciar-dini (1483–1540), and Edward Hyde, Earl of Clarendon (1609–1674): famous histo-rians of Greece, Mexico, Italy, and England.

is shaped like a Lilliput monkey, and there it sits, like the larger monkeys on the barrel-organs of those pedestrian *virtuosi* (as Jenkins himself would say) who grind you off hap'orths of Mozart or Donizetti. There is the monkey-soul of Jenkins! And see you not his nether monkey, glowing in red plush? That is Jenkins' soul in full livery; and for that soul, so habited, we must (it is a public duty) continue to flog Jenkins.

Within these few days, Jenkins has had the audacity to give his opinion on the proper position and requisite beverage of a gentleman. He says:—

> We believe that a man of genius may be seen arm-in-arm with a gentleman, without any derogation from his intellectual elevation, and that it is somewhat *more respectable for him* to take his *glass of sherry at his club in respectable society*, than to frequent taverns in very questionable company.

This is all very well, Jenkins, about the glass of sherry. It is pretty upon paper; but it is not the belief of Jenkins. No, no: he tastes not sherry: he writes not "too well," as he always does, upon sherry; but owes his nerve to plebeian half-and-half. All his beautiful flowers of speech are raised in good, honest pewter. Do they not smack of Barclay—have they not the aroma of Perkins?[25]

Jenkins now comes to female society; and, considering the hours he has, in his time, waited at Howell & James's, he must be allowed to know something of the matter. He says:—

> Nor do we believe that refined female society will injure his intellect, any more than we imagine that a first-rate coat will crook his spine.

Jenkins has a painful recollection of a certain coat. He remembers, in his early footman life, when he was compelled to wear the cast livery of a stout predecessor; he still shudders when he ponders on the awful wrinkles down the back; on the sack-like fit of the blue plush, big enough for the Flying Dutchman. But this was before Jenkins lived with the baronet. Then he was no longer drab and blue, but gray and scarlet.

---

25 Barclay, Perkins, owners of a well-known brewery in Park Street, Southwark.

LETTERS, "thick as the leaves of Vallambrosa,"[26] come upon us, demanding the whereabout of Jenkins? Some of the writers—we forgive the slander—boldly aver that we, *Punch*, have killed, murdered outright, the said Jenkins. We loved him too much; too deeply were we indebted to him to slay the flunky: no, the man was serviceable to us. Nevertheless, we ourselves have been puzzled to know what has become of Jenkins. Again and again, since the opera opened, have we looked in the *Post*, but Jenkins was no longer there. No his flourishes are gone—his fine, subtle, very long ear for music is not to be seen. We no longer roar over the criticisms of the opera; once they were fine and volant as dragonflies, and now are they flat as flat-fish. Jenkins is departed!

However, not to leave the reader in despair—no longer to torture him, we state, for his comfort, that we have found Jenkins. But how!

[26] "Thick as autumnal leaves that strow the brooks / In Vallombrosa . . . ." (*Paradise Lost*, Bk. I, ll. 302-303.)

*Quantum mutatus*—as Jenkins himself would say. Let us narrate our adventure.

On Saturday last we attended the opera. Coming out, we looked around in the hope of espying Jenkins. A linkman—with the fine sense belonging to "his order"—interpreted our wish. He sidled up to us, and in few words told us the fate of Jenkins.

He had been mesmerised past hope of recovery at a neighbouring pot-house. We saw him, and immediately put him on paper. Yes, gentle reader, Jenkins, who has so oft delighted you, is in a trance. Should he, however, recover—should he by any accident return to pen and ink—depend upon it you shall have the earliest notice of his doings. In the meanwhile, Jenkins, "rosy dreams and slumbers light."[27] Farewell, Jenkins.

## PUNCH'S PARTING TRIBUTE TO JENKINS.[*]
### [W. M. Thackeray]

THE ILLUSTRIOUS nobody who has long afforded our readers much amusement cannot be consigned to the obscurity from which we reluctantly dragged him, without some appropriate memorial of his value and pretension. The annexed engraving, intended for that purpose, is a magnified design for a tobacco-stopper, to be cast—need we add—in brass. The inscription in Jenkins-French has been submitted to the Editor of the *Morning Post,* who perfectly reciprocates the sentiments expressed in it.

> Oh! Jenkins, homme du peuple—mangez bien,[28]
> Désormais avec toi nous ferons rien,
> Vous êtes tout usé—chose qui montre la corde,[29]
> Nos lecteurs étaient mal de toi d'abord:
> Allez-vous-en—votre bâton coupez vîte,
> En Ponch jamais votre nom—désormais sera dite.

---

[27] "To all, to each, a fair good-night, / And pleasing dreams, and slumbers light." (Sir Walter Scott, *Marmion,* "L'Envoy, To the Reader.")

[28] [*Thackeray's note*] *Mangez bien,* is a Jenkinsonian French expression signifying literally—fare well.

[29] [*Thackeray's note*] A threadbare subject. The Jenkinsonian French for "threadbare" being *qui montre la corde.*

[*] *Punch*, V, 123; VI, 153.

GEMS FROM JENKINS.
[W. M. Thackeray]

OUR DEAR FRIEND has begun lately a very artful way of conciliating the aristocracy of the country: viz., by *writing bad French* in his Journal. Witness the two following paragraphs extracted from Tuesday's Journal, and profound specimens of Jenkinsonian dissimulation:—

Authors' Miseries. No. VI. Thackeray and Jerrold on the left.

Un jeune homme, age de 30 ans, parlant Francais, Allemande et Anglais,
que a servie de famille destingue deseire se placer comme Valet d'chambre,
ou Courier, que peura donne de bon aclemmation.

Une personne Francaise, .... elle sais faire les robes, et bien coiffee; elle
n'a point d'objection de prendre le soin d'une petite Demoiselle si necessaire, point d'objection pour la campagne ni Londre, mais une Famille pour
voyager sera preferable.

They are copied from our fashionable contemporary with laborious
accuracy, and contain specimens of a noble eccentricity of style, which
we never believed to have existed in any person below the rank of the
Marquis of Londonderry. Even he could not write worse French than the
Courier of the *Post*. And little boys of six years old will remark with
pleasure that out of the last twenty-two words in the paragraph, only
four are right. Was it the *Morning Post* who wrote, or was it the *Courier*?
Only the fashionable contemporary knows this awful secret.

The *Femme de Chambre* announcement is evidently the writing of an
English person, *"une petite demoiselle si necessaire,"* a little girl so
necessary, and *"une famille pour voyager sera preferable,"* "a family to
travel will be preferable," are, we fearlessly assert, the expressions of
Betty the housemaid, not of Manon the *Femme de Chambre*. Or is there
a presiding genius at the office of the *Post*, who himself composes these

remarkable advertisements? and who writes about *"que a servie,"* and *"de bon aclemmation,"* and *"elle sais faire,"* and *"elle sais coiffee?"*

We are inclined to think that Jenkins writes bad French, not because he knows no better, but because in the fashionable world good French would not be understood. They don't like it there. They like their French loaded and doctored like their wine; and J.—knowing his public will only consume a bad article,—supplies that bad article to their hearts' content. If Lady Londonderry, if Lady Blessington, if Lady Bulwer, if Mrs. Trollope, if the fashionable world in a word proves its dislike of good French by constantly practising bad, why should a journalist venture to differ from such authorities, or pretend to better behaviours than his betters?

# THE WINE CELLAR.*

## A "MORALITY."

STEPHEN CURLEW was a thrifty goldsmith in the reign of the Second Charles. His shop was a mine of metal; he worked for the court, although, we fear, his name is not to be found in any record in the State-Paper Office. Stephen was a bachelor, and, what is strange, he never felt, that is, he never complained of, his loneliness. His chased ewers, his embossed goblets, his gold in bars, were to him wife and children. Midas was his only kinsman. He would creep among his treasures, like an old gray rat, and rub his hands, and smile, as if communing with the wealth about him. He had so long hugged gold to his heart, that it beat for nothing else. Stephen was a practical philosopher; for he would meekly take the order—nay, consult the caprice—of the veriest popinjay with the humility of a pauper, when, at a word, he might have outblazoned lords and earls. If this be not real philosophy, thought Stephen, as he walked slip-shod at the heels of his customers, what is?

Stephen was a man of temperance. He was content to see venison carved on his hunting-cups; he cared not to have it in his larder. His eyes would melt at clustering grapes chased on banquet goblets; but no drop of the living juice passed the goldsmith's lips. Stephen only gave audience to Bacchus when introduced by Plutus. Such was the frugality of Stephen to his sixty-fifth year; and then, or his name had not been eternised in this our page, temptation fell upon him.

It was eight o'clock, on a raw spring evening, and Stephen sat alone in his back room. There was no more fire upon the hearth than might have lain in a tinder-box, but Stephen held his parchment hands above it, and would not be cold. A small silver lamp, with a short wick—for the

* *The Writings of Douglas Jerrold* (8 vols.; London, 1851–1858), IV, 264–269.

keen observation of Stephen had taught him the scientific truth, that the less the wick, the less the waste of oil—glowed, a yellow speck in the darkness. On the table lay a book, a treatise on precious stones; and on Stephen's knee, "Hermes, the True Philosopher."[1] Stephen was startled from a waking dream by a loud and hasty knocking at the door. Mike, the boy, was out, but it could not be he. Stephen took up the lamp, and was creeping to the door, when his eye caught the silver, and he again placed it upon the table, and felt his way through the shop. Unbolting the five bolts of the door, but keeping fast the chain, Stephen demanded "who was there?"

"I bear a commission from Sir William Brouncker, and I'm in haste."

"Stay you a minute—but a minute;" and Stephen hurried back for the lamp, then hastily returned, opened the door, and the visitor passed the threshold.

" 'Tis not Charles," cried Stephen, alarmed at his mistake, for he believed he had heard the voice of Sir William's man.

"No matter for that, Stephen; you work for men, and not for Christian names. Come, I have a job for you;" and the visitor, with the easy, assured air of a gallant, lounged into the back parlour, followed by the tremulous Stephen.

"Sir William"——began the goldsmith.

"He bade me use his name; the work I'd have you do is for myself. Fear not; here's money in advance," and the stranger plucked from his pocket a purse, which, in its ample length lay like a bloated snake upon the table.

Stephen smiled and said, "Your business, sir?"

"See here," and the stranger moved the lamp immediately between them, when, for the first time, Stephen clearly saw the countenance of his customer. His face was red as brick, and his eyes looked deep as the sea, and glowed with good humour. His mouth was large and frank; and his voice came as from the well of truth. His hair fell in curls behind his ears, and his moustache, black as coal, made a perfect crescent on his lip, the points upwards. Other men may be merely good fellows, the stranger seemed the best. "See here," he repeated, and produced a drawing on a small piece of paper, "can you cut me this in a seal ring?"

"Humph!" and Stephen put on his spectacles, "the subject is"——

"Bacchus squeezing grape-juice into the cup of Death," said the stranger.

1 "Hermes, the True Philosopher," perhaps an ironic foreshadowing of Stephen's fate, since one of Hermes' many functions in Greek mythology was to conduct souls to the underworld.

"An odd conceit," cried the goldsmith.

"We all have our whims, or woe to the sellers," said the customer. "Well, can it be done?"

"Surely, sir, surely. On what shall it be cut?"

"An emerald, nothing less. It is the drinker's stone. In a week, Master Curlew?"

"This day week, sir, if I live in health."

The day came, Stephen was a tradesman of his word, and the stranger sat in the back parlour, looking curiously into the ring.

"*Per Bacco!* Rarely done. Why, Master Curlew, thou has caught the very chops of glorious Liber; his swimming eyes, and blessed mouth. Ha! ha! thou has put thy heart into the work, Master Curlew; and how cunningly hast thou all but hid the dart of Death behind the thyrsus of the god. How his life-giving hand clutches the pulpy cluster, and with what a gush comes down the purple rain, plashing into rubies in the cup of Mors!"

"It was my wish to satisfy, most noble sir," said Stephen, meekly; somewhat confounded by the loud praises of the speaker.

"May you never be choked with a grape-stone, Master Curlew, for this goodly work. Ha!" and the speaker looked archly at the withered goldsmith; "it hath cost thee many a headache ere thou couldst do this."

"If I may say it, I have laboured hard at the craft—have been a thrifty, sober man," said Stephen.

"Sober! Ha! ha! ha!" shouted the speaker, and his face glowed redder, and his eyes melted; "sober! why, thou wast begot in a wine cask, and suckled by a bottle, or thou hadst never done this. By the thigh of Jupiter! he who touched this," and the stranger held up the ring to his eye, and laughed again, "he who touched this, hath never known water. Tut! man, were I to pink thee with a sword, thou'dst bleed wine!"

"I," cried Stephen, "I bleed;" and he glanced fearfully towards the door, and then at the stranger, who continued to look at the ring.

"The skin of the sorriest goat shall sometimes hold the choicest liquor," said the stranger, looking into the dry face of the goldsmith. "Come, confess, art thou not a sly roisterer? Or art thou a hermit over thy drops, and dost count flasks alone? Ay! ay! well, to thy cellar, man; and,—yes,—thine arms are long enough,—bring up ten bottles of thy choicest Malaga."

"I!—my cellar!—Malaga!" stammered Stephen.

"Surely thou hast a cellar?" and the stranger put his hat upon the table with the air of a man set in for a carouse.

"For forty years, but it hath never known wine," cried the goldsmith. "I—I have never known wine." The stranger said nothing; but turning full upon Stephen, and placing his hands upon his knees, he blew out his flushing cheeks like a bagpipe, and sat with his eyes blazing upon the heretic. "No, never!" gasped Stephen, terrified, for a sense of his wickedness began to possess him.

"And dost thou repent?" asked the stranger, with a touch of mercy towards the sinner.

"I—humph! I'm a poor man," cried Curlew; "yes, though I'm a goldsmith, and seem rich, I—I'm poor! poor!"

"Well, 'tis lucky I come provided;" and the stranger placed upon the table a couple of flasks. Whether he took them from under his cloak, or drew them through the floor, Stephen knew not; but he started at them as they stood rebukingly upon his table, as if they had been two sheeted ghosts. "Come, glasses," cried the giver of the wine.

"Glasses!" echoed Stephen, "in my house!"

"Right, glasses! No—cups, and let them be gold ones,"—and the bacchanal, for it was plain he was such, waved his arm with an authority which Stephen attempted not to dispute, but rose, and hobbled into the shop, and returned with two cups, just as the first cork was drawn. "Come, there's sunlight in that, eh?" cried the stranger, as he poured the wine into the vessels. "So, thou hast never drunk wine? Well, here's to the baptism of thy heart." And the stranger emptied the cup, and his lips smacked like a whip.

And Stephen Curlew tasted the wine, and looked around, below, above; and the oaken wainscot did not split in twain, nor did the floor yawn, nor the ceiling gape. Stephen tasted a second time; thrice did he drink, and he licked his mouth as a cat licks the cream from her whiskers, and putting his left hand upon his belly, softly sighed.

"Ha! ha! another cup? I know thou wilt," and Stephen took another, and another; and the two flasks were in brief time emptied. They were, however, speedily followed by two more, placed by the stranger on the table, Stephen opening his eyes and mouth at their mysterious appearance. The contents of these were duly swallowed, and lo! another two stood before the goldsmith, or, as he then thought, four.

"There never was such a Bacchus!" cried Stephen's customer, eyeing the ring. "Why, a man may see his stomach fairly heave, and his cheek ripen with wine; yet, till this night, thou hadst never tasted the juice? What—what could have taught thee to carve the god so capitally?"

"Instinct—instinct," called out the goldsmith, his lips turned to clay by too much wine.

"And yet," said the stranger, "I care not so much for—How old art thou, Stephen?"

"Sixty-five," and Stephen hiccuped.

"I care not so much for thy Death, Stephen; instinct should have made thee a better hand at Death."

" 'Tis a good Death," cried the goldsmith, with unusual boldness, "a most sweet Death."

" 'Tis too broad—the skeleton of an alderman with the flesh dried upon him. He hath not the true desolation—the ghastly nothingness of the big bugbear. No matter; I'm content; but this I'll say, though thou hast shown thyself a professor at Bacchus, thou art yet but a poor apprentice at Death."

Stephen Curlew answered not with words, but he snored very audibly. How long he slept he could not well discover; but when he awoke, he found himself alone; no, not alone, there stood upon the table an unopened flask of wine. In a moment the mystery broke upon him—and he sprang to his feet with a shriek, and rushed into the shop. No, he had not been drugged by thieves—all was as it should be. The stranger, like an honest and a courteous man, had taken but his own; and, without disturbing the sleeper, had quitted the house. And Stephen Curlew, the wine glowing in his heart—yea down to his very nails, stood and smiled at the unopened flask before him.

Stephen continued to eye the flask; and though its donor had shared with him he know not how many bottles, Stephen was resolved that not one drop of the luscious juice before him should wet an alien throat. But how—where to secure it? For in the new passion which seized upon the goldsmith, the one flask seemed to him more precious than the costly treasure in his shop—a thing to be guarded with more scrupulous affection—more jealous love. In what nook of his house to hide the glorious wealth—what corner, where it might escape the profane glances and itching fingers of his workmen? The thought fell in a golden flash upon him—the cellar—ay, the cellar! who of his household ever thought of approaching the cellar? Stephen seized the flask and lamp, and paused. The cellar had no lock! no matter; he had a bag of three-inch nails and a stout hammer.

The next morning, neighbours met at the closed door and windows of the goldsmith, and knocked and shouted—shouted and knocked. They were, however, reduced to a crowbar, and, at length, burst into the house. Every place was searched, but there was nowhere visible old

Stephen Curlew. Days passed on, and strange stories filled the ears of men. One neighbour vowed that he had had a dream or vision, he knew not which, wherein he saw the goldsmith whirled down the Strand in a chariot drawn by a lion and a tiger, and driven by a half-naked young man, wearing a panther skin, and on his head vine-leaves and ivy. An old woman swore that she had seen Stephen carried away by a dozen devils (very much in liquor), with red faces and goat legs. However, in less than a month, the goldsmith's nephew, a scrivener's clerk, took possession of Curlew's wealth, and became a new-made butterfly with golden wings. As for Stephen, after various speculations, it was concluded to the satisfaction of all parties, that he must have been carried away by Satan himself, and the nephew cared not to combat popular opinions. But such, in truth, was not the end of the goldsmith. Hear it.

Stephen, possessed by the thought of the cellar, with the one flask, a lamp, nails and hammer, proceeded to the sacred crypt. He arrived in the vault, and having kissed the flask, reverently put it down, and straightway addressed himself to the work. Closing the door, he drove the first nail, the second, third; and borrowing new strength from the greatness of his purpose, he struck each nail upon the head with the force and precision of a Cyclops, burying it deep in the oak. With this new-found might, he drove eleven nails; the twelfth was between his thumb and finger, when looking round,—oh; sad mishap, heavy mischance! awful error!—he had driven the nails from the wrong side!—In a word, he had nailed himself in! There he stood, and there stood the flask. He gasped with horror; his foot stumbled, struck the lamp, it fell over, and the light went out.

Shall we write further on the agony of Stephen Curlew? Shall we describe how he clawed and struck at the door, now in the hope to wrench a nail, and now to alarm the breathing men above? No; we will not dwell upon the horror; it is enough that the fate of the goldsmith was dimly shadowed forth in the following paragraph of last Saturday.

"Some labourers, digging a foundation near"—no, we will not name the place, for the family of the Curlews is not yet extinct, and there may be descendants in the neighbourhood—"near———, found a skeleton; a hammer was beside it, with several long nails: a small wine-flask was also found near the remains, which it is considered, could not have been in the vault in which they were discovered, less than a century and three-quarters!"

Oh, ye heads of families—and oh, ye thrifty, middle-aged bachelors, boarding with families, or growing mouldy by yourselves, never, while ye live, forget the terrible end of Stephen Curlew. And oh, ye heads of families—and oh, ye aforesaid bachelors, albeit ye have only one bottle left, never—NEVER NAIL UP THE WINE-CELLAR!

# SELECTED BIBLIOGRAPHY

EDITIONS OF JERROLD'S WORKS

*The Works of Douglas Jerrold*, with an introductory memoir by his son, W. Blanchard Jerrold. 5 vols. London: Bradbury and Evans, n.d.

*The Writings of Douglas Jerrold.* 8 vols. London: Bradbury and Evans, 1851–1858. (Although the most complete collection of his writings, many essays, serials, and plays are not included.)

MISCELLANEOUS COLLECTIONS

*Bon-mots of Charles Lamb and Douglas Jerrold*, ed. Walter Jerrold. London: J. M. Dent and Co., 1893.

*The Brownrigg Papers*, ed. Blanchard Jerrold. London: J. C. Hotten, 1860.

*Douglas Jerrold and 'Punch'.* London: Macmillan and Co., 1910. (Part I is an account by Walter Jerrold of Douglas Jerrold's career with the magazine; Part II reprints four of Jerrold's serials from *Punch*: "Capsicum House for Young Ladies," "The Life and Adventures of Miss Robinson Crusoe," "Our Honeymoon," and "Exhibition of the English in China.")

*Fireside Saints, Mr. Caudle's Breakfast Talk, and other Papers.* Boston: Lee and Shepard, 1888.

*The Handbook of Swindling, and Other Papers*, ed., with an introduction, by Walter Jerrold. London: Scott, n.d.

CONTRIBUTIONS TO *Punch*

Jerrold's contributions to *Punch* are too numerous to be listed here. For a near-complete record of his publications in that journal see the bibliography in Walter Jerrold's *Douglas Jerrold and 'Punch'*.

BIOGRAPHIES, RECENT CRITICISM, AND RELATED WORKS

Jerrold, Walter. *Douglas Jerrold, Dramatist and Wit.* 2 vols. London:

Hodder and Stroughton, 1914. (The most accurate account of Jerrold's life and a valuable source of information about his career in the theater.)

Jerrold, W. Blanchard. *The Life of Douglas Jerrold.* Vol. V in *The Works of Douglas Jerrold.* (Important source of biographical data but marred by factual errors and sentimentality.)

Kelly, Richard. "The American in England: An Examination of a Hitherto Neglected Satire by Douglas Jerrold," *Victorian Newsletter* (Spring, 1967), pp. 28–31. (A study of "The English in Little.")

————. "Mrs. Caudle, a Victorian Curtain Lecturer," *University of Toronto Quarterly,* XXXVIII (April, 1969), 295–309.

————. "Punch's Letters to His Son," *Satire Newsletter,* IV (1967), 58–62.

Price, R. G. G. *A History of Punch.* London: Collins, 1957. (A very readable history that brings Spielmann's work up to date.)

Spielmann, M. H. *The History of Punch.* New York: Cassell Publishing Co., 1895. (The definitive work for the first fifty-four years of *Punch's* development.)

Taube, Myron. "The Parson-Snob Controversy and *Vanity Fair,*" *Victorian Newsletter* (Fall, 1968), pp. 25–29. (An account of Thackeray's feuds with Jerrold and their effect upon the writing of *Vanity Fair.*)

# INDEX

Numbers in italics refer to illustration pages

*The Best of Mr. Punch*

has been set on the Linotype in 10-point Baskerville with two points
spacing between lines. Certain display elements have been adapted
from handdrawn type used in the original *Punch*. Text illus-
trations are also taken from the original source. The paper
on which this book is printed is designed for an effec-
tive life of at least three hundred years.